BATEMAN CONTEMPORARY ATLAS NEW ZEALAND

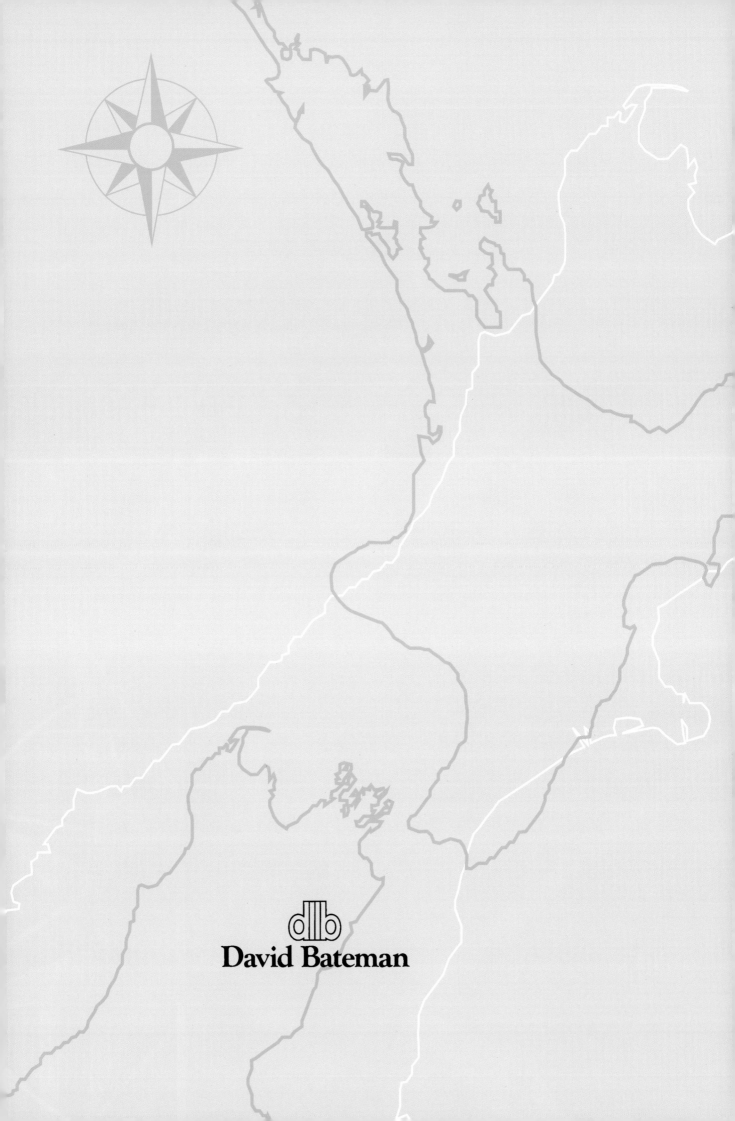

David Bateman

BATEMAN
CONTEMPORARY
ATLAS
NEW ZEALAND

The Shapes of Our Nation

Russell Kirkpatrick

First published 1999 by David Bateman Ltd, 30 Tarndale Grove, Albany,
Auckland, New Zealand

Reprinted 2003

ISBN 1-86953-408-5(hbk)

The cover photograph, taken during a NASA Space Shuttle mission, is
reproduced with the kind permission of NASA.

Cover and book design by Shelley Watson
Plates and cartographic design by Russell Kirkpatrick, Mediamerge
Mapping
Pre-press by Apple Laser Set, Auckland
Printed in China by Everbest Printing Co

CONTENTS

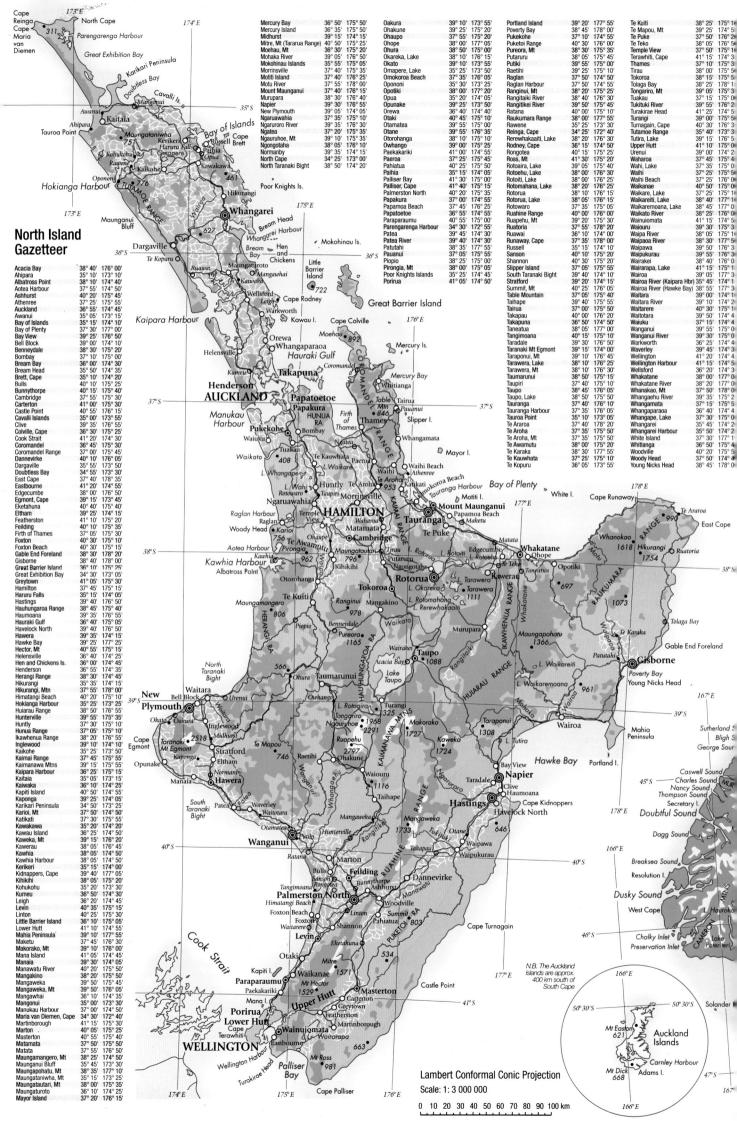

PREFACE

New Zealanders have long been without an up-to-date, comprehensive thematic atlas of their country. It is 23 years since the 1976 *New Zealand Atlas* was published, and since then New Zealand's geography has been irrevocably altered by economic, social and environmental transformation. The way geographers think about these changes and the way they research them have also changed radically. Moreover, the methods used to show the changes cartographically have undergone an equally significant transformation. It is well past time that New Zealanders were provided with a contemporary thematic atlas which encourages them to put their own experiences in a physical, environmental, historical, economic and social context.

The *Contemporary Atlas New Zealand* is designed to fill this gap. From its inception in 1997, the aims of the project have been:

* to circulate among the wider community a document which captures the essence of New Zealand geography as we approach the new millennium;
* to challenge the geographical community to re-examine the virtues of the map, particularly the ability of cartography to represent current geographical thought;
* to make the best use of the New Zealand Census and other research data, and to use both as the basis for future editions of the *Atlas*.

The making of the *Atlas*

The first comprehensive New Zealand atlas, *A Descriptive Atlas of New Zealand* (McLintock, 1960), was produced by an advisory committee set up by the Cabinet in an attempt to make use of the expertise originally developed for the ill-fated Centennial Historical Atlas project of the 1940s. After five years of work the committee produced an atlas which contained 48 pages of general and largely physical maps and 80-odd pages of comprehensive scientific text, a combination which did not sit comfortably together. This atlas sold well and was soon reprinted, but did not satisfy the critics (Lister, 1979). At best it was seen as a commendable first effort, a precursor to a real national atlas.

By the late 1960s serious consideration was being given to revising the *Descriptive Atlas* and in 1970 a new committee commenced work. This committee, drawn from the Department of Lands and Survey and the Historical Branch of the Department of Internal Affairs, sought to refine the formula used in the 1960 atlas, with longer and more specialist scientific articles, many more maps and a large photographic section. The work was published in 1976, in a blaze of publicity, under the title *New Zealand Atlas* (Wards, 1976). Over 100 pages of text, 73 pages of photographs and 80 pages of maps were welded together into a well-marketed publication. It was a commercial success but was ridiculed by the critics (Brockie and Moran, 1977). The atlas committee had failed to realise that the intellectual climate of the nation had changed. While fifteen years earlier a mere book of maps, nice photographs and weighty articles of conservative scholarship might have satisfied some, by the mid 1970s reviewers were looking for something that reflected the changing faces both of New Zealand and of geographical thought. That they did not find this in the *New Zealand Atlas* has contributed to the decline of the thematic atlas as a geographical tool.

Since this time the thematic atlases which have appeared have been aimed squarely at the school market. These atlases are generated from a formula that involves purchasing world maps from an overseas cartographic house, and combining these with a few pages of New Zealand maps aimed at the secondary school syllabus. Even the best of these fall far short of offering a balanced insight into the geographies of New Zealand.

Then, in 1997, as a result of seven years' work and a considerable sum from the Lotteries Commission, the *New Zealand Historical Atlas* (McKinnon et al, 1997) was published. This endeavour, like the 1976 *New Zealand Atlas*, was a joint effort between the state mapping agency (then called the Department of Survey and Land Information) and the Historical Branch of the Department of Internal Affairs. What made the difference between this work and the previous effort was that the scholarship was based on current historiography, and that the cartography was sympathetic to the scholarship rather than to tradition.

The *New Zealand Historical Atlas* has been received enthusiastically by reviewers:

"... a superb record of journeys into this country's histories: sweeping in its scope, highly innovative in its design, and immediately engaging in its appeal" (Overton, 1997).

PHYSICAL

The New Zealand physical shape is best for showing areas that need to be compared. This shape is a 'bird's eye' view, with all places on the map an equal distance from the reader's eye. Traditionally this shape has communicated a scientific, impartial message, but it is not always the best way of showing social and cultural issues.

My involvement in the *New Zealand Historical Atlas* project gave me, as Deputy Editor and the link between the editorial team and the cartographers, a chance to apply my geographic training in a practical manner. The overwhelmingly positive reaction to the last section of the *New Zealand Historical Atlas* ('From Progress to Uncertainty', which was in essence a geography of the 1970s and 1980s) convinced me that this approach could be applied to New Zealand's contemporary geographies. The publisher, David Bateman Ltd, agreed that a new atlas was needed as the new millennium approached. Hence the production of the *Contemporary Atlas New Zealand*.

What kind of *Atlas* is it?

Atlases are reference books. A reader expects to pick up an atlas and answer the question: "Where is it?" This atlas is no exception. It is comprehensive in scope, showing the reader where the mountains are, where the rivers flow, where the people live and where they go to work. It has soil maps, maps showing internal migration, climate maps, maps of indigenous vegetation, exotic forests and overseas trade. This is the familiar, traditional territory of geography, the sort of things lay people expect geographers to be studying.

But the *Contemporary Atlas New Zealand* deals with more than just the traditional territory. Modern geography does not content itself with just asking, "Where is it?" It progresses on to ask, "Why is it there?" Maps are eminently suitable to show the answers to both questions.

The strongest criticism of atlases in the past has been their narrow choice of subject matter. Atlas makers favour the physical, static, tangible and measurable aspects of the world – those easiest to map – over the invisible, intangible, dynamic and the human. But human experience is shaped by dynamic and intangible factors. Those map makers who limit themselves to a narrow and traditional choice of empirical subject matter will inevitably fail to provide a map of human life. Reviewers reserved their strongest criticism of the two previous national atlases for their failure to illustrate the human aspects of our nation's geography. An atlas maker must ask the question: "What geographies should I record?"

While I am happy to give ground to arguments for constructing a national atlas in other ways, I will not concede that we must return to a conventional assessment of geography and atlases as page after page of New Zealand maps showing traditional topics. This is not an 'alternative' atlas. It is a mainstream atlas for the new millennium.

The shapes of our nation

New Zealand has more than one geographical shape. We are familiar with the irregular, elongated outline of our coasts; so much so that advertisers use the physical shape of New Zealand as an icon to sell us all kinds of things (Kirkpatrick, 1987). But it is not the only shape our nation takes. New Zealand has a population shape, for example. Half our country's people live in the northern half of the North Island, and parts of the South Island are virtually uninhabited. This shape appears top-heavy to our conditioned eyes, and the South Island looks too small. But the population shape is not simply a distortion of the 'real' geographical shape. Our population is just as real as our coastline, so it is just as valid to map New Zealand using a population-based cartogram as using a physical map – indeed, if it is being used to examine population issues, it is more valid.

For the sake of clarity, the shapes of our nation are gathered together under six section headings: Physical Shapes, Environmental Shapes, Historical Shapes, Population Shapes, Economic Shapes, and Social and Cultural Shapes.

The first section of the *Atlas* explores the physical shapes underpinning our nation – geology, topography, climate, soils and vegetation. The broad outline of New Zealand's physical shape continues to evolve as a complex interaction of these factors, but humans have had a significant impact on them. This impact, and the reasons for it, are examined in the second section, Environmental Shapes. This section focuses on the shapes of resource exploitation (farming, forestry, fishing), environmental management and natural hazards. Together these two sections make up the first 25 plates of the *Atlas*; roughly corresponding to those topics considered the substance of physical geography as taught in schools and universities.

The other four sections of the *Atlas* comprise New Zealand's human geography. Here the choices of sections and themes are not so straightforward. I have chosen to begin with a short review of historical shapes. While not wanting to retrace the ground traversed by the *New Zealand Historical Atlas*, I do consider it important to emphasise that our human actions are embedded in time as well as space. These historical shapes are followed by an examination of the demographic characteristics of New Zealand's population shapes. This is not only important in its own right, but is also a necessary background to the exploration of the economic and social/cultural shapes of our nation.

The last two sections (Economic Shapes and Social and Cultural Shapes) are the most problematic. What is presented here is a small but careful selection from the hundreds of possibilities. The shapes emphasised in these sections include business and trade, the supply of energy and infrastructure, political links to the world, race, class and labour issues, access to health and education, economic and social deprivation, and sport and recreation.

Social issues are generally characterised by a relative lack of mappable data and by rapid change, so that whatever data are assembled go rapidly out of date. Nevertheless, this *Atlas* presents a broader range of social issues than has been mapped in any other atlas. It is my hope that those dissatisfied with the choice of topics or the coverage of topics they are familiar with might feel sufficiently stimulated to generate maps based on those topics.

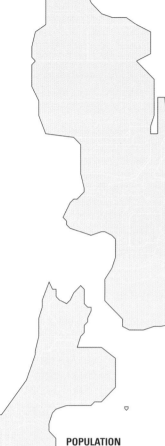

POPULATION CARTOGRAM

This shape reflects the population of New Zealand. The size of each region is determined by how many people live there, not by physical size. Many social issues require the use of a cartogram. For example, it is a mistake to use a physical shape to show population change, as areas with few people show up as more important than they ought to, and vice versa.

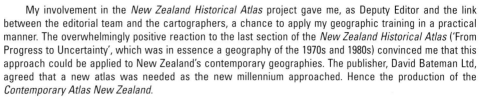

Case studies

Each major theme within the *Atlas* has at least one plate devoted to it, and in some cases (climate, for example) two or even three. A number of these themes are illustrated using case studies, a feature which I consider to be crucial to the understanding of the regional and local impacts of national and global trends. A small-scale case study allows the reader to personalise the discussion, and encourages the question, "Is something similar happening in my area?"

The social context of cartography

The wide variety of map styles which appear in this *Atlas* (and appeared in the *New Zealand Historical Atlas*) are not the result of 'playing around' with a computer. Each map projection has been carefully chosen to suit the intellectual content of the map subject, and many of the choices I have made are explained in the section 'Map Notes and Sources' which follows the plates. Moreover, there is a clear intellectual foundation for offering alternatives to the standard physical shape of New Zealand: the alternatives are firmly based in an understanding of the social context of cartography.

Social interaction is full of rituals. Everyone is familiar with the ritual apology. Both parties know it is insincere. Nevertheless, the apology is acceptable because it assists another person to save face or to avoid conflict (Goffman, 1967). Writers claim that such rituals are ubiquitous among humankind (Brown and Levinson, 1987).

Cartography is a form of social interaction. A heavily ritualised, mostly one-way communication to be sure, but one that operates using the same rules which govern all forms of communication. These rules are not formulated by cartographic theorists, who are generally mired in theories which attempt understanding of the mechanics of map design and interpretation devoid of any social context (Keates, 1982). Instead, they are the rules which govern the complex interaction of honesty, deception, half-truth, exaggeration, inference, misunderstanding and so on, those things which give meaning to – or take it from – our interactions as human beings.

Maps have often been part of formal interactions on a broad social scale. A careful historical review entitles one to assert that the map has been used as an empire-building tool developed to measure, and thereby control, physical resources and the people who depend on them. Maps are not the objective, value-free documents that one might assume, despite their scientific appearance.

As capitalism developed in Western Europe, "concern for accuracy of navigation and the definition of territorial rights (both private and collective) meant that mapping and cadastral survey became basic tools of the geographer's art" (Harvey, 1984: 2). Mercantile capitalism became associated with imperialism, in which the state acted to protect its economic interests abroad; and colonialism, in which imperialism is extended to the annexing of foreign territory to secure economic advantage. Maps have been potent weapons for imperialist designs, as "surveyors marched alongside soldiers, initially mapping for reconnaissance, then for general information, and eventually as a tool of pacification, civilisation and exploitation"(Harley, 1988: 282). To Louis XV of France, "mapping was nothing less than the identification, measurement, and description of the physical characteristics of state sovereignty" (Southard, 1983:5). Topographical information was essential to field commanders and backroom planners alike. Strategists were provided crucial information on infrastructure, communications, battle sites, line-of-sight for artillery fire, location of vital installations, cover for approach and ambush, and the details of population centres.

The use of maps by emerging imperial powers threatened whole cultures. The use of a map to discover, annex, partition and control territory imposed severe restraints on indigenous people's freedom of action. The builders of empire claimed the resources of the world: "Shall we English who inherit so large a part of the world not acquaint ourselves with our inheritance and the conditions under which we can retain and make the most of it?" (Freshfield, 1886: 701). Neil Smith reminds us that in 1917 Colonel Sir Thomas H. Holdich, president of the Royal Geographical Society, made his case for the rule of Empire thus: "The right of the white man to fill the earth and subdue it has always been unquestioned, because it is based on the principle that his dominance and lordship tend to the betterment of the world and straightens out the highways for the peace and the blessings of civilisations to follow" (Holdich, 1917: quoted in Smith, 1979: 371).

One of the first acts of a colonial power was to institute authoritative resources, such as the map, which were controlled by the state. "The surveyor is the pioneer of the development; if the country is to be opened up, he must get there beforehand; in general, capital, either in men or means, is not going to waste itself in unknown land" (Report of the British Colonial Survey Committee, 1928: 17; quoted in Balogun, 1985: 159). The map becomes a legal document which defines the extent and ownership of resources, thereby giving illocutionary force (legally binding power) to the western notion of land as a commodity to be bought and sold, and enshrining in law this particular cultural perspective on the relationship between land and people. Such things matter greatly: a line drawn hastily on a Royal Engineers map separated Pakistan from India in 1947, condemning antagonistic communities to economic ruin unless they could co-operate, as it divided resources from mills and ports. The result was widespread conflict, with minority enclaves suffering genocide (Collins and Lapierre, 1972). In this stark case of illocutionary force the map decreed "the lives and deaths of millions of people" (Harley, 1988: 283).

Neil Smith explains how British geography was influenced by the needs of the Empire: "By 1900 the major empire building nations had established distinct national schools of geography within which geographers directed their research to the colonies... refining their talents as explorers, mapmakers, land-use chroniclers, students of natural process and artists depicting and describing natural harmony" (Smith, 1979: 371). The legacy of this is still found in the geography classroom. Peter Haggett said recently that "no other [discipline] insists that students include courses on map making, map reading, map projections and the like in the core curriculum"(Haggett, 1990: 8).

The oblique shape allows an area to be emphasised from a particular perspective. Viewing from a perspective more closely approximates the way we see our everyday environment, horizontally rather than vertically. Such a shape can be used to emphasise movement, as it portrays a feeling of depth, allowing the viewer to 'insert' him or herself into the map. It has proven useful in portraying Māori space.

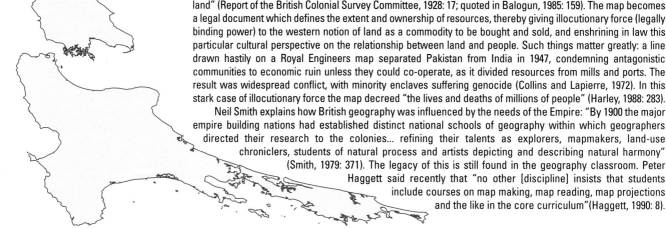

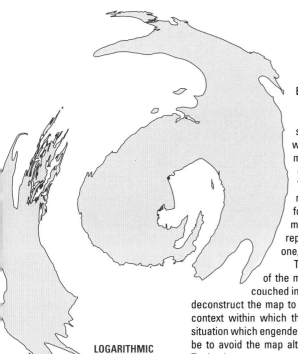

LOGARITHMIC

This shape is centred on Wellington, and the scale decreases out from the centre of the shape. The effect is like looking through a fish-eye lens. This shape allows the map maker to highlight a central place at a detailed scale, then show linkages to other places. It makes one part of our nation seem more important than the others.

But unless educators consciously divest the map of its imperialist legacy, they will continue to inculcate such values into their students.

Standard physical maps have also aided environmental exploitation. All places on such maps appear equally far from the reader's eye – a 'bird's eye' view. The forest, which may be the subject of logging rights, is shown not as a stand of trees on a mountainside but as a green colour on a map. Therefore "policy decisions based on conventional map reading may invalidate the basic humanity of planning efforts", as "mapping environmental phenomena planimetrically and at a greatly reduced scale may well abstract that informational attribute which is most crucial in related policy formulation and decision making... the 'bird's-eye' map view is not what we see when moving about at ground level" (Muehrcke, 1974: 13). The fundamental mistake of representing the different shapes of New Zealand using the one kind of map is a serious one, and in this *Atlas* is deliberately addressed.

The map generators may have ideas other than those suggested by a cursory reading of the map. They might be hiding another intention behind the literal meaning of the map, couched in terms of scientific truth and accuracy. To challenge the map generator, one must first deconstruct the map to reveal its underlying context. Because most map users lack the knowledge of the context within which the map was generated, they will misunderstand the map generator's intention, a situation which engenders confusion. After a time, the most common strategy used by critical geographers will be to avoid the map altogether, thus jeopardising the discipline. And this is exactly what we find in New Zealand.

Atlases and social change

Near the end of the post-war 'long boom' period (1945-1970) many nations financed lavish national atlases. These atlases portrayed their nations as resource-rich and ready for continued expansion, and the governments which funded their production used them as a nation-building tool. Within a decade this optimistic view was proven wrong. Resources were indeed finite, and the negative environmental effects of their unchecked use had embedded themselves in popular consciousness. An aging infrastructure and an inability to supply a demand-driven consumer society placed pressure on local and central governments. In the 1980s economic and social restructuring initiatives were introduced to many western nations. It is not surprising that the proliferation of national atlases seen in the 1960s and 1970s petered out in the 1980s. Indeed, the 1980s and 1990s saw the rise of historical atlas projects in Australia, Canada, the United States and New Zealand, as scholars reassessed history, and as the general public began to look back in nostalgia rather than to look forward to continued progress.

The restructuring that characterised the 1980s and 1990s was not a one-time change. It is a continued reorganisation of the economy and of society in the interests of capital. Included in this reorganisation are attempts to introduce competition in the marketplace by asset sales, the formation of State-owned Enterprises (SOEs), restructuring of the labour market and social service provision. Though the general thrust of restructuring appears to be deregulatory, it is more correct to argue that the protective regulations of the 'long boom' era have been replaced by new sets of regulations. These sets of regulations are intensely geographical, as they act at different scales: APEC, GATT, intellectual copyright laws and the Montreal Protocol on CFCs, for example, operate on a global scale, while the Treaty of Waitangi, the Resource Management Act, anti-monopoly legislation and the Employment Contracts Act function on a national scale. Locally, such things as district plans and resource consents shape our lives. The market has assumed an informal regulatory function, sorting out winners and losers, and as a result the mean income has risen while the median income has fallen: that is, while we are slightly better off on average, most of us are actually worse off in fact.

These processes are embedded in space and time. The impacts of restructuring are manifest even in the physical environment (for example, in the number of farms underproducing as a result of the high interest rates and debt levels of the late 1980s). Just as New Zealand's physical shapes continue to change at a variety of speeds and scales, so do our social, environmental, population, economic and cultural shapes. Geographers have adopted alternative ways of thinking about these changes, using Marxist, behaviouralist, feminist and post-modern perspectives to inform their research. But geographers, nervous of its positivist origins, have abandoned the map as a means of portraying these changing shapes. Fewer maps appear in geographical journals. The gulf between popular geography (perhaps most powerfully represented by the *National Geographic* magazine) and scholarly geography continues to widen; we speak different languages.

I seek ways to bridge this gulf. Maps are powerful and are intuitively understood by many people: stripped of their empire-building baggage, they become more powerful still. The overwhelmingly positive public reaction to the innovative cartography I introduced in the *New Zealand Historical Atlas* convinces me that I am on the right track. Carefully drawn maps that show the many different shapes of our nation will help people understand more clearly the changes taking place around them, and may provide a common language for academic geographers to once again speak with the general population.

Dr Russell Kirkpatrick
Honorary Fellow
Department of Geography
University of Canterbury
August 1999

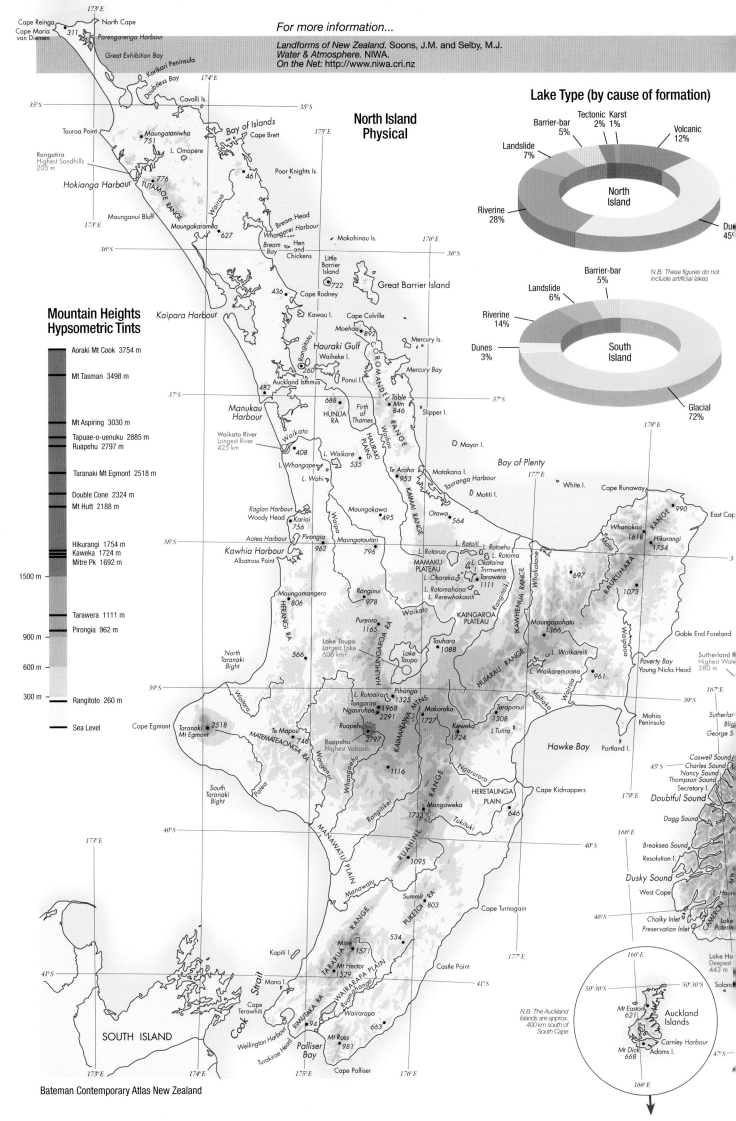

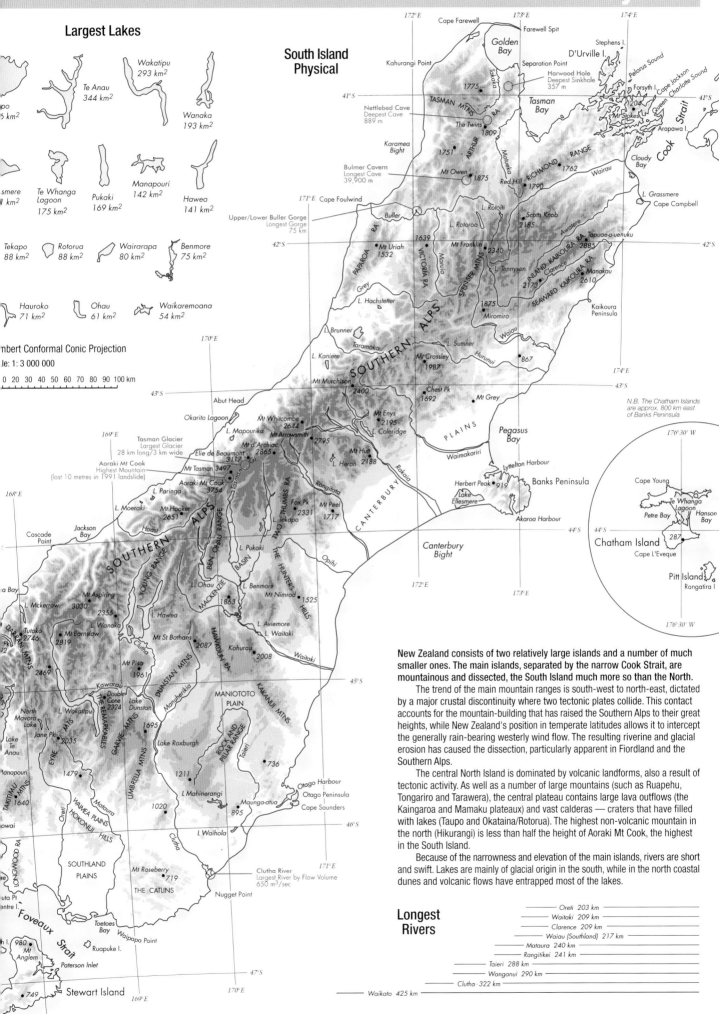

Largest Lakes

Te Anau 344 km²
Wakatipu 293 km²
Wanaka 193 km²
Te Whanga Lagoon 175 km²
Pukaki 169 km²
Manapouri 142 km²
Hawea 141 km²
…smere … km²
Tekapo 88 km²
Rotorua 88 km²
Wairarapa 80 km²
Benmore 75 km²
Hauroko 71 km²
Ohau 61 km²
Waikaremoana 54 km²

Lambert Conformal Conic Projection
Scale 1: 3 000 000

0 10 20 30 40 50 60 70 80 90 100 km

South Island Physical

N.B. The Chatham Islands are approx. 800 km east of Banks Peninsula

New Zealand consists of two relatively large islands and a number of much smaller ones. The main islands, separated by the narrow Cook Strait, are mountainous and dissected, the South Island much more so than the North.

The trend of the main mountain ranges is south-west to north-east, dictated by a major crustal discontinuity where two tectonic plates collide. This contact accounts for the mountain-building that has raised the Southern Alps to their great heights, while New Zealand's position in temperate latitudes allows it to intercept the generally rain-bearing westerly wind flow. The resulting riverine and glacial erosion has caused the dissection, particularly apparent in Fiordland and the Southern Alps.

The central North Island is dominated by volcanic landforms, also a result of tectonic activity. As well as a number of large mountains (such as Ruapehu, Tongariro and Tarawera), the central plateau contains large lava outflows (the Kaingaroa and Mamaku plateaux) and vast calderas — craters that have filled with lakes (Taupo and Okataina/Rotorua). The highest non-volcanic mountain in the north (Hikurangi) is less than half the height of Aoraki Mt Cook, the highest in the South Island.

Because of the narrowness and elevation of the main islands, rivers are short and swift. Lakes are mainly of glacial origin in the south, while in the north coastal dunes and volcanic flows have entrapped most of the lakes.

Longest Rivers

Oreti 203 km
Waitaki 209 km
Clarence 209 km
Waiau (Southland) 217 km
Mataura 240 km
Rangitikei 241 km
Taieri 288 km
Wanganui 290 km
Clutha 322 km
Waikato 425 km

1

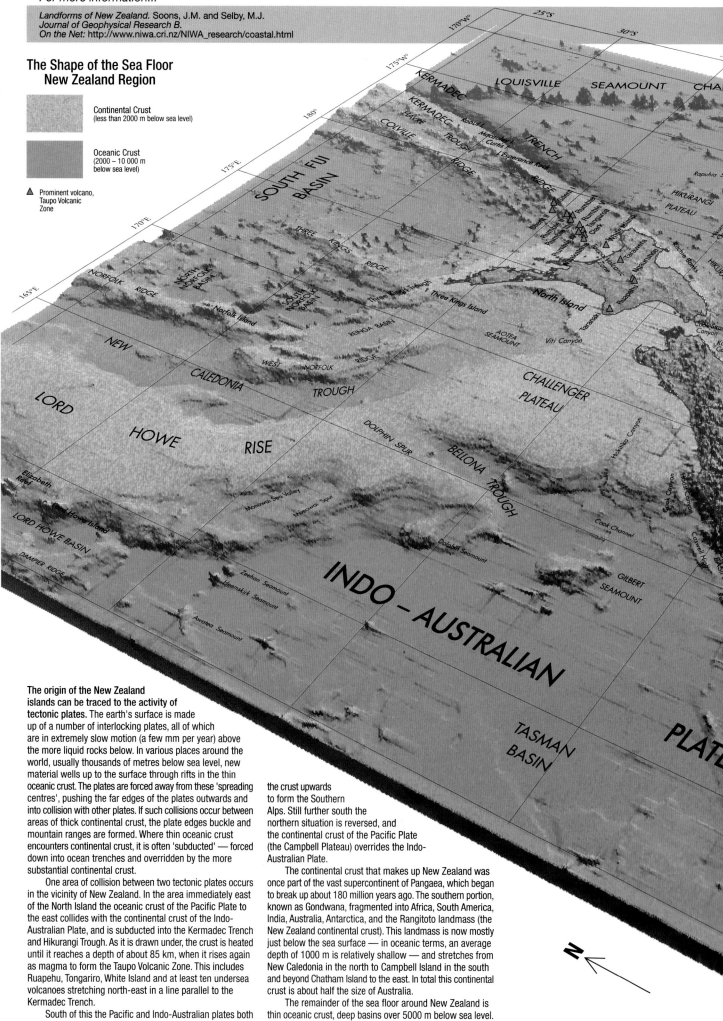

For more information...

Landforms of New Zealand. Soons, J.M. and Selby, M.J.
Journal of Geophysical Research B.
On the Net: http://www.niwa.cri.nz/NIWA_research/coastal.html

The Shape of the Sea Floor
New Zealand Region

Continental Crust
(less than 2000 m below sea level)

Oceanic Crust
(2000 – 10 000 m
below sea level)

▲ Prominent volcano,
Taupo Volcanic
Zone

The origin of the New Zealand islands can be traced to the activity of tectonic plates. The earth's surface is made up of a number of interlocking plates, all of which are in extremely slow motion (a few mm per year) above the more liquid rocks below. In various places around the world, usually thousands of metres below sea level, new material wells up to the surface through rifts in the thin oceanic crust. The plates are forced away from these 'spreading centres', pushing the far edges of the plates outwards and into collision with other plates. If such collisions occur between areas of thick continental crust, the plate edges buckle and mountain ranges are formed. Where thin oceanic crust encounters continental crust, it is often 'subducted' — forced down into ocean trenches and overridden by the more substantial continental crust.

One area of collision between two tectonic plates occurs in the vicinity of New Zealand. In the area immediately east of the North Island the oceanic crust of the Pacific Plate to the east collides with the continental crust of the Indo-Australian Plate, and is subducted into the Kermadec Trench and Hikurangi Trough. As it is drawn under, the crust is heated until it reaches a depth of about 85 km, when it rises again as magma to form the Taupo Volcanic Zone. This includes Ruapehu, Tongariro, White Island and at least ten undersea volcanoes stretching north-east in a line parallel to the Kermadec Trench.

South of this the Pacific and Indo-Australian plates both consist of continental crust, and their collision has buckled the crust upwards to form the Southern Alps. Still further south the northern situation is reversed, and the continental crust of the Pacific Plate (the Campbell Plateau) overrides the Indo-Australian Plate.

The continental crust that makes up New Zealand was once part of the vast supercontinent of Pangaea, which began to break up about 180 million years ago. The southern portion, known as Gondwana, fragmented into Africa, South America, India, Australia, Antarctica, and the Rangitoto landmass (the New Zealand continental crust). This landmass is now mostly just below the sea surface — in oceanic terms, an average depth of 1000 m is relatively shallow — and stretches from New Caledonia in the north to Campbell Island in the south and beyond Chatham Island to the east. In total this continental crust is about half the size of Australia.

The remainder of the sea floor around New Zealand is thin oceanic crust, deep basins over 5000 m below sea level. These are little known and currently being explored.

The Louisville Seamount Chain

The Louisville Seamount Chain has been formed (over the last 75 m.y.) by a lone 'hot spot' beneath the thin oceanic crust. It sends periodic magmatic pulses to the surface, forming a sequence of volcanoes as the Pacific Plate slides north-westwards over it. Each active volcano rose somewhere near the surface, in many cases forming an atoll. When the magmatic pulse ceases, the sea floor drops by as much as a kilometre, lowering the extinct volcano down into the sea and leaving an undersea remnant (guyot). The seamount chain is gradually being drawn, along with the Pacific Plate, into the Kermadec Trench. Only the north-western end of the chain is shown here.

Louisville Seamount Chain profile labels:

Kermadec Trench

-4990m 100km³ 74.4mya

Osbourn -1953m 4300km³ 73.6mya

-1220m 3800km³ 71.9mya

-1530m 3900km³ 68mya

-1770m 2200km³ 64.9mya

Seafox -1630m 2400km³ 62.2mya

name / summit height (below s.l.) / volume / age

-1085m 3200km³ 44.5mya

-274m 21400km³ 42.2mya

-1085m 5200km³ 69.7mya

-1375m 5300km³ 66.7mya

Currituck -1630m 2700km³ 63.6mya

Louisville -1135m 8700km³ 60.1mya

Burton -1490m 3400km³ 57.2mya

-1250m 3900km³ 54.7mya

-1150m 2500km³ 52.2mya

Forde -980m 3500km³ 50.1mya

-1025m 4000km³ 46.5mya

-1035m 3300km³ 44.9mya

-880m 8400km³ 40mya

Map labels:

PACIFIC

Broughton Gap

Reihu Seavalley

NORTH CHATHAM RISE

CHATHAM RISE

Reserve Bank

Veryan Bank

Gap

Pitt I.

Chatham I.

BOUNTY TROUGH

BOUNTY CHANNEL

Bounty Is.

BOUNTY PLATEAU

Antipodes Is.

BOLLONS SEAMOUNT

SOUTHWEST PACIFIC BASIN

South Island

uth Island

PUKAKI RISE

PLATE

SUBANTARCTIC

50°S

45°S

Endeavour Banks

Stewart I.

CAMPBELL PLATEAU

CAMPBELL RISE

CAMPBELL I.

SLOPE

The Snares

SOLANDER

YSEGUR TRENCH

kersgill mount

Auckland Is.

AUCKLANDS TROUGH

AUCKLANDS

SLOPE

MACQUARIE

EMERALD BASIN

RIDGE

2

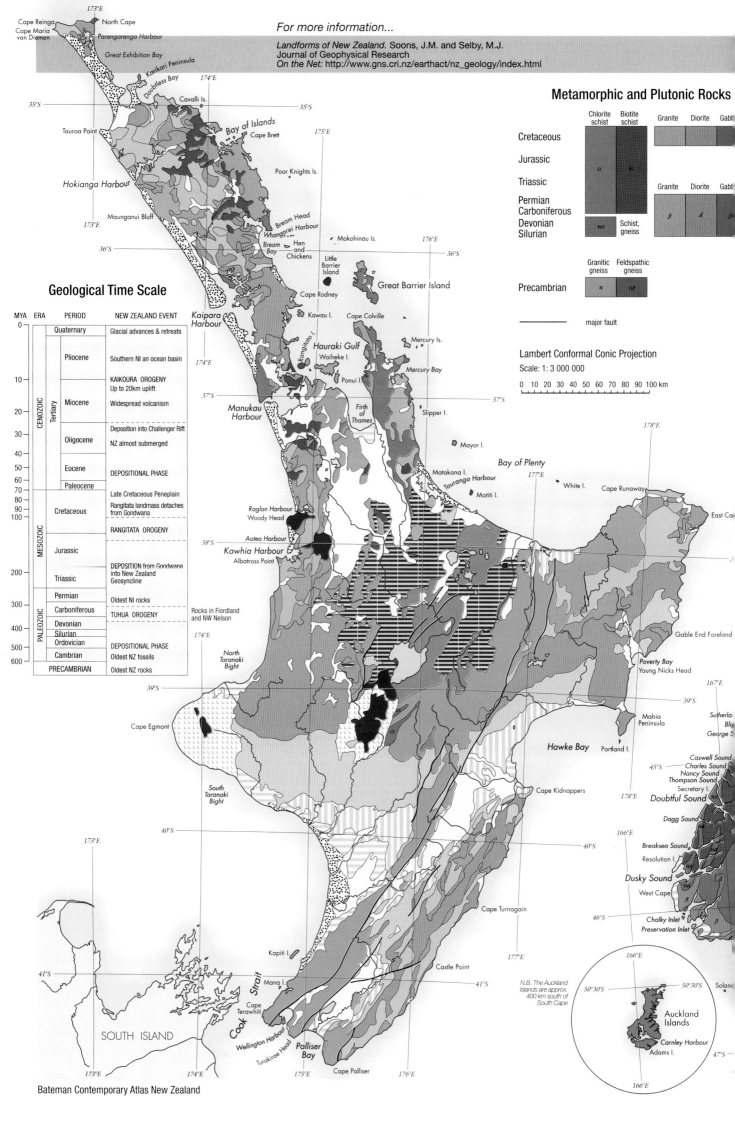

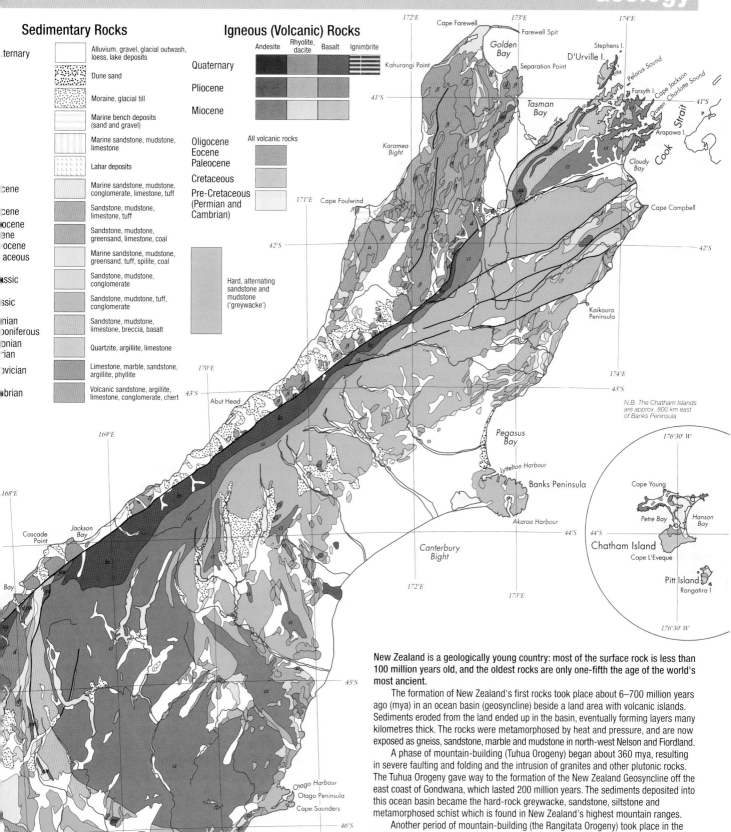

Sedimentary Rocks

ternary
- Alluvium, gravel, glacial outwash, loess, lake deposits
- Dune sand
- Moraine, glacial till
- Marine bench deposits (sand and gravel)
- Marine sandstone, mudstone, limestone
- Lahar deposits

cene
- Marine sandstone, mudstone, conglomerate, limestone, tuff

cene
- Sandstone, mudstone, limestone, tuff

ocene
ene
ocene
- Sandstone, mudstone, greensand, limestone, coal

aceous
- Marine sandstone, mudstone, greensand, tuff, spilite, coal

ussic
- Sandstone, mudstone, conglomerate

ssic
- Sandstone, mudstone, tuff, conglomerate

nian
oniferous
onian
rian
- Sandstone, mudstone, limestone, breccia, basalt

- Quartzite, argillite, limestone

ovician
- Limestone, marble, sandstone, argillite, phyllite

brian
- Volcanic sandstone, argillite, limestone, conglomerate, chert

Igneous (Volcanic) Rocks

	Andesite	Rhyolite, dacite	Basalt	Ignimbrite

Quaternary

Pliocene

Miocene

Oligocene
Eocene
Paleocene

Cretaceous

Pre-Cretaceous (Permian and Cambrian)

All volcanic rocks

Hard, alternating sandstone and mudstone ('greywacke')

N.B. The Chatham Islands are approx. 800 km east of Banks Peninsula

New Zealand is a geologically young country: most of the surface rock is less than 100 million years old, and the oldest rocks are only one-fifth the age of the world's most ancient.

The formation of New Zealand's first rocks took place about 6–700 million years ago (mya) in an ocean basin (geosyncline) beside a land area with volcanic islands. Sediments eroded from the land ended up in the basin, eventually forming layers many kilometres thick. The rocks were metamorphosed by heat and pressure, and are now exposed as gneiss, sandstone, marble and mudstone in north-west Nelson and Fiordland.

A phase of mountain-building (Tuhua Orogeny) began about 360 mya, resulting in severe faulting and folding and the intrusion of granites and other plutonic rocks. The Tuhua Orogeny gave way to the formation of the New Zealand Geosyncline off the east coast of Gondwana, which lasted 200 million years. The sediments deposited into this ocean basin became the hard-rock greywacke, sandstone, siltstone and metamorphosed schist which is found in New Zealand's highest mountain ranges.

Another period of mountain-building (the Rangitata Orogeny) took place in the Cretaceous period, exposing sediment from the New Zealand Geosyncline as well as older Tuhua rocks. After the orogeny ended the land eroded until a peneplain formed in the late Cretaceous. At about this time the landmass broke away from Gondwana, moving eastwards on the Pacific Plate. The sea then invaded the low-lying land, which was almost submerged in the Oligocene. Sediment was eroded into the Challenger Rift.

The land re-emerged as the Kaikoura Orogeny began, about 25–30 mya. The Alpine Fault developed and rock deposits were divided and pulled apart, so that Tuhua rocks are now separated by 450 km between Fiordland and Nelson. The Pacific Plate began to be subducted under the Indo-Australian Plate, resulting in folding which, in turn, caused mountain-building in the eastern North Island. Tectonic volcanoes appeared, first in Northland, then in stages drawing closer to the plate boundary off the North Island's east coast. The southern North Island, and latterly the Marlborough Sounds, subsided as the Pacific Plate was drawn down. During the Quaternary period glaciation modified the landscape. The Kaikoura Orogeny continues to this day.

For more information...

Mineral Wealth of New Zealand. Thompson, B.N., Brathwaite, R.L. and Christie, A.B.
Mineral Resources of New Zealand, 1996 Edition. New Zealand Crown Minerals, 1996.
On the Net: http://www.gns.cri.nz/earthres/minerals/index.html

New Zealand Minerals

Metallic Minerals

△ aluminium
▲ antimony
▲ chromium
▲ copper
△ gold
▲ iron
▲ lead, zinc
△ manganese
▲ mercury
▲ molybdenum
▲ nickel
▲ platinum
△ rare earths
△ silver
▲ tin
▲ titanium
△ tungsten
△ uranium

Non-metallic Minerals

☐ asbestos
■ building stone
☐ clays
☐ diatomite
☐ dolomite
■ feldspar
☐ greenstone
☐ limestone
■ marble
■ mica
■ perlite
☐ phosphate
■ pumice
☐ salt
■ serpentine
■ silica
☐ sulphur
☐ talc-magnesite
☐ zeolites

Energy Minerals

small   la
● coal
✳ geothermal
● oil and gas

☒ old mines, close
✕ (any mineral typ

Aggregate Deposits

quaternary sediments for gravel and sand
greywacke for roa
basalt for road chip
andesite for roa

Selected Stone Resources used by pre-contact Māori

☆ argillite
★ basalt
★ chert
☆ greywacke
☆ limestone flint
★ obsidian
☆ pahutane flint
★ porcellanite
★ pounamu
☆ silcrete

Lambert Conformal Conic Projection

Scale: 1: 3 000 000

0 10 20 30 40 50 60 70 80 90 100 km

Gold Production by Mining Area 1994–98

total gold production
Golden Cross
Macraes
Otago/Westland alluvial
Martha Hill

Kilograms: 0, 2000, 4000, 6000, 8000, 10,000, 12,000
Year: 1994 1995 1996 1997 1998

Geoth
8% ($200n

Iron
1.22% ($30

0.29% ($

9.61% ($23

N.B. The Auckland Islands are approx. 400 km south of South Cape

Auckland Islands
Carnley Harbour
Adams I.

Bateman Contemporary Atlas New Zealand

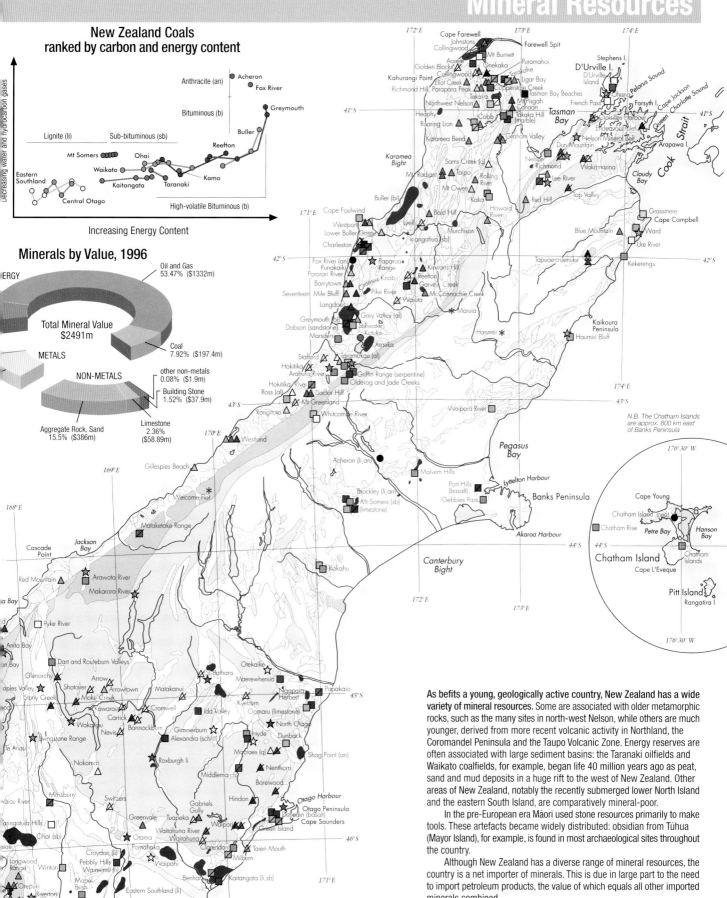

New Zealand Coals
ranked by carbon and energy content

decreasing water and hydrocarbon gases

Anthracite (an)   • Acheron
                  • Fox River

Bituminous (b)   • Greymouth

Lignite (li)   Sub-bituminous (sb)   • Buller

Mt Somers   Ohai   • Reefton

Waikato   • Kamo

Eastern   Kaitangata   Taranaki
Southland

Central Otago

High-volatile Bituminous (b)

Increasing Energy Content

Minerals by Value, 1996

ENERGY

Oil and Gas
53.47% ($1332m)

Total Mineral Value
$2491m

METALS

Coal
7.92% ($197.4m)

NON-METALS

other non-metals
0.08% ($1.9m)

Building Stone
1.52% ($37.9m)

Aggregate Rock, Sand
15.5% ($386m)

Limestone
2.36%
($58.89m)

N.B. The Chatham Islands
are approx. 800 km east
of Banks Peninsula

As befits a young, geologically active country, New Zealand has a wide variety of mineral resources. Some are associated with older metamorphic rocks, such as the many sites in north-west Nelson, while others are much younger, derived from more recent volcanic activity in Northland, the Coromandel Peninsula and the Taupo Volcanic Zone. Energy reserves are often associated with large sediment basins: the Taranaki oilfields and Waikato coalfields, for example, began life 40 million years ago as peat, sand and mud deposits in a huge rift to the west of New Zealand. Other areas of New Zealand, notably the recently submerged lower North Island and the eastern South Island, are comparatively mineral-poor.

In the pre-European era Māori used stone resources primarily to make tools. These artefacts became widely distributed: obsidian from Tūhua (Mayor Island), for example, is found in most archaeological sites throughout the country.

Although New Zealand has a diverse range of mineral resources, the country is a net importer of minerals. This is due in large part to the need to import petroleum products, the value of which equals all other imported minerals combined.

Energy minerals have proven to be the most valuable to the economy, with oil, gas, coal and geothermal energy being present. While the coal resource is substantial, oil, geothermal and gas reserves meet only a small proportion of New Zealand's needs. Abundant metallic minerals include gold, iron and silver, while the remaining metals need to be imported. The most important non-metallic minerals are limestone, building stone and aggregate, used primarily in roading and filling. Salt is produced locally, but not in sufficient quantities. Diatomite, nitrate, large amounts of phosphate, potash, gypsum, talc and sulphur are imported.

4

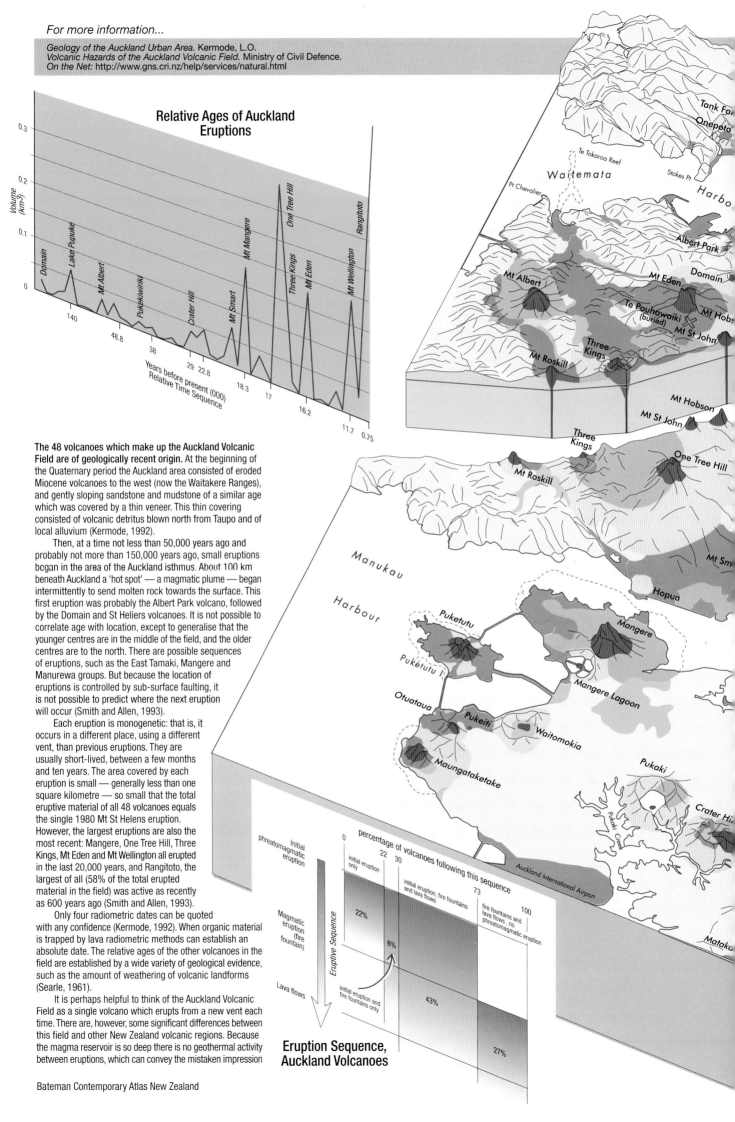

For more information...

Geology of the Auckland Urban Area. Kermode, L.O.
Volcanic Hazards of the Auckland Volcanic Field. Ministry of Civil Defence.
On the Net: http://www.gns.cri.nz/help/services/natural.html

Relative Ages of Auckland Eruptions

The 48 volcanoes which make up the Auckland Volcanic Field are of geologically recent origin. At the beginning of the Quaternary period the Auckland area consisted of eroded Miocene volcanoes to the west (now the Waitakere Ranges), and gently sloping sandstone and mudstone of a similar age which was covered by a thin veneer. This thin covering consisted of volcanic detritus blown north from Taupo and of local alluvium (Kermode, 1992).

Then, at a time not less than 50,000 years ago and probably not more than 150,000 years ago, small eruptions began in the area of the Auckland isthmus. About 100 km beneath Auckland a 'hot spot' — a magmatic plume — began intermittently to send molten rock towards the surface. This first eruption was probably the Albert Park volcano, followed by the Domain and St Heliers volcanoes. It is not possible to correlate age with location, except to generalise that the younger centres are in the middle of the field, and the older centres are to the north. There are possible sequences of eruptions, such as the East Tamaki, Mangere and Manurewa groups. But because the location of eruptions is controlled by sub-surface faulting, it is not possible to predict where the next eruption will occur (Smith and Allen, 1993).

Each eruption is monogenetic: that is, it occurs in a different place, using a different vent, than previous eruptions. They are usually short-lived, between a few months and ten years. The area covered by each eruption is small — generally less than one square kilometre — so small that the total eruptive material of all 48 volcanoes equals the single 1980 Mt St Helens eruption. However, the largest eruptions are also the most recent: Mangere, One Tree Hill, Three Kings, Mt Eden and Mt Wellington all erupted in the last 20,000 years, and Rangitoto, the largest of all (58% of the total erupted material in the field) was active as recently as 600 years ago (Smith and Allen, 1993).

Only four radiometric dates can be quoted with any confidence (Kermode, 1992). When organic material is trapped by lava radiometric methods can establish an absolute date. The relative ages of the other volcanoes in the field are established by a wide variety of geological evidence, such as the amount of weathering of volcanic landforms (Searle, 1961).

It is perhaps helpful to think of the Auckland Volcanic Field as a single volcano which erupts from a new vent each time. There are, however, some significant differences between this field and other New Zealand volcanic regions. Because the magma reservoir is so deep there is no geothermal activity between eruptions, which can convey the mistaken impression

Eruption Sequence, Auckland Volcanoes

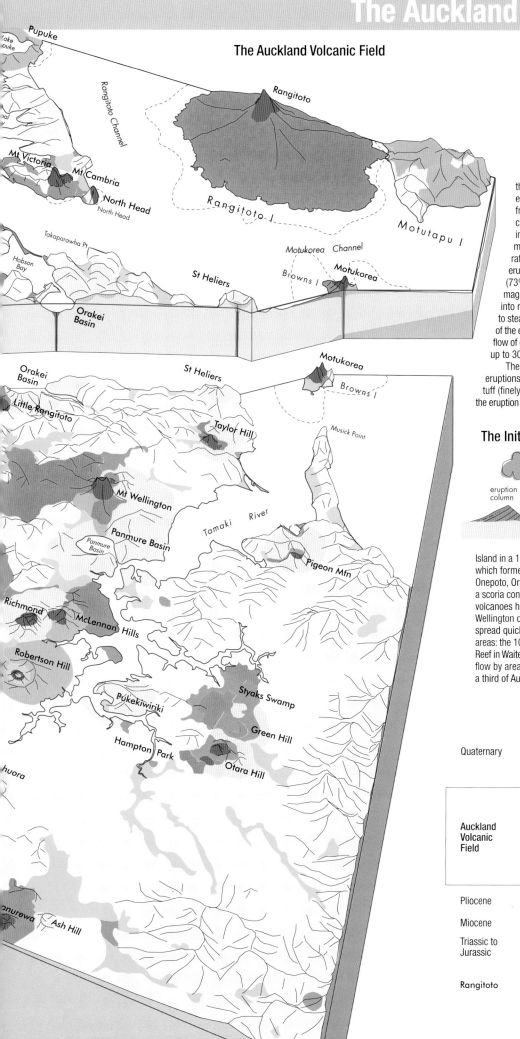

The Auckland Volcanic Field

that the field is extinct (Smith and Allen,1993). The eruptions consist of basaltic material, which differs from the rhyolite, andesite and dacite of the larger central North Island volcanoes. Basalt eruptions in the Auckland Volcanic Field are of a low viscosity, meaning that lava flows easily, spreading into fields rather than building large volcanic cones. The initial eruption from each vent is generally phreatomagmatic (73% of cases), an explosive mix generated by the magma contacting water: the magma cools and breaks into readily ejected fragments, while the water turns to steam, adding to the blast. The most destructive part of the eruption is the pyroclastic surge, a ground-hugging flow of gas and tephra which spreads outwards at speeds up to 300 km/h for distances of 1.5 km or more.

The landforms associated with phreatomagmatic eruptions include the maar, or crater itself; a blanket of tuff (finely powdered debris); ash deposited downwind of the eruption (in the case of Rangitoto, ash fell across Motutapu

The Initial Phreatomagmatic Eruption

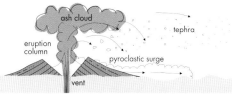

Island in a 12 km swath); a tuff-ring, created by base surges, which formed in over half the field's volcanoes (Pupuke, Onepoto, Orakei, Panmure and Pukaki are good examples); a scoria cone, formed by fire-fountaining (77% of Auckland's volcanoes have evidence of fire-fountaining, with the Mt Wellington cone being the largest); and lava flows, which spread quickly across the landscape, following low-lying areas: the 10 km flow from Three Kings volcano to Te Tokaroa Reef in Waitemata Harbour is the longest lava flow. The largest flow by area is on Rangitoto Island, which makes up about a third of Auckland's 75 km^2 of lava fields.

Geology of the Auckland Area

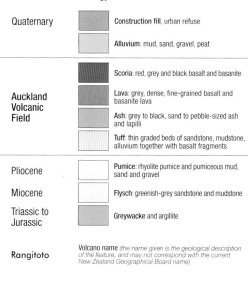

Quaternary		Construction fill, urban refuse
		Alluvium: mud, sand, gravel, peat
Auckland Volcanic Field		Scoria: red, grey and black basalt and basanite
		Lava: grey, dense, fine-grained basalt and basanite lava
		Ash: grey to black, sand to pebble-sized ash and lapilli
		Tuff: thin graded beds of sandstone, mudstone, alluvium together with basalt fragments
Pliocene		Pumice: rhyolite pumice and pumiceous mud, sand and gravel
Miocene		Flysch: greenish-grey sandstone and mudstone
Triassic to Jurassic		Greywacke and argillite
Rangitoto		Volcano name (the name given is the geological description of the feature, and may not correspond with the current New Zealand Geographical Board name)

5

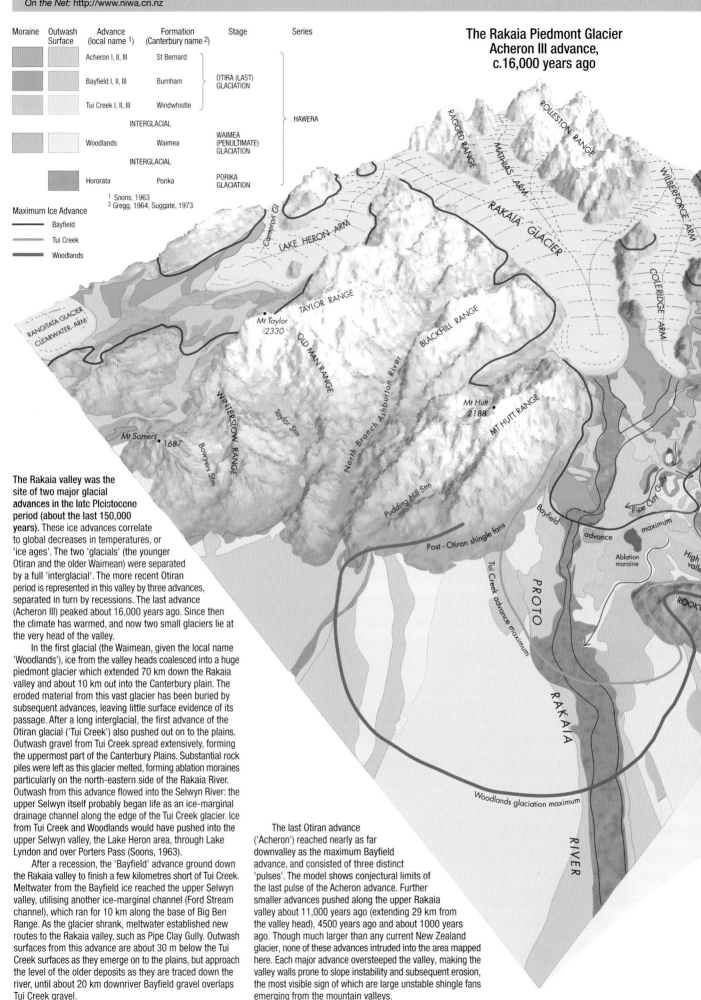

For more information...

Landforms of New Zealand. Soons, J.M. and Selby, M.J.
Prehistoric New Zealand. Stevens, G.R., McGlone, M.S. and McCulloch, B.
On the Net: http://www.niwa.cri.nz

**The Rakaia Piedmont Glacier
Acheron III advance,
c.16,000 years ago**

Moraine	Outwash Surface	Advance (local name [1])	Formation (Canterbury name [2])	Stage	Series
		Acheron I, II, III	St Bernard		
		Bayfield I, II, III	Burnham	OTIRA (LAST) GLACIATION	
		Tui Creek I, II, III	Windwhistle		
		INTERGLACIAL			HAWERA
		Woodlands	Waimea	WAIMEA (PENULTIMATE) GLACIATION	
		INTERGLACIAL			
		Hororata	Porika	PORIKA GLACIATION	

[1] Soons, 1963
[2] Gregg, 1964, Suggate, 1973

Maximum Ice Advance
— Bayfield
— Tui Creek
— Woodlands

Mt Taylor 2330

RAGGED RANGE
ROLLESTON RANGE
MATHIAS ARM
RAKAIA GLACIER
WILBERFORCE ARM
COLERIDGE ARM

Cameron Gl
LAKE HERON ARM
TAYLOR RANGE
OLD MAN RANGE
BLACKHILL RANGE
WINTERSLOW RANGE
Taylor Stm
North Branch, Ashburton River
Mt Hutt 2188
MT HUTT RANGE

RANGITATA GLACIER
CLEARWATER ARM

Mt Somers • 1687
Bowyers Stm
Pudding Hill Stm
Post - Otiran shingle fans

Bayfield
Pipe Clay Gully
Ford Stream
advance   maximum
Ablation moraine
High Peak valley
Tui Creek advance maximum
PROTO
RAKAIA
ROOKWO
Woodlands glaciation maximum
RIVER

The Rakaia valley was the site of two major glacial advances in the late Pleistocene period (about the last 150,000 years). These ice advances correlate to global decreases in temperatures, or 'ice ages'. The two 'glacials' (the younger Otiran and the older Waimean) were separated by a full 'interglacial'. The more recent Otiran period is represented in this valley by three advances, separated in turn by recessions. The last advance (Acheron III) peaked about 16,000 years ago. Since then the climate has warmed, and now two small glaciers lie at the very head of the valley.

In the first glacial (the Waimean, given the local name 'Woodlands'), ice from the valley heads coalesced into a huge piedmont glacier which extended 70 km down the Rakaia valley and about 10 km out into the Canterbury plain. The eroded material from this vast glacier has been buried by subsequent advances, leaving little surface evidence of its passage. After a long interglacial, the first advance of the Otiran glacial ('Tui Creek') also pushed out on to the plains. Outwash gravel from Tui Creek spread extensively, forming the uppermost part of the Canterbury Plains. Substantial rock piles were left as this glacier melted, forming ablation moraines particularly on the north-eastern side of the Rakaia River. Outwash from this advance flowed into the Selwyn River: the upper Selwyn itself probably began life as an ice-marginal drainage channel along the edge of the Tui Creek glacier. Ice from Tui Creek and Woodlands would have pushed into the upper Selwyn valley, the Lake Heron area, through Lake Lyndon and over Porters Pass (Soons, 1963).

After a recession, the 'Bayfield' advance ground down the Rakaia valley to finish a few kilometres short of Tui Creek. Meltwater from the Bayfield ice reached the upper Selwyn valley, utilising another ice-marginal channel (Ford Stream channel), which ran for 10 km along the base of Big Ben Range. As the glacier shrank, meltwater established new routes to the Rakaia valley, such as Pipe Clay Gully. Outwash surfaces from this advance are about 30 m below the Tui Creek surfaces as they emerge on to the plains, but approach the level of the older deposits as they are traced down the river, until about 20 km downriver Bayfield gravel overlaps Tui Creek gravel.

The last Otiran advance ('Acheron') reached nearly as far downvalley as the maximum Bayfield advance, and consisted of three distinct 'pulses'. The model shows conjectural limits of the last pulse of the Acheron advance. Further smaller advances pushed along the upper Rakaia valley about 11,000 years ago (extending 29 km from the valley head), 4500 years ago and about 1000 years ago. Though much larger than any current New Zealand glacier, none of these advances intruded into the area mapped here. Each major advance oversteeped the valley, making the valley walls prone to slope instability and subsequent erosion, the most visible sign of which are large unstable shingle fans emerging from the mountain valleys.

Retreat of Permanent Snowline, 23,000 years ago to the Present

Time before present (thousands of years)

End of the large South Island glaciers

last Acheron advances

Late Glacial

The 'Hypsothermal' warm period

New Zealand at the Last Glacial Maximum (St Bernard formation, Otiran stage) 20,000 years ago

permanent snow and ice

fellfield: rock and gravel, low-growing vegetation

shrubland and grassland

grassland

forest: conifer-broadleaf in the north, beech elsewhere

present coastline

Waikato

Piarere gap

Taranaki

Cape Farewell

Rakaia

Avoca Glacier

Mt Enys
2195

CRAGIEBURN RANGE

Broken River

Lake Lyndon

TORLESSE RA.

Porters Pass

Ben More
1657

BIG BEN RANGE

Kowai River

lwyn River

NGE

Piarere Gap
an old outlet of the Waikato River, the gap is now traversed by S.H. 29 between Hinuera and Lake Karapiro

see map at left

Notes:
1. Shrubland and grassland contained small areas of forest; forested regions had open grassland on floodplains and exposed sites.
2. The coastline 20,000 years ago is inferred from oceanographic soundings, and in some places is of questionable reliability.

The Quaternary Period was influenced by the latter stage of the 'Ice Age', where global temperatures in the coolest periods ('glacials') often fell by 5°C or more. Massive ice sheets formed in the high latitudes of both hemispheres, taking up so much water that sea levels dropped by over a hundred metres. Glaciation had a profound shaping effect on New Zealand landscapes. Virtually all South Island high country valleys have been eroded and their sides oversteepened by glacial action. An ice sheet covered the South Island alpine chain, extending ice tongues 50 km and more down valleys. Increased sediment supply from these vast glaciers resulted in widespread sediment deposition in lowland areas. Fine silt was blown from these areas, settling on adjacent hills, forming thick sheets of loess.

During the last glacial maximum (around 20,000 years ago) sea level receded about 120 m below the present level, exposing continuous land from Stewart Island to beyond North Cape. New Zealand at this time was 50% larger than at present, the extra land consisting of lowland outwash surfaces and large areas of dunes, particularly between Cape Farewell and Taranaki where outwash sediment was transported north along the coast. At times during this period the Waikato River flowed northwards through the Piarere gap, over the Hauraki Plain and emptied into the Pacific Ocean.

At the last glacial maximum the climate was not only cooler by 5°C, but also it was much drier, and the winds were stronger. This harsh climate limited forest growth to the north of the North Island. Further south scrub and grassland dominated, interspersed with small patches of beech forest. The South Island was generally cold, arid and treeless.

The bleak conditions affected bird communities. Open-land birds, such as the moa, kea and giant eagle, expanded their range, while forest-dwellers survived in isolated sheltered pockets of forest or in the far north.

6

Southern Hemisphere Pressure Field
(mean sea level, hPa)

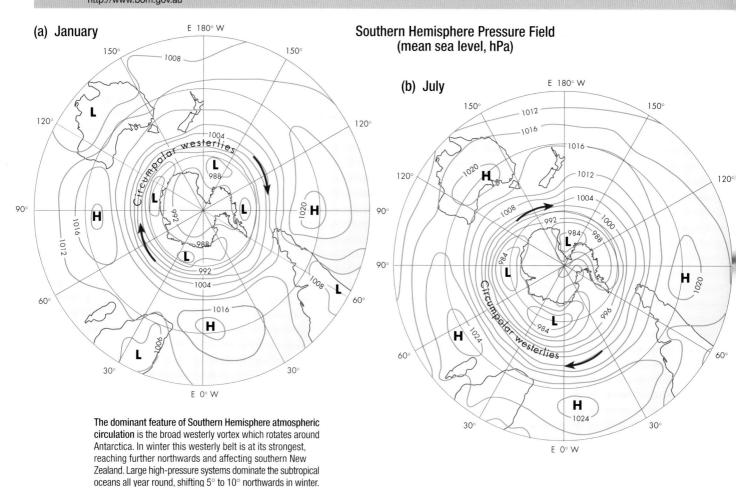

(a) January

(b) July

The dominant feature of Southern Hemisphere atmospheric circulation is the broad westerly vortex which rotates around Antarctica. In winter this westerly belt is at its strongest, reaching further northwards and affecting southern New Zealand. Large high-pressure systems dominate the subtropical oceans all year round, shifting 5° to 10° northwards in winter.

Southern Hemisphere Cyclonic and Anticyclonic Activity

In January high pressure systems are found just to the west of the southern continents in a broad belt wrapped around the globe between 30°S and 40°S latitude. Local anticyclonic activity is focused in the Great Australian Bight and in the Tasman Sea to the west of the North Island. Cyclones, often with embedded cold fronts, are forced southwards of 60°S, though some breed over north-west Australia (Sturman and Tapper, 1996).

In July anticyclonic activity decreases and moves northwards to about 30°S, though the occasional 'blocking high' is found to the east of the South Island. By contrast cyclonic activity intensifies, spreading into the 40°S to 60°S area and increasing greatly near Antarctica. New Zealand experiences a winter mixture of cyclonic and anticyclonic activity.

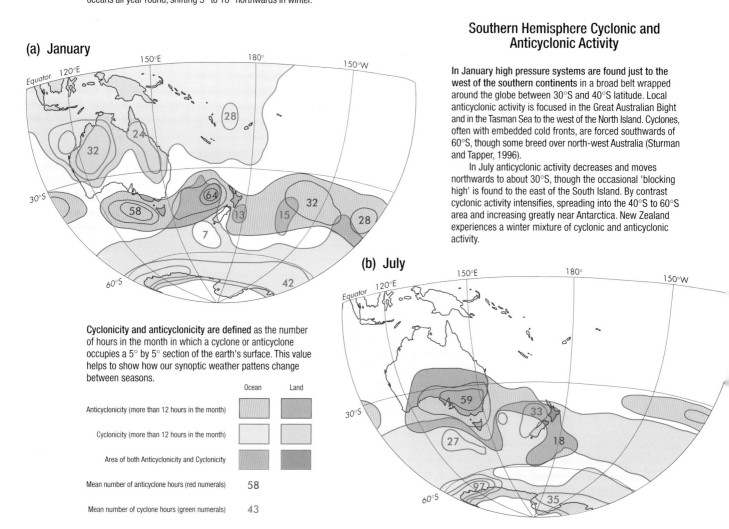

(a) January

(b) July

Cyclonicity and anticyclonicity are defined as the number of hours in the month in which a cyclone or anticyclone occupies a 5° by 5° section of the earth's surface. This value helps to show how our synoptic weather pattens change between seasons.

	Ocean	Land
Anticyclonicity (more than 12 hours in the month)		
Cyclonicity (more than 12 hours in the month)		
Area of both Anticyclonicity and Cyclonicity		
Mean number of anticyclone hours (red numerals)	58	
Mean number of cyclone hours (green numerals)	43	

New Zealand Climate Districts

A1   Warm humid summers, mild winters. Annual rainfall 1000mm to 1500mm with a winter maximum. Prevailing wind south-west but occasional strong gales and heavy rain from the east or north-east from Hamilton northwards.

A2   Similar to A1 but much wetter. Rainfall 1500mm to 2500mm.

B1   Sunny rather sheltered areas which receive rains of very high intensity at times from the north-east and north. Very warm summers and mild winters. Annual rainfall 1000mm to 2000mm with a winter maximum.

B2   Less sunny than B1. Cooler winters with frequent ground frosts.

C1   Very warm summers, day temperatures occasionally rise above 30°C with dry fohn north-westerlies. Annual rainfall 1000mm to 1500mm; marked decrease in amount and reliability of rain in spring and summer. Moderate winter temperatures with maximum rainfall in this season.

C2   Drier than C1; rainfall 600mm to 1000mm. Summer droughts common.

C3   Cooler and wetter than C1. Very heavy rains at times from south and south-east. Annual rainfall mainly 1500mm to 2500mm.

D1   West to north-west winds prevail with relatively frequent gales. Annual rainfall 900mm to 1300mm. Rainfall reliable and evenly distributed throughout the year. Warm summers and mild winters.

D2   Wetter than D1 with annual rainfall 1300mm to 2000mm.

E1   Small temperature range. High rainfall increasing rapidly inland with height. Minimum rainfall in winter in the south. Prevailing winds south-west but gales infrequent in spite of exposed coastline.

E2   More sheltered than E1. Little seasonal variation in rainfall but a larger range in temperature with frequent winter frosts.

F1   Low annual rainfalls of 500mm to 800mm; in the south, slightly more in summer than in other seasons. Warm summers with occasional hot fohn north-westerlies giving temperatures above 30°C. Cool winters with frequent frost and occasional snow. North-easterlies prevail with north-westerlies more frequent inland.

F2   Cooler and wetter than F1 with rainfall 800mm to 1500mm. North-westerlies predominate with occasional very strong gales especially along river valleys. Snow may lie for weeks in winter.

F3   Semi-arid areas with annual rainfall 300mm to 500mm. Very hot summers and cold winters.

G1   Warm summers and cool winters. Rainfall 500mm to 900mm evenly distributed but slight winter minimum.

G2   Wetter than G1 with rainfall 900mm to 1300mm. Generally windier with frequent showers in coastal districts.

M   High rainfall mountain climate. Conditions vary greatly with altitude and exposure.

Lambert Conformal Conic Projection
Scale: 1: 5 640 000

50   100   150   200   250   300 km

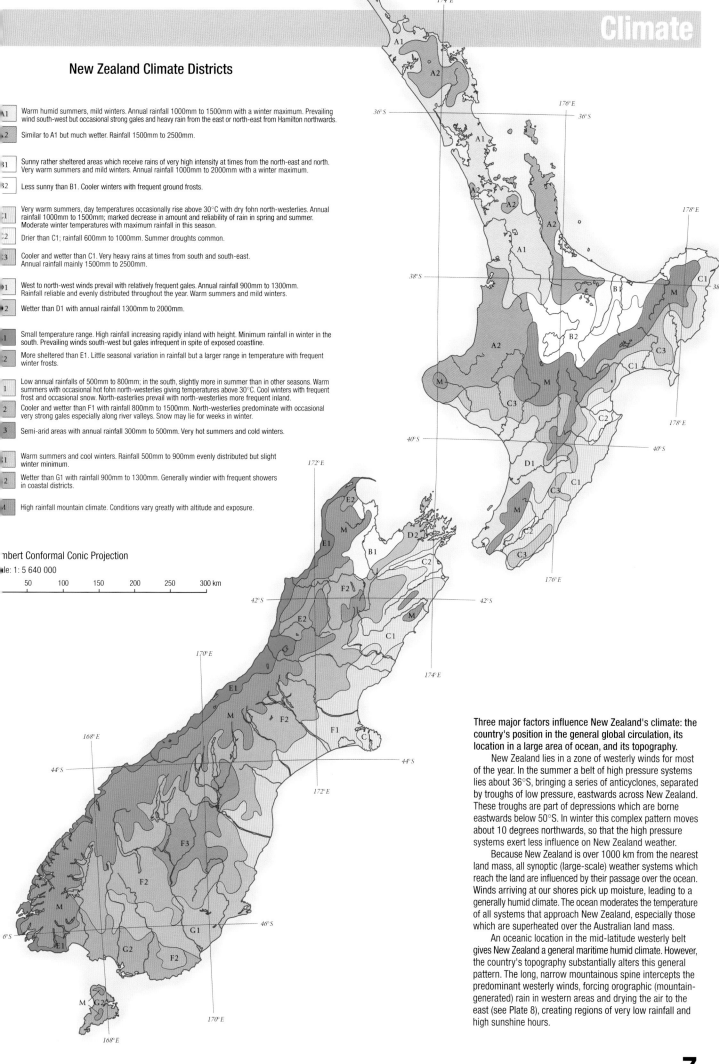

Three major factors influence New Zealand's climate: the country's position in the general global circulation, its location in a large area of ocean, and its topography.

New Zealand lies in a zone of westerly winds for most of the year. In the summer a belt of high pressure systems lies about 36°S, bringing a series of anticyclones, separated by troughs of low pressure, eastwards across New Zealand. These troughs are part of depressions which are borne eastwards below 50°S. In winter this complex pattern moves about 10 degrees northwards, so that the high pressure systems exert less influence on New Zealand weather.

Because New Zealand is over 1000 km from the nearest land mass, all synoptic (large-scale) weather systems which reach the land are influenced by their passage over the ocean. Winds arriving at our shores pick up moisture, leading to a generally humid climate. The ocean moderates the temperature of all systems that approach New Zealand, especially those which are superheated over the Australian land mass.

An oceanic location in the mid-latitude westerly belt gives New Zealand a general maritime humid climate. However, the country's topography substantially alters this general pattern. The long, narrow mountainous spine intercepts the predominant westerly winds, forcing orographic (mountain-generated) rain in western areas and drying the air to the east (see Plate 8), creating regions of very low rainfall and high sunshine hours.

For more information...

Waters of New Zealand. Mosley, M.P.
Water & Atmosphere. NIWA.
On the Net: http://www.niwa.cri.nz

There are three major producers of rainfall in New Zealand: major (synoptic) weather systems, such as troughs of low pressure and cyclones; orographic uplift, in which moisture-laden clouds are forced upwards by mountain barriers, at which time the moisture condenses and rain falls; and mesoscale systems such as thunderstorms and squalls along the line of fronts (Tomlinson, 1992).

The regional difference in average annual rainfall is determined mainly by topography. The result of a large alpine barrier which runs the length of both main islands is that western regions receive much more orographic rain than eastern regions, the difference being marked in the south.

Latitude has little to do with rainfall amount. However, the weather systems which generate this rainfall differ greatly between northern and southern areas. Northern and central North Island areas are subject to heavy short-period rainfalls from convective showers, thunderstorms and the remnants of tropical cyclones. The West Coast receives longer-period rain, falling from regular troughs of low pressure crossing the South Island from the west. Annual totals in this region are some of the highest in the world. Areas lying in the lee of the Southern Alps receive much less rain. The westerly airflow is warmed and dried by the time it reaches eastern districts: most of the rain received by these areas is associated with southerly fronts, convective storms and coastal drizzle.

Rainfall is distributed uniformly thoughout the year in most regions. The greatest variation in *seasonal* rainfall is in the north: almost twice as much rain falls in winter as in summer in Northland. The pattern gradually reverses as one progresses southwards, so that in inland Southland rain falls in a summer maximum generated by convective storms.

The areas of greatest *annual* variability in rainfall are eastern and northern districts, which are therefore most likely to suffer droughts or unusually wet years. These areas tend to receive weather patterns that are decaying — southerly fronts, mid-latitude cyclones — and are difficult to forecast.

Annual Rainfall

Rainfall (mm)

	12800
	9600
	6400
	4800
	3200
	2400
	1600
	1200
	800
	600
	400

Whenuapai
Highest 1-hour rainfall
107mm, 16 February 1966

Tauranga
Highest 10-minute rainfall
34mm, 17 April 1948

Dawson Falls
Highest 48-hour rainfall
844mm, 10-11 August 1967

Lambert Conformal Conic Projection

Scale: 1: 5 640 000

0   50   100   150   200   250   300 km

Colliers Creek
Highest 12-hour rainfall
473mm, 22 January 1994
Highest 24-hour rainfall
682mm, 21-22 January 1994

Tuke Hut
Highest 1-month rainfall
2747mm, October 1988

Waterfall Creek
Highest 12-month rainfall
14108mm, Nov 1982 - Oct 1983

A

B

Clyde
Lowest 3-month rainfall
10mm, July-September 1966

Alexandra
Lowest 6-month rainfall
53mm, March-August 1966
Lowest 12-month rainfall
167mm, Nov 1963 - Oct 1964

Bateman Contemporary Atlas New Zealand

Rainfall Cross-Section
Bruce Bay to Banks Peninsula

N.B. The physical cross-section scale (brown scale) rises in increments of 1000 metres above sea level, while the rainfall cross-section (blue scale) increases in increments of 1000 mm rainfall per annum. While rainfall often increases with elevation, the two scales are not causally linked. Thus 4000 metres above sea level is not an annual rainfall of 4000 mm. So, at point X on the cross section annual rainfall is 6500 mm, and the elevation of the physical cross-section is 2600 metres.

Area of highest rainfall. The air is now about -3°C, and snow may fall.

Air cools as it rises, causing condensation and rainfall; convection storms may form. The air loses 6°C/km of ascent altitude.

North-west 'fohn' winds warm as they descend the eastern side of the mountains. The air gains 10°C/km of descent altitude, reaching about 27°C by sea level.

Westerly winds bring moist air at 15°C. Air 'dams up' west of the mountains.

Rainfall 'spillover' extends eastwards, feeding hydro lakes in the Mackenzie Basin.

A region of light air may form immediately upwind of the mountains.

Annual Rainfall (mm)

13
12
11
10
90
80
70
60
50

metres a.s.l.
4000
3000
2000
1000
0

Bruce Bay

Aoraki Mt Cook 3754

MAIN DIVIDE

SOUTHERN   ALPS

TWO TH RANG

A

X

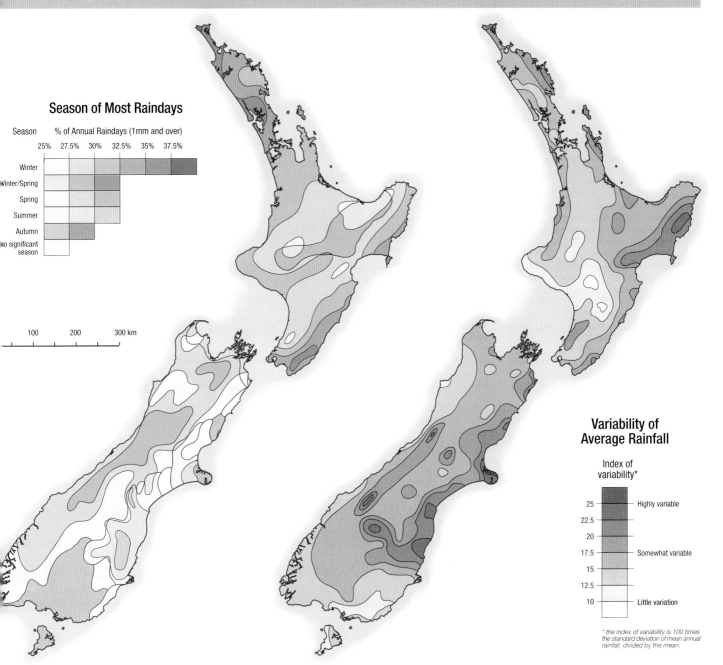

Season of Most Raindays

Season	% of Annual Raindays (1mm and over)
	25% 27.5% 30% 32.5% 35% 37.5%
Winter	
Winter/Spring	
Spring	
Summer	
Autumn	
No significant season	

100   200   300 km

Variability of Average Rainfall

Index of variability*

25	Highly variable
22.5	
20	
17.5	Somewhat variable
15	
12.5	
10	Little variation

* the index of variability is 100 times the standard deviation of mean annual rainfall, divided by the mean.

Westerly Rainfall Events and SALPEX

…e processes involved in a westerly rainfall event across … central South Island are understood as follows: (1) moist … is brought by westerly winds from the Tasman Sea; (2) air …locked, and 'dams' up to 100 km west of the mountains, …ing sufficient time for the formation of rain, which (3) rises …d is cooled. Since cold air holds less moisture, some of the …isture condenses and falls as rain or snow; (4) the air may … unstable, or already contain significant cloud: if so, a small …ward surge will lead to convective storms; (5) the area of …hest rainfall is just west of the main divide, where up to …m may fall annually; (6) rain is blown downwind by the …sterly, sometimes 'spilling over' 10-20 km downwind. The …ount of spillover is determined by the strength of the wind, … stability of the air, and the volume of moisture in the air; … the air warms as it descends. Dry air warms faster than …ist air cools, so the air temperature becomes warmer than …ore it reached the mountains; and (8) the dry nor'westerly … flow spreads across the Canterbury Plains, but near the

coast it is sometimes blocked by the north-east sea breeze.

Meteorologists seeking a better understanding of mountain influences on New Zealand weather have begun a study called the Southern Alps Experiment (SALPEX). In particular, they want to understand factors determining the intensity and distribution of heavy rainfall, the west to east spread of precipitation across the Southern Alps, and the intensity of lee wind storms and associated warming.

SALPEX is a joint venture between NIWA, CSIRO (Australia), the Meteorological Service, and universities in New Zealand and overseas. It consists of three phases, each of which combines archived weather data, computer modelling and field campaigns.

Results from SALPEX will generate a clearer picture of what happens during intense rainfall events, helping to develop a predictive model, which will be useful for the management of the hydro-electric power stations to the east of the main divide. It will also be of benefit to recreationists and farmers.

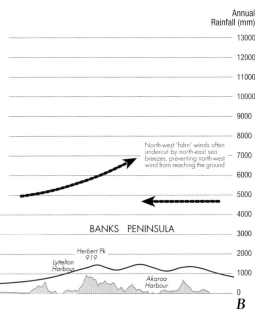

Annual Rainfall (mm)

13000
12000
11000
10000
9000
8000
7000
6000
5000
4000
3000
2000
1000
0

North-west 'fohn' winds often undercut by north-east sea breezes, preventing north-west wind from reaching the ground

Low relative humidities associated with north-west winds are unusually low for the temperate climate

Rainfall on the plains is a mixture of convective storms, easterly storms and south-easterly frontal events

BANKS PENINSULA

Mt Somers 1687

…gitata …ver

Rakaia River   CANTERBURY PLAINS

Herbert Pk 919

Lyttelton Harbour

Akaroa Harbour

For more information...

Newsletter. Meteorological Society of New Zealand (quarterly).
On the Net: http://www.niwa.cri.nz/NIWA_research/climate.html
http://www.pmel.noaa.gov/toga-tao/el-nino/nino-home-low.html

El Niño and La Niña climatic conditions have a marked effect on New Zealand's rainfall. This can be demonstrated with a comparison of rainfall between January 1997 and January 1998.

The Southern Oscillation Index (SOI) measures pressure differences between Tahiti and Darwin, the recognised indication of which phase of the El Niño/La Niña cycle affects our weather. Highly negative SOI values, with high pressures over Australia and low pressures over the eastern Pacific, occur a few months before an El Niño episode. The reverse situation, with positive SOI values, heralds a La Niña event.

High positive SOI values had by January 1997 developed into a weak La Niña episode. Conditions were very dry in the north of the North Island and in the west and south of the South Island (between 25% and 50% of normal), with record low rainfall in Fiordland (less than 25% of normal). Cyclone Drena brought above-average rainfall in the east from Wairarapa to Otago. An unusually high number of anticyclones to the south of New Zealand brought frequent cool east and south-east winds to eastern districts. Rainfall in the east was between 150% and 250% of normal. Temperatures were well below average, particularly in Canterbury and Marlborough, due to a lack of warm north-westerlies.

By January 1998 New Zealand was in the grip of an El Niño event. Initially forecasters thought this event, which began in mid-1997, would be worse than the deep El Niño event of 1982–83, but it had moderated somewhat by year's end. Even so, it was a significant event. The westerly pattern was restored, with the south-west changes containing little or no rain. Overall rainfall was well down, with only a few stations recording above average rain, and many sites experienced record temperatures. Northern and eastern areas had little precipitation (in most places less than 15% of normal), a reversal of the 1997 situation. Drought spread throughout these areas, the severest conditions being experienced in Marlborough.

air pressure difference between Tahiti and Darwin

Southern Oscillation Index
1967–1998

Rainfall January 1997
La Niña conditions
Selected Climate Stations

Rainfall below normal

(mm)
100 — January Average
— January Actual
0 —
Rainfall Station

1cm : 125mm

Rainfall above normal

(mm) — January Actual
100 — January Average
0 —
Rainfall Station

NB: Oblique Distortion:
not a true projection

6. Weakening of east
trade winds can resul
droughts in Indonesia,
Australia and New Zea

Normal Conditions
in the Tropical Paci

Convective Loop

5. Rainfall generated in
rising air above warmest
water: western Pacific wet,
eastern Pacific relatively dry

1. Easterly Trade winds
blow across equatorial Po

2. Sea surface 0.5m higher
at Indonesia than at Ecuador

3. Sea Surface Temperature
(SST) 8°C higher in the west

Equator

Trade Winds

AUSTRALIA

17°C Thermocline

Bateman Contemporary Atlas New Zealand.

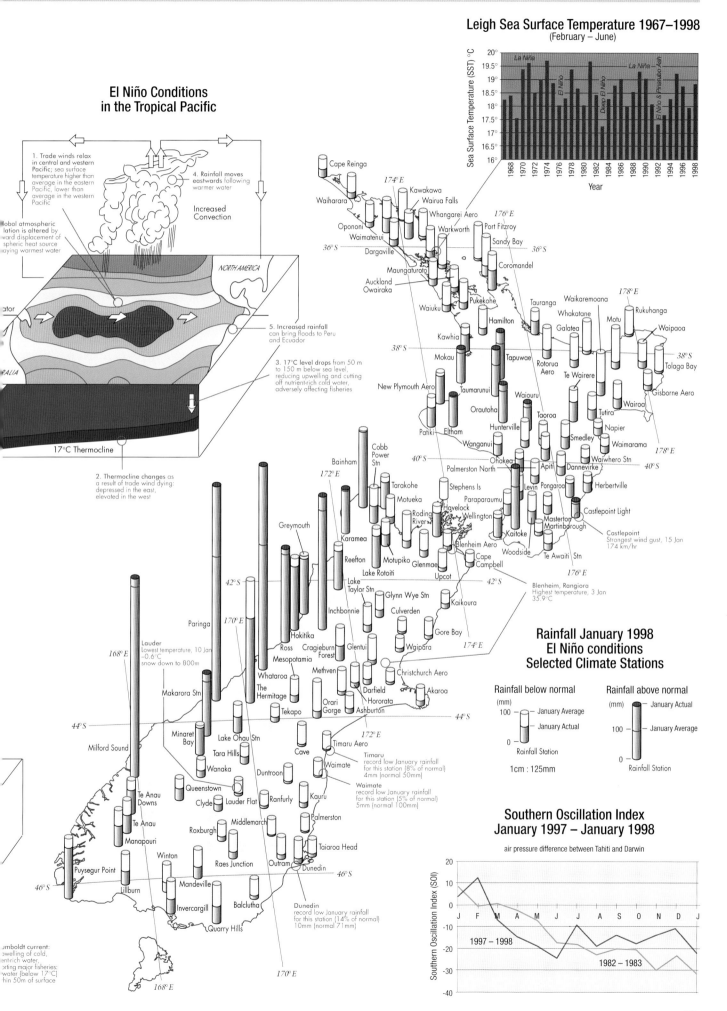

El Niño Conditions in the Tropical Pacific

1. Trade winds relax in central and western Pacific; sea surface temperature higher than average in the eastern Pacific, lower than average in the western Pacific

Global atmospheric circulation is altered by eastward displacement of atmospheric heat source overlaying warmest water

4. Rainfall moves eastwards following warmer water

Increased Convection

NORTH AMERICA

AUSTRALIA

equator

5. Increased rainfall can bring floods to Peru and Ecuador

3. 17°C level drops from 50 m to 150 m below sea level, reducing upwelling and cutting off nutrient-rich cold water, adversely affecting fisheries

17°C Thermocline

2. Thermocline changes as a result of trade wind dying: depressed in the east, elevated in the west

Humboldt current: upwelling of cold, nutrient-rich water, supporting major fisheries; water (below 17°C) within 50m of surface

Leigh Sea Surface Temperature 1967–1998
(February – June)

La Niña
El Niño
Deep El Niño
La Niña
El Niño & Pinatubo Ash

Sea Surface Temperature (SST) °C

20°
19.5°
19°
18.5°
18°
17.5°
17°
16.5°
16°

1968 1970 1972 1974 1976 1978 1980 1982 1984 1986 1988 1990 1992 1994 1996 1998

Year

Rainfall January 1998
El Niño conditions
Selected Climate Stations

Rainfall below normal
(mm)
100 — January Average
— January Actual
0
Rainfall Station

Rainfall above normal
(mm)
— January Actual
100 — January Average
0
Rainfall Station

1cm : 125mm

Southern Oscillation Index
January 1997 – January 1998

air pressure difference between Tahiti and Darwin

Southern Oscillation Index (SOI)

20
10
0
-10
-20
-30
-40

J F M A M J J A S O N D J

1997 – 1998

1982 – 1983

Cape Reinga
Waiharara
Kawakawa
Wairua Falls
Whangarei Aero
Opononi
Warkworth
Port Fitzroy
Sandy Bay
Waimatenui
Dargaville
Coromandel
Maungaturoto
Auckland
Owairaka
Pukekohe
Tauranga
Waikaremoana
Rukuhanga
Waiuku
Hamilton
Whakatane
Galatea
Motu
Waipaoa
Kawhia
Mokau
Tapuwae
Rotorua Aero
Te Wairere
Tolaga Bay
New Plymouth Aero
Taumarunui
Waiouru
Wairoa
Gisborne Aero
Orautoha
Taoroa
Tutira
Patiki
Eltham
Hunterville
Smedley
Napier
Wanganui
Waimarama
Ohakea
Apiti
Waiwhero Stn
Dannevirke
Cobb Power Stn
Bainham
Palmerston North
Stephens Is
Levin
Pongaroa
Herbertville
Tarakohe
Paraparaumu
Castlepoint Light
Motueka
Roding River
Havelock
Wellington
Masterton
Martinborough
Castlepoint
Greymouth
Karamea
Kaitoke
Woodside
Te Awaiti Stn
Reefton
Motupiko
Blenheim Aero
Cape Campbell
Lake Rotoiti
Glenmae
Upcot
Lake Taylor Stn
Glynn Wye Stn
Kaikoura
Inchbonnie
Culverden
Paringa
Hokitika
Cragieburn Forest
Glentui
Waipara
Gore Bay
Ross
Mesopotamia
Lauder
Whataroa
Methven
Christchurch Aero
Makarora Stn
The Hermitage
Darfield
Akaroa
Tekapo
Orari Gorge
Hororata
Ashburton
Minaret Bay
Lake Ohau Stn
Timaru Aero
Tara Hills
Cave
Timaru
Milford Sound
Wanaka
Duntroon
Waimate
Queenstown
Lauder Flat
Ranfurly
Kauru
Te Anau Downs
Clyde
Middlemarch
Palmerston
Te Anau
Roxburgh
Manapouri
Winton
Raes Junction
Taiaroa Head
Puysegur Point
Mandeville
Outram
Dunedin
Lillburn
Invercargill
Balclutha
Quarry Hills

Castlepoint
Strongest wind gust, 15 Jan
174 km/hr

Blenheim, Rangiora
Highest temperature, 3 Jan
35.9°C

Lauder
Lowest temperature, 10 Jan
-0.6°C
snow down to 800m

Timaru
record low January rainfall for this station (8% of normal)
4mm (normal 50mm)

Waimate
record low January rainfall for this station (5% of normal)
5mm (normal 100mm)

Dunedin
record low January rainfall for this station (14% of normal)
10mm (normal 71mm)

168° E
170° E
172° E
174° E
176° E
178° E

36° S
38° S
40° S
42° S
44° S
46° S

9

For more information...

The New Zealand Weather Book. Brenstaum, E.
Newsletter. Meteorological Society of New Zealand (quarterly).
On the Net: http://www.niwa.cri.nz/NIWA_research/climate.html

Along with rainfall (see Plate 8), temperature, sunshine and wind comprise the four major components of climate. Each factor interacts with the others to give New Zealand its long-term climatic patterns.

Mean annual temperature is influenced by both seasonal and diurnal (day/night) variation. Though extreme temperature maximums are just as high in the south as in the north — Dunedin and Invercargill have recorded temperatures as high as any recorded at Auckland (Tomlinson, 1976) — the south experiences much colder winters. This means that temperature variation is much greater in the South Island, with inland Central Otago having a temperature regime nearest to a continental climate (warm days and cold nights; warm summers and cold winters). Diurnal variation is not as important a factor in a temperate maritime climate.

The amount of sunshine received by any location is a factor of latitude (southern locations have shorter days in winter and longer days in summer) and cloudiness. The sunniest areas are in Nelson and Marlborough, with a substantial portion of the country receiving more than 2000 hours of sunshine annually. The southernmost parts of the South Island lie at the northern edge of a zone of increasing cloudiness: Invercargill receives 1600 sunshine hours annually, while Auckland Island 400 km to the south receives an average of less than 1000 hours of sunshine each year.

Predominant winds are generally from the west, in keeping with the synoptic weather patterns. These tend to be stronger in southern districts, but are influenced by topography: strong winds are funnelled through the Manawatu Gorge, Cook Strait and Foveaux Strait. The West Coast and most of the southern and central South Island is subjected to south-westerlies, while eastern districts experience north-westerlies inland, and north-easterly sea breezes near the coast. Seasonal variations include periods of calm in the winter and sea breezes in summer.

Lambert Conformal Conic Projection

Scale: 1: 5 640 000

0   50   100   150   200   250   300 km

Mean Annual Temperature

°C

- 15
- 14
- 13
- 12
- 11
- 10
- 9
- 8

Ruatoria
Highest North Island maximum temperature
39.2°C, 7 February 1973

Chateau Tongariro
Lowest North Island minimum temperature
-13.6°C, 7 July 1937

Rangiora & Jordan
Highest maximum temperature
42.4°C, 7 February 1973

Ophir
Lowest minimum temperature
–21.6°C, 3 July 1995

not analysed
under 8°C

Extreme Temperature Maximums

average number of days per year
with a maximum temperature of
25°C or greater

Days

- 30
- 20
- 10
- 5
- 1

0   100   200   300 k

Bateman Contemporary Atlas New Zealand

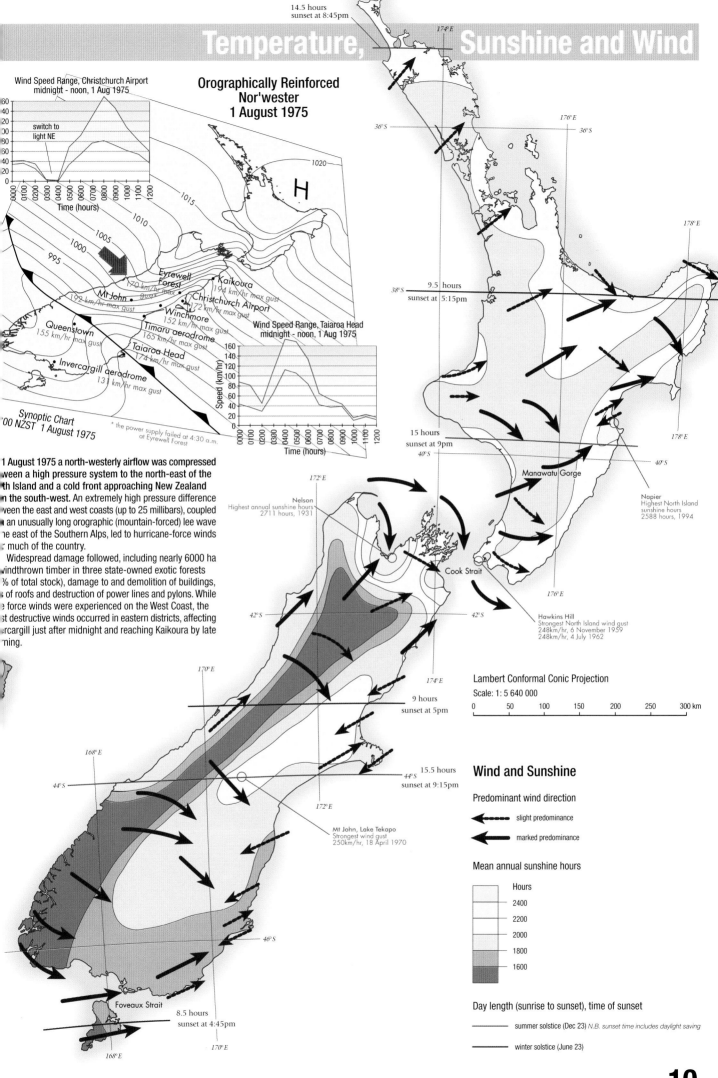

Wind Speed Range, Christchurch Airport
midnight - noon, 1 Aug 1975

switch to light NE

Time (hours)

Orographically Reinforced Nor'wester
1 August 1975

H

1020
1015
1010
1005
1000
995

Eyrewell Forest
170 km/hr max gust

Kaikoura
194 km/hr max gust

Mt John
192 km/hr max gust

Christchurch Airport
172 km/hr max gust

Winchmore

Queenstown
155 km/hr max gust

Timaru aerodrome
152 km/hr max gust

Taiaroa Head
165 km/hr max gust
174 km/hr max gust

Invercargill aerodrome
131 km/hr max gust

Synoptic Chart
00 NZST 1 August 1975

* the power supply failed at 4:30 a.m. at Eyrewell Forest

Wind Speed Range, Taiaroa Head
midnight - noon, 1 Aug 1975

Speed (km/hr)

Time (hours)

1 August 1975 a north-westerly airflow was compressed
ween a high pressure system to the north-east of the
th Island and a cold front approaching New Zealand
n the south-west. An extremely high pressure difference
ween the east and west coasts (up to 25 millibars), coupled
an unusually long orographic (mountain-forced) lee wave
e east of the Southern Alps, led to hurricane-force winds
much of the country.

Widespread damage followed, including nearly 6000 ha
indthrown timber in three state-owned exotic forests
% of total stock), damage to and demolition of buildings,
of roofs and destruction of power lines and pylons. While
force winds were experienced on the West Coast, the
t destructive winds occurred in eastern districts, affecting
rcargill just after midnight and reaching Kaikoura by late
ning.

14.5 hours
sunset at 8:45pm

174° E
176° E
178° E
36° S

9.5 hours
sunset at 5:15pm
38° S

15 hours
sunset at 9pm
40° S

Manawatu Gorge

Napier
Highest North Island
sunshine hours
2588 hours, 1994

Nelson
Highest annual sunshine hours
2711 hours, 1931

Cook Strait

Hawkins Hill
Strongest North Island wind gust
248km/hr, 6 November 1959
248km/hr, 4 July 1962

176° E

172° E
170° E
168° E

42° S
44° S
46° S

9 hours
sunset at 5pm

15.5 hours
sunset at 9:15pm

Mt John, Lake Tekapo
Strongest wind gust
250km/hr, 18 April 1970

Foveaux Strait

8.5 hours
sunset at 4:45pm

170° E
168° E

174° E
172° E

Lambert Conformal Conic Projection
Scale: 1: 5 640 000

0   50   100   150   200   250   300 km

Wind and Sunshine

Predominant wind direction

slight predominance

marked predominance

Mean annual sunshine hours

Hours
2400
2200
2000
1800
1600

Day length (sunrise to sunset), time of sunset

summer solstice (Dec 23) N.B. sunset time includes daylight saving

winter solstice (June 23)

10

North Island Soils by area

North Island Soils
11 134 157ha

Ultic 637,788 ha (5.73%)
Recent 1,163,846 ha (10.45%)
Allophanic 1,367,388 ha (12.28%)
Raw 152,488 ha (1.37%)
Pumice 1,721,087 ha (15.46%)
Podzol 636,931 ha (5.72%)
Pallic 847,861 ha (7.61%)
Oxidic 44,090 ha (0.4%)
Organic 151,300 ha (1.36%)
Granular 292,787 ha (2.63%)
Gley 450,672 ha (4.05%)
Melanic 50,892 ha (0.46%)
Brown 3,617,02... (32.49%)

New Zealand Soil Classification

Allophanic Soils
Low bulk density, well structured and friable soils. Mostly from weathered pyroclastic parent materials.

Anthropic Soils
Disturbed soils made by stripping or mixing soil material or by addition of fill, such as dredge tailings.

Brown Soils
Yellowish-brown in the upper subsoil. Moderate to low fertility. Mainly in areas that are moist throughout the year. On a variety of parent materials.

Gley Soils
Saturated by water for prolonged periods and with pale greyish subsoils. Affected mainly by groundwater in their natural state.

Granular Soils
Well structured clayey soils from weathered pyroclastic deposits, or basalt or andesite rocks on old land surfaces.

Melanic Soils
Very dark, well-structured topsoils and weakly acid or alkaline subsoils. High fertility. From parent materials rich in calcium and/or magnesium.

Organic Soils
Formed in the partly decomposed remains of wetland plants (peat) or thick forest litter. Organic materials predominate.

Oxidic Soils
Clayey soils, dominated by iron and aluminium oxides. Well structured and friable but low fertility. From weathered basic volcanic rocks on old land surfaces.

Pallic Soils
Pale colours, high bulk density, moderate or high fertility. Dry in summer.

Podzol Soils
Strongly acid with a bleached subsurface horizon overlying accumulations of iron, aluminium and silicon rich materials. Very low fertility. Occurring in areas of high rainfall and generally under forest.

Pumice Soils
Coarse-textured and dominated by pumice or volcanic glass with a low clay content. Yellow-brown upper subsoils.

Raw Soils
Very young soils or materials lacking a distinct topsoil. Occur in active eroding environments or areas of sedimentation.

Recent Soils
Distinct topsoil, but absent or only weakly developed subsurface horizons. Generally deep rooting and fertile, but may be shallow, particularly on sloping land.

Semiarid Soils
Dry for most of growing season. Lime or salts in the subsoil. Fertile, low in organic matter and plant growth is limited by droughtiness.

Ultic Soils
Clayey soils with low fertility. Subsurface horizons are acid. Mainly from weathered sedimentary rocks on old land surfaces.

Black represents urban areas

SOUTH ISLAND

N.B. The Auckland Islands are approx. 400 km south of South Cape

The NZSC has not been completed for this area: soils are mostly organic

Auckland Islands

Bateman Contemporary Atlas New Zealand

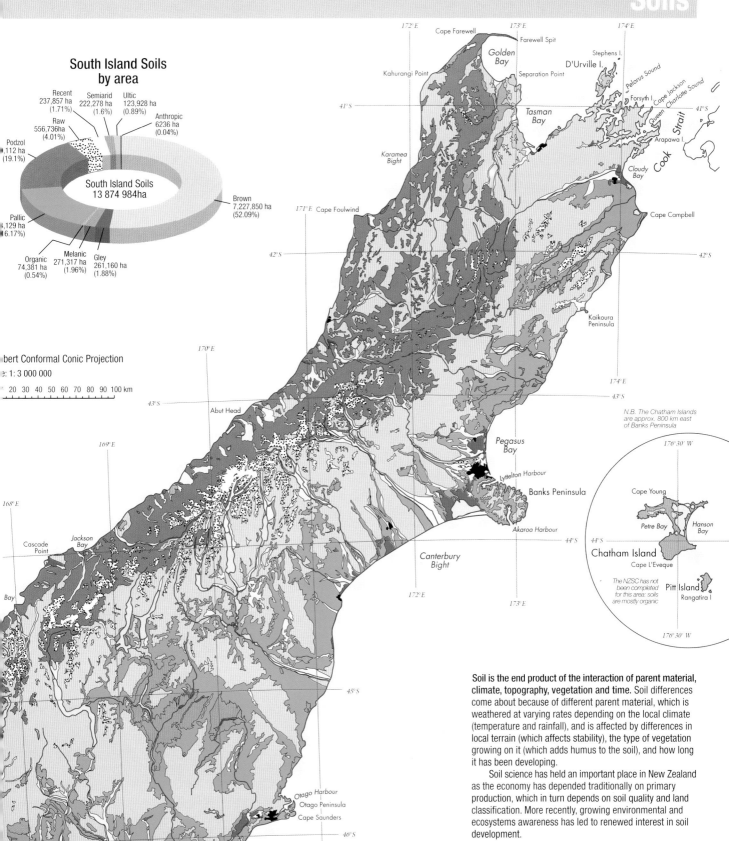

South Island Soils by area

South Island Soils
13 874 984ha

Recent 237,857 ha (1.71%)
Semiarid 222,278 ha (1.6%)
Ultic 123,928 ha (0.89%)
Anthropic 6236 ha (0.04%)
Raw 556,736ha (4.01%)
Podzol ,112 ha (19.1%)
Brown 7,227,850 ha (52.09%)
Pallic ,129 ha 6.17%)
Organic 74,381 ha (0.54%)
Melanic 271,317 ha (1.96%)
Gley 261,160 ha (1.88%)

bert Conformal Conic Projection
e: 1: 3 000 000

20 30 40 50 60 70 80 90 100 km

N.B. The Chatham Islands are approx. 800 km east of Banks Peninsula

Chatham Island
Cape Young
Petre Bay
Hanson Bay
Cape L'Eveque
Pitt Island
Rangatira I
The NZSC has not been completed for this area: soils are mostly organic

Manaaki Whenua
Landcare Research
NEW ZEALAND LTD

Soil is the end product of the interaction of parent material, climate, topography, vegetation and time. Soil differences come about because of different parent material, which is weathered at varying rates depending on the local climate (temperature and rainfall), and is affected by differences in local terrain (which affects stability), the type of vegetation growing on it (which adds humus to the soil), and how long it has been developing.

Soil science has held an important place in New Zealand as the economy has depended traditionally on primary production, which in turn depends on soil quality and land classification. More recently, growing environmental and ecosystems awareness has led to renewed interest in soil development.

Soil classification in New Zealand dates back to Māori gardeners (Best, 1925), who named soils such as oneharuru (a light but good sandy loam) and onetea (white soil from volcanic materials). A comprehensive soil classification was published in 1948 (the New Zealand Genetic Classification; Taylor, 1948), but by the late 1970s many of the theories of soil development on which this classification was based were becoming outmoded. The New Zealand Soil Classification (NZSC), of which this map is an example, was developed in the 1980s and is based on "the similarities of observable and measurable soil properties" (Hewitt, 1993). This should ensure that the NZSC better adapts to changes in theories of soil development. This map shows the fifteen NZSC soil orders, the highest and most generalised level of soil classification.

For more information...

Vegetation of New Zealand. Wardle, P.
New Zealand Historical Atlas. McKinnon, M.A. (ed).
On the Net: http://www.landcare.cri.nz

Contemporary New Zealand Vegetation

CROPLANDS

- Horticulture, orchards, vineyards
- Pasture; improved and unimproved

GRASSLAND

- Tussock grassland
- Grassland and forest

SCRUBLAND

- Scrubland, grassland and scrub, forest and scrub

FOREST

- Indigenous forest
- Exotic forest

OTHER VEGETATION

- Alpine herbfields
- Dune vegetation
- Wetland vegetation, pākihi

NO VEGETATION

- Urban areas, perennial ice and snow, sand, rock and scree, braided riverbeds

New Zealand's vegetative cover has been altered conside
from its pre-human state, though the pattern can still be
discerned. A number of large fires helped turn dry eastern fo
into tussock grassland during the period when Māori alone
in the New Zealand islands: scientists are unsure whether t
fires were 'cultural' — deliberately lit in order to facilitate hu
— or natural, perhaps started by lightning strikes.

Since the beginning of the nineteenth century, and the a
of Europeans, the floral landscape has undergone a startlin
transformation. Native plants have largely been replaced in r
areas by exotic species, particularly near population concentra
and most of the more fragile ecosystems, such as wetlands,
simply disappeared, having been swept away before urban
agricultural development. The influx of immigrants in the m
nineteenth century introduced many floral and faunal specie
of which altered New Zealand's vegetation pattern.

Even without the added human factor, the vegetative pa
is constantly changing in response to climatic change. At th
height of the last glaciation (Plate 6) colder temperatures lin
forests to the northernmost areas of the country, from which
spread southwards as the climate warmed.

Lambert Conformal Conic Projection

Scale: 1: 3 000 000

0 10 20 30 40 50 60 70 80 90 100 km

Manaaki Whenua
Landcare Research
NEW ZEALAND LTD

N.B. The Auckland
Islands are approx.
400 km south of
South Cape

Auckland Islands

Carnley Harbour
Adams I.

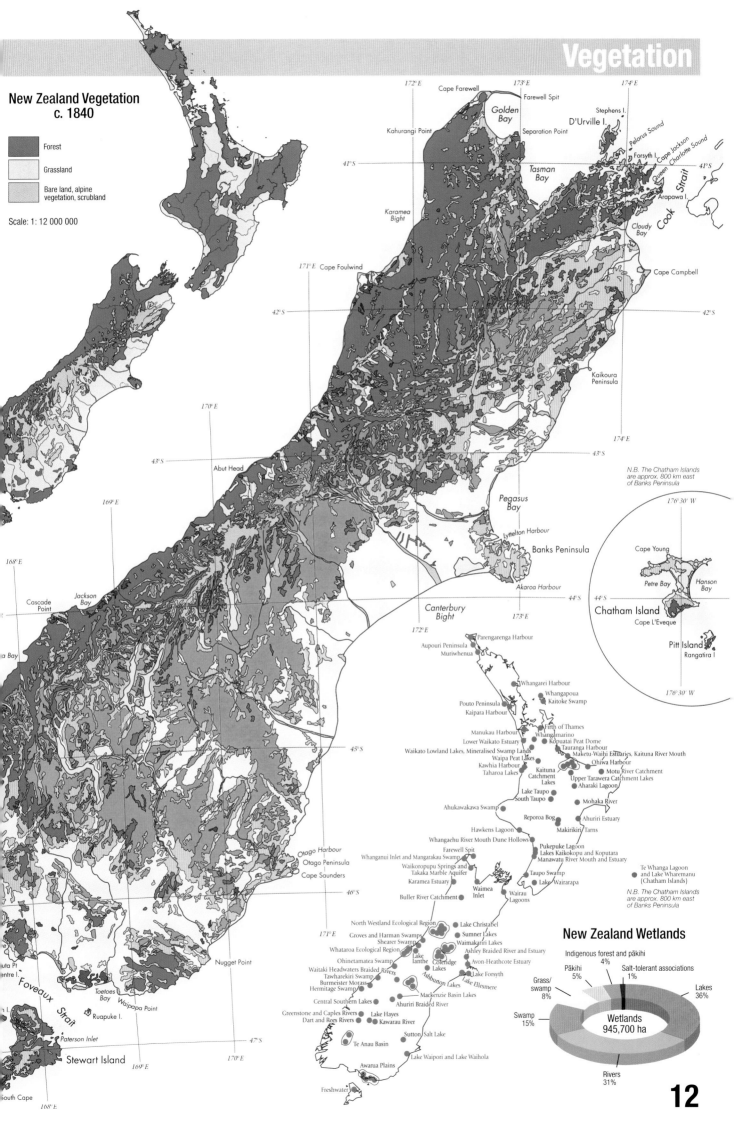

New Zealand Vegetation c. 1840

Forest

Grassland

Bare land, alpine vegetation, scrubland

Scale: 1: 12 000 000

173° E

174° E

172° E

Cape Farewell
Farewell Spit
Stephens I.
Golden Bay
D'Urville I.
Kahurangi Point
Separation Point
Pelorus Sound
41° S
Forsyth I.
Cape Jackson
Tasman Bay
Queen Charlotte Sound
41° S
Arapawa I.
Cook Strait
Karamea Bight
Cloudy Bay
171° E Cape Foulwind
Cape Campbell
42° S
42° S
Kaikoura Peninsula
170° E
43° S
43° S
Abut Head
174° E
N.B. The Chatham Islands are approx. 800 km east of Banks Peninsula
169° E
176° 30' W
Pegasus Bay
Cascade Point
Jackson Bay
Cape Young
Lyttelton Harbour
Petre Bay
Hanson Bay
168° E
a Bay
Banks Peninsula
44° S
44° S
Chatham Island
Cape Saunders
Akaroa Harbour
Cape L'Eveque
Canterbury Bight
173° E
Pitt Island
Rangatira I.
172° E
176° 30' W
Parengarenga Harbour
45° S
Aupouri Peninsula
Muriwhenua
Whangarei Harbour
Whangapoua
Pouto Peninsula
Kaitoke Swamp
Kaipara Harbour
Manukau Harbour
Firth of Thames
Whangamarino
Lower Waikato Estuary
Koputai Peat Dome
Waipa Peat Lakes
Tauranga Harbour
Waikato Lowland Lakes, Mineralised Swamp Lands
Maketu-Waihi Estuaries, Kaituna River Mouth
Kawhia Harbour
Ohiwa Harbour
Taharoa Lakes
Kaituna Catchment Lakes
Motu River Catchment
Upper Tarawera Catchment Lakes
Aharaki Lagoon
Lake Taupo
South Taupo
Mohaka River
Ahukawakawa Swamp
Reporoa Bog
Ahuriri Estuary
Makirikiri Tarns
Hawkens Lagoon
Whangaehu River Mouth Dune Hollows
Pukepuke Lagoon
Farewell Spit
Lakes Kaikokopu and Koputara
Whanganui Inlet and Mangarakau Swamp
Manawatu River Mouth and Estuary
Waikoropupu Springs and Takaka Marble Aquifer
Taupo Swamp
Te Whanga Lagoon and Lake Wharemanu (Chatham Islands)
Karamea Estuary
Lake Wairarapa
46° S
Waimea Inlet
Wairau Lagoons
N.B. The Chatham Islands are approx. 800 km east of Banks Peninsula
Buller River Catchment
Otago Harbour
Otago Peninsula
171° E
North Westland Ecological Region
Lake Christabel
New Zealand Wetlands
Groves and Harman Swamps
Sumner Lakes
Shearer Swamp
Waimakariri Lakes
Whataroa Ecological Region
Ashley Braided River and Estuary
Indigenous forest and pākihi 4%
Ohinetamatea Swamp
Lake Ianthe
Coleridge Lakes
Avon-Heathcote Estuary
Pākihi 5%
Salt-tolerant associations 1%
Waitaki Headwaters Braided Rivers
Ashburton Lakes
Lake Forsyth
Tawharekiri Swamp
Lake Ellesmere
Grass/ swamp 8%
Lakes 36%
Burmeister Morass
Hermitage Swamp
Mackenzie Basin Lakes
Central Southern Lakes
Ahuriri Braided River
Greenstone and Caples Rivers
Lake Hayes
Swamp 15%
Wetlands 945,700 ha
Dart and Rees Rivers
Kawarau River
Sutton Salt Lake
Foveaux Strait
Toetoes Bay
Waipapa Point
Te Anau Basin
Lake Waipori and Lake Waihola
Ruapuke I.
Rivers 31%
Paterson Inlet
170° E
Stewart Island
169° E
Awarua Plains
Freshwater
168° E

For more information...

Vegetation of the Pureora Mountain Ecological Area. Leathwick, J.R.
The State of New Zealand's Environment. Ministry for the Environment.
On the Net: http://www.doc.govt.nz/local/waik.html

The Pureora Mountain Ecological Area is one of ten scientific reserves within the Pureora Forest Park, and contains large stands of lowland to montane podocarp forest unmodified by humans. This virgin forest on the mountain slopes, and the altitudinal zones in which it is arranged, makes the area interesting to study. The Ecological Area is centred around Pureora Mountain, a large andesite volcanic cone about 2 million years old. The vegetation, especially that on the slopes of the mountain, is arranged in concentric zones: the tallest forest is found at the lowest altitudes, and canopy height decreases as altitude increases. This is as a result of increased exposure to rain, wind and lower temperatures.

The vegetation within the reserve provides habitats for kōkako, kākā, kākāriki and falcon (Leathwick, 1990). It also contains significant areas of shrubland and wetland (mire). The reserve is managed by the Department of Conservation, which maintains a headquarters about 9 km from the mountain.

The last major Taupo eruption, about 1800 years ago, deposited 50–100 cm of pumice on the reserve. This, allied with fast-flowing ignimbrite from the same eruption, undoubtedly destroyed the forests on Pureora Mountain: what now exists has regenerated since then. The resulting soils are infertile yellow-brown podzols. This infertility, coupled with the site's high elevation and steepness, prevented its exploitation. Most of the surrounding lower elevation forests have been cleared and replanted in exotic species, mostly pine.

Vegetation Types by area
Pureora Mountain Ecological Area

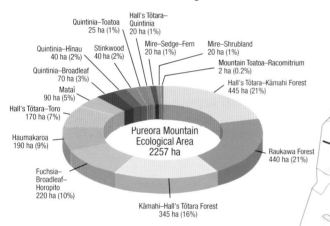

Quintinia–Toatoa 25 ha (1%)
Hall's Tōtara–Quintinia 20 ha (1%)
Quintinia–Hinau 40 ha (2%)
Stinkwood 40 ha (2%)
Mire–Sedge–Fern 20 ha (1%)
Mire–Shrubland 20 ha (1%)
Quintinia–Broadleaf 70 ha (3%)
Mountain Toatoa–Racomitrium 2 ha (0.2%)
Matāī 90 ha (5%)
Hall's Tōtara–Kāmahi Forest 445 ha (21%)
Hall's Tōtara–Toro 170 ha (7%)
Haumakaroa 190 ha (9%)
Fuchsia–Broadleaf–Horopito 220 ha (10%)
Raukawa Forest 440 ha (21%)
Kāmahi–Hall's Tōtara Forest 345 ha (16%)

Pureora Mountain Ecological Area 2257 ha

Generalised Distribution of Vegetation Types by Altitude and Topography
Pureora Mountain Ecological Area

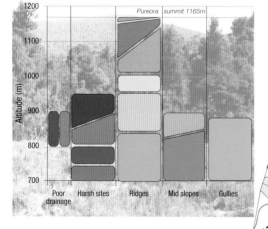

Pureora summit 1165m

Altitude (m)

1200
1100
1000
900
800
700

Poor drainage | Harsh sites | Ridges | Mid slopes | Gullies

Manaaki Whenua
Landcare Research
NEW ZEALAND LTD

PUREORA FOREST PARK

Logged area

Logged area

Exotic Forest

Ongarue River

PUREORA FOREST PARK

0

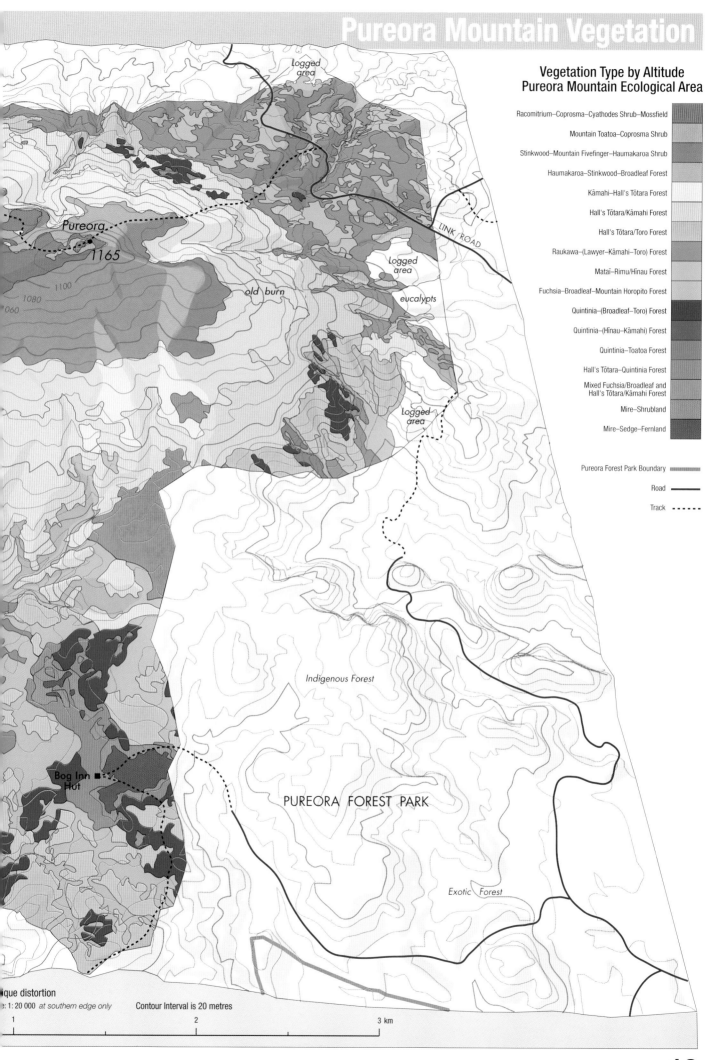

Vegetation Type by Altitude
Pureora Mountain Ecological Area

Racomitrium–Coprosma–Cyathodes Shrub–Mossfield

Mountain Toatoa–Coprosma Shrub

Stinkwood–Mountain Fivefinger–Haumakaroa Shrub

Haumakaroa–Stinkwood–Broadleaf Forest

Kāmahi–Hall's Tōtara Forest

Hall's Tōtara/Kāmahi Forest

Hall's Tōtara/Toro Forest

Raukawa–(Lawyer–Kāmahi–Toro) Forest

Mataī–Rimu/Hīnau Forest

Fuchsia–Broadleaf–Mountain Horopito Forest

Quintinia–(Broadleaf–Toro) Forest

Quintinia–(Hīnau–Kāmahi) Forest

Quintinia–Toatoa Forest

Hall's Tōtara–Quintinia Forest

Mixed Fuchsia/Broadleaf and Hall's Tōtara/Kāmahi Forest

Mire–Shrubland

Mire–Sedge–Fernland

Pureora Forest Park Boundary

Road

Track

Logged area

Logged area

eucalypts

Logged area

LINK ROAD

Pureora

1165

old burn

1100

1080

1060

Indigenous Forest

Bog Inn Hut

PUREORA FOREST PARK

Exotic Forest

que distortion

: 1: 20 000 *at southern edge only*   Contour Interval is 20 metres

1   2   3 km

Comparative City Sizes, Asia-Pacific Rim

Los Angeles 8,375,000
Sydney 2,850,000
Singapore 2,600,000
Auckland 991,000
Wellington 334,0
Christchurch 325,000
Bombay 8,250,000
Hong Kong 4,450,000
Hamilton 109,000
Dune 111,0

N.B. Population figures are 1996 estimates, or the closest availab
date to 1996. City boundaries correspond to the built-up areas, a
in some cases these are uncertain.

Settlement Populations

- • under 500
- ○ 500-1000
- ○ 1000-5000
- ○ 5000-10,000
- ◉ 10,000-20,000
- ◎ 20,000-100,000
- ⬡ **over 100,000**

Communications

——— State Highway roading network

——— Railways

Environmental classification

- Alpine barren land; subalpine scrubland
- Forest
- Forest and grazing land
- Forest and cropland
- Grassland
- Grassland and cropland

Cape Reinga
Cape Maria van Diemen
North Cape
Parengarenga Harbour
Great Exhibition Bay
Karikari Peninsula
Doubtless Bay
Cavalli Is.
Mangonui
Kaitaia
Awanui
Ahipara
Tauroa Point
Maungataniwha 751
Kerikeri
Haruru Falls
(Waitangi)
Russell
Paihia
Opua
Bay of Islands
Cape Brett
Kaikohe
Kawakawa
461
Poor Knights Is.
Kohukohu
Rawene
Opononi
Kaikou
Hokianga Harbour
Hikurangi
Whangarei
776
Maunganui Bluff
627
Bream Head
Whangarei Harbour
Mokohinau Is.
Dargaville
Te Kopuru
Ruawai
Maungaturoto
Mangawhai
Bream Bay
Hen and Chickens
Little Barrier Island
722
Great Barrier Island
Wellsford
Leigh
Warkworth
Cape Rodney
Kawau I.
Cape Colville
Kaipara Harbour
Helensville
Orewa
Whangaparaoa
Kumeu
Hauraki Gulf
Moehau 892
Coromandel
Mercury Is.
Takapuna
Mercury Bay
Whitianga
Henderson
AUCKLAND
Papatoetoe
Papakura
HUNUA RA
Firth of Thames
Thames
Table Mtn 846
Pauanui
Slipper I.
Manukau Harbour
Pukekohe
Bombay
Ngatea
Whangamata
Waiuku
Tuakau
408
L. Kauwhata
Paeroa
Waihi
Waihi Beach
Athenree
Mayor I.
Waikato
L. Whangape
Huntly
Te Aroha
Te Aroha 953
Katikati
Omokoroa Beach
Tauranga Harbour
Bay of Plenty
White I.
Cape Runaway
L. Waikare
L. Wahi
Rotowaro
Taupiri
Ngaruawahia
Morrinsville
Motiti I.
Mount Maunganui
Papamoa Beach
Maketu
Te Araroa
990
Temple View
HAMILTON
Tauranga
Te Puke
Matata
RANGE
Raglan Harbour
Raglan
Waharoa
Matamata
KAIMAI RANGE
Edgecumbe
Whakatane
Ohope
Whanokao 1618
Hikurangi 1754
Ruatoria
Woody Head
Cambridge
Hirau
L. Rotorua
L. Rotoiti
Rotoehu
Te Teko
Opotiki
Aotea Harbour
Te Awamutu
756
Ohaupo
Pirongia
Maungatautari
Putaruru
Ngongotaha
Kawerau
Taneatua
697
RAUKUMARA RANGE
1073
Albatross Point
Kawhia Harbour
962
Kihikihi
Rotorua
L. Okareka
L. Okataina
L. Tarawera
Tarawera 1111
L. Rotomahana
L. Rerewhakaaiti
Murupara
Waioeka
Te Karaka
Tolaga Bay
Otorohanga
Te Kuiti
Tokoroa
Gable End Foreland
Maungamangero
Ranginui 978
Mangakino
Waikato
Wairakei
Maungapohatu 1366
Patutahi
Gisborne
HERANGI RA
806
Piopio
Benneydale
Pureora 1165
Taupo 1088
Acacia Bay
RANGITAIKI
L. Waikareiti
Poverty Bay
Young Nicks Head
Taumarunui
Ohura
566
Owhango
Lake Taupo
HAUHUNGAROA RA
Makorako 1727
Kaweka 1724
Taraponui 1308
L. Waikaremoana
961
Wairoa
Mahia Peninsula
North Taranaki Bight
Waitara
Bell Block
Urenui
L. Rotoaira
Turangi 1325
Tongariro
Ngauruhoe 1968 2291
KAIMANAWA MTNS
L. Tutira
Portland I.
New Plymouth
Okato
Oakura
Inglewood
Midhirst
Ruapehu 2797
Ohakune
Taranaki Mt Egmont 2518
Cape Egmont
Stratford
Eltham
Kaponga
Waiouru 1116
Taihape
HUIARAU RANGE
Bay View
Napier
Clive
Haumoana
Taradale
Opunake
Normanby
Te Mapou 746
Raetihi
Whangaehu
RUAHINE RANGE
Hastings
Havelock North
Cape Kidnappers
Manaia
Hawera
Kaponga
Patea
South Taranaki Bight
Waverley
Waitotara
Wanganui
Mangaweka 1733
Mangaweka
Otane
646
Waipawa
Cook Strait
Putiki
Hunterville
Rangitikei
Takapau
Waipukurau
Ratana
Marton
Bulls
Sanson
Rongotea
Feilding
Bunnythorpe
Ashhurst
Dannevirke
Cape Turnagain
Tangimoana
Palmerston North
Himatangi Beach
Woodville
Manawatu
PUKETOI RA
803
Foxton Beach
Foxton
Linton
Waitarere
Shannon
Pahiatua
Kapiti I.
Levin
Eketahuna
534
Otaki
Mitre 1571
Castle Point
Waikanae
Mt Hector 1529
Paraparaumu
Paekakariki
Mana I.
Upper Hutt
Masterton
Porirua
Lower Hutt
Greytown
Featherston
Martinborough
Wainuiomata
Cape Terawhiti
WELLINGTON
Eastbourne
Wairarapa
663
Wellington Harbour
Mt Ross 981
Palliser Bay
Turakirae Head
Cape Palliser

SOUTH ISLAND

178°E
177°E
East Cap
Sutherla
Blig
George S
Caswell Sound
Charles Sound
Nancy Sound
Thompson Sound
Secretary I.
Doubtful Sound
Dagg Sound
Breaksea Sound
Resolution I.
Dusky Sound
West Cape
Chalky Inlet
Preservation Inlet
166°E
167°E
178°E
45°S
46°S
177°E
Solanc
50°30'S
Auckland Islands
Mt Easton 621
Mt Dick 668
Adams I.
Carnley Harbour
47°S
166°E

N.B. The Auckland Islands are approx. 400 km south of South Cape

Bateman Contemporary Atlas New Zealand.

human imprint is clearly visible on the New Zealand dscape. It is shown here not only as cities and towns, the roads and railways that link them, but also as the cultural modification of rural areas. Only the mountain tops the most inaccessible forests are relatively free from ct human influence.

Much of New Zealand's prime sheep and dairy country s originally forest-covered. Bush clearance was a major occupation of farmers and governments last century, ticularly in the lower and central North Island. Rural towns, ds and railways sprang up to service the farming community, the major cities serving as provincial hubs. Today urban as and their hinterlands dominate the cultural landscape, 'wild' New Zealand pushed back to the fringes of society.

New Zealand's urban areas are of relatively low density, sisting largely of fully detached, single-storey housing, have been designed around the automobile. The largest es of our closest international neighbours of the Pacific and Asia are much more densely populated. Hong Kong, extreme example, is considerably smaller in area than llington but has over ten times the population. The eptions are the large Australian and American cities, even densely settled than those in New Zealand.

mbert Conformal Conic Projection
le: 1: 3 000 000

0 20 30 40 50 60 70 80 90 100 km

N.B. The Chatham Islands are approx. 800 km east of Banks Peninsula

New Zealand is not a large country and, though not experiencing the population pressures of other Pacific Rim countries, the inhabitants have to manage the land carefully.

Over two-thirds of New Zealand's 270,534 square kilometres slopes at greater than 12 degrees, and nearly half at greater than 28 degrees. Three-fifths of the country is over 300 metres in altitude, with one-fifth over 900 metres. Half of the country is farmed, with another 30% forested. Humans make use of even the barren areas, pursuing mountain recreation and tourism. The land therefore comes under considerable pressure from competing users.

Land Use by Area

Other Land 19%
(51,400 km²)

Urban Areas 1%
(2700 km²)

Planted Production Forest
5% (13,500 km²)

Total Land Area
270,534 km²

Pasture and
Arable Land
51%
(138,000 km²)

Natural Forest 24%
(65,000 km²)

For more information...

Farm Monitoring Reports. Ministry of Agriculture and Forestry.
Situation and Outlook for New Zealand Agriculture. MAF Agriculture Policy Group.
On the Net: http://www.maf.govt.nz/MAFnet/index.html

Farming remains a major industry in New Zealand, despite significant structural changes in the last fifteen years. Land use maps of New Zealand continue to show the majority of the country's land area in farmland, with the traditional farming types centred around sheep and cattle, producing meat, wool, dairy produce and hides. A comparison of this pattern with that of 25 years ago shows only small-scale changes: the growth of urban areas, an increase in area devoted to horticulture, and the reversion of some marginal land. However, the map alone cannot show that the mix of farming types has changed. Total sheep numbers continue to fall, from 70.3 million in 1983 to 47.4 million in 1997, while the beef and dairy cattle herds continue to grow. Mixed sheep/beef farms now derive a larger proportion of their income from beef.

The period from the mid-1980s to the early 1990s was one of structural change and economic hardship for many farmers, due to agricultural reform and the removal of long-standing farm subsidies. New Zealand farmers are currently exposed to world market forces to a greater extent than any other developed country. Proponents of change in the agricultural sector advocate further reorganisation, such as the removal of the powers of producer boards. Prudence has seen many farmers adopting a broader base, perhaps mixing their livestock to cover fluctuations in world commodity prices, and trying new types of livestock, such as deer, goats and ostriches. Other farming families, trapped by circumstances or less open to innovation, rely on supplementary income from 'off-farm' work to survive.

Land Use by Farm Type
1996

Horticulture 1%
Deer Farming 2%
Beef Farming 7%
Mixed Livestock 3%
Dairy Farming 12%
Exotic Forest 14%
Sheep Farming 43%
Other Farming and Idle Land 3%
Sheep with Beef 15%

Total Farming area
16,547,113 ha

Agricultural Land Use
1996

- Exotic Forest
- Horticulture: viticulture, orchards, market gardens
- Dairying, with some finishing of sheep and beef
- Intensive Pastoralism: sheep, cash crops, some beef
- Semi-intensive Pastoralism: sheep and beef
- Semi-extensive Pastoralism: sheep, some beef
- Extensive Pastoralism: sheep and beef
- Non-agricultural: indigenous forests, alpine areas, conservation estate, urban areas

Southland 13090 ha

Lambert Conformal Conic Projection

Scale: 1: 5 640 000

| 0 | 50 | 100 | 150 | 200 | 250 | 300 km |

Relative Farm Expenditure on Sheep Farms
during the period of restructuring, 1981–1992

Base Year = 100

Wages
Feed, Graz
Animal He
Interest
Contract V
and Cartag
Maintenan
Fertiliser, l
and Seeds

Percentage of 1985 expenditure (in current $)

Year

Bateman Contemporary Atlas New Zealand

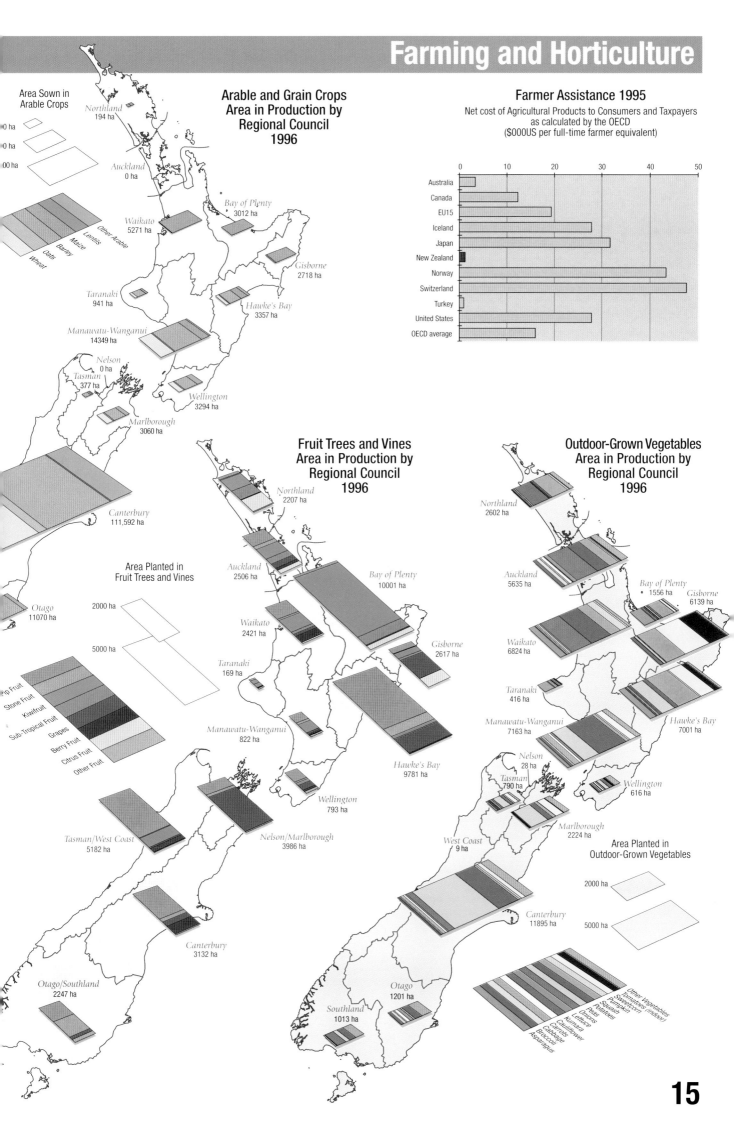

Area Sown in Arable Crops

0 ha
0 ha
00 ha

Lentils
Maize
Barley
Oats
Other Arable
Wheat

Arable and Grain Crops
Area in Production by
Regional Council
1996

Northland 194 ha

Auckland 0 ha

Bay of Plenty 3012 ha

Waikato 5271 ha

Gisborne 2718 ha

Taranaki 941 ha

Hawke's Bay 3357 ha

Manawatu-Wanganui 14349 ha

Nelson 0 ha

Tasman 377 ha

Wellington 3294 ha

Marlborough 3060 ha

Canterbury 111,592 ha

Otago 11070 ha

Otago/Southland 2247 ha

Farmer Assistance 1995
Net cost of Agricultural Products to Consumers and Taxpayers
as calculated by the OECD
($000US per full-time farmer equivalent)

	0	10	20	30	40	50
Australia						
Canada						
EU15						
Iceland						
Japan						
New Zealand						
Norway						
Switzerland						
Turkey						
United States						
OECD average						

Fruit Trees and Vines
Area in Production by
Regional Council
1996

Northland 2207 ha

Auckland 2506 ha

Bay of Plenty 10001 ha

Waikato 2421 ha

Gisborne 2617 ha

Taranaki 169 ha

Hawke's Bay 9781 ha

Manawatu-Wanganui 822 ha

Wellington 793 ha

Nelson/Marlborough 3986 ha

Tasman/West Coast 5182 ha

Canterbury 3132 ha

Otago/Southland 2247 ha

Southland 1013 ha

Area Planted in Fruit Trees and Vines

2000 ha
5000 ha

Pip Fruit
Stone Fruit
Kiwifruit
Sub-Tropical Fruit
Grapes
Berry Fruit
Citrus Fruit
Other Fruit

Outdoor-Grown Vegetables
Area in Production by
Regional Council
1996

Northland 2602 ha

Auckland 5635 ha

Bay of Plenty 1556 ha

Gisborne 6139 ha

Waikato 6824 ha

Taranaki 416 ha

Hawke's Bay 7001 ha

Manawatu-Wanganui 7163 ha

Nelson 28 ha

Tasman 790 ha

Wellington 616 ha

Marlborough 2224 ha

West Coast 9 ha

Canterbury 11895 ha

Otago 1201 ha

Area Planted in Outdoor-Grown Vegetables

2000 ha
5000 ha

Other Vegetables
Tomatoes (indoor)
Sweetcorn
Pumpkin
Squash
Peas
Potatoes
Onions
Lettuce
Kumara
Cauliflower
Carrots
Cabbage
Broccoli
Asparagus

15

For more information...

The Atlas of Area Codes and TACCS. Clement and Associates.
Water & Atmosphere. NIWA.
On the Net: http://www.niwa.cri.nz/NIWA_research/fisheries.html

The Quota Management System (QMS) was introduced in 1986 as part of an effort to reduce pressure on New Zealand's fish stocks. Before 1980 the New Zealand fishery was confined to coastal waters, mostly within the 12-mile territorial zone. Large fleets from Japan, South Korea and the USSR fished the deeper waters beyond the 12-mile limit.

In the 1970s the government offered incentives to increase participation in the fishing industry, with the result that certain stocks were overfished and a great deal of pressure was put on coastal waters. Then, in the late 1970s, world governments agreed to bring Exclusive Economic Zones (EEZs) into law, extending sovereignty over resources to 200 nautical miles beyond the coast of each nation. This left New Zealand with the fourth-largest EEZ in the world, at 1.2 million square nautical miles. However, the catch is not in proportion to the size of the fishery. While the annual worldwide fish catch is well over 100 million tonnes, New Zealand waters contribute only 600,000 tonnes. The majority of the EEZ is deeper than 1000 metres and low in nutrients, in which few resources are found.

Having learned from the chaos of the inshore fishery, the government set up the QMS to manage this resource. Each prospective player in the industry must lease or purchase the right to fish for an Individual Transferable Quota (ITQ) of each species, and the cost of this, coupled with the expense of deep-sea vessels and equipment, is now a significant barrier to smaller participants. By 1999 three companies (Amaltal, Sanford and Sealord) held 60% of the quota between them. The QMS thereby acts as an effective tool for maintaining sustainable commercial catch limits, but at a high cost to small fishing enterprises.

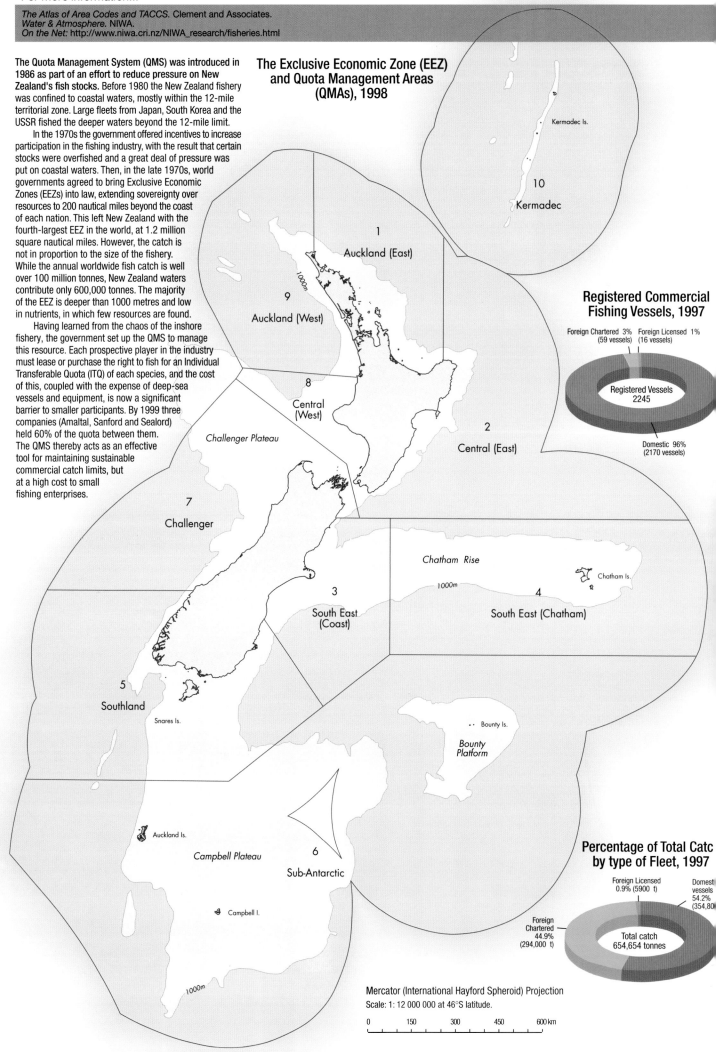

The Exclusive Economic Zone (EEZ) and Quota Management Areas (QMAs), 1998

Kermadec Is.

10
Kermadec

1
Auckland (East)

9
Auckland (West)

8
Central
(West)

2
Central (East)

Challenger Plateau

7
Challenger

Chatham Rise

Chatham Is.

1000m

3
South East
(Coast)

4
South East (Chatham)

5
Southland

Snares Is.

Bounty Is.

*Bounty
Platform*

Auckland Is.

Campbell Plateau

6
Sub-Antarctic

Campbell I.

1000m

Registered Commercial Fishing Vessels, 1997

Foreign Chartered 3%
(59 vessels)

Foreign Licensed 1%
(16 vessels)

Registered Vessels
2245

Domestic 96%
(2170 vessels)

Percentage of Total Catch by type of Fleet, 1997

Foreign Licensed
0.9% (5900 t)

Domestic
vessels
54.2%
(354,80...)

Foreign
Chartered
44.9%
(294,000 t)

Total catch
654,654 tonnes

Mercator (International Hayford Spheroid) Projection
Scale: 1: 12 000 000 at 46°S latitude.

0   150   300   450   600 km

Bateman Contemporary Atlas New Zealand

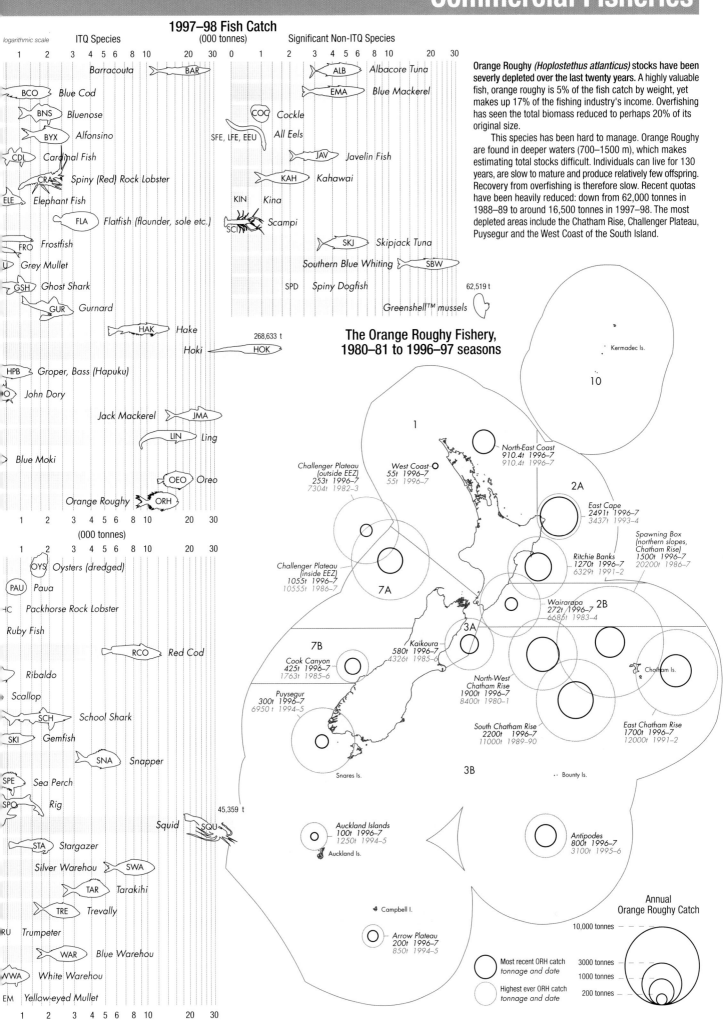

1997–98 Fish Catch

logarithmic scale

ITQ Species

(000 tonnes)

Significant Non-ITQ Species

Barracouta — BAR

BCO Blue Cod

BNS Bluenose

BYX Alfonsino

CDL Cardinal Fish

CRA Spiny (Red) Rock Lobster

ELE Elephant Fish

FLA Flatfish (flounder, sole etc.)

FRO Frostfish

Grey Mullet

GSH Ghost Shark

GUR Gurnard

HAK Hake

Hoki HOK — 268,633 t

HPB Groper, Bass (Hapuku)

John Dory

Jack Mackerel JMA

LIN Ling

Blue Moki

OEO Oreo

Orange Roughy ORH

ALB Albacore Tuna

EMA Blue Mackerel

COC Cockle

SFE, LFE, EEU All Eels

JAV Javelin Fish

KAH Kahawai

KIN Kina

SCI Scampi

SKJ Skipjack Tuna

Southern Blue Whiting SBW

SPD Spiny Dogfish

Greenshell™ mussels — 62,519 t

(000 tonnes)

OYS Oysters (dredged)

PAU Paua

Packhorse Rock Lobster

Ruby Fish

RCO Red Cod

Ribaldo

Scallop

SCH School Shark

SKI Gemfish

SNA Snapper

SPE Sea Perch

SPO Rig

Squid SQU — 45,359 t

STA Stargazer

Silver Warehou SWA

TAR Tarakihi

TRE Trevally

Trumpeter

WAR Blue Warehou

WWA White Warehou

EM Yellow-eyed Mullet

The three-letter abbreviations are QMS codes for each species.

Orange Roughy (Hoplostethus atlanticus) stocks have been severly depleted over the last twenty years. A highly valuable fish, orange roughy is 5% of the fish catch by weight, yet makes up 17% of the fishing industry's income. Overfishing has seen the total biomass reduced to perhaps 20% of its original size.

This species has been hard to manage. Orange Roughy are found in deeper waters (700–1500 m), which makes estimating total stocks difficult. Individuals can live for 130 years, are slow to mature and produce relatively few offspring. Recovery from overfishing is therefore slow. Recent quotas have been heavily reduced: down from 62,000 tonnes in 1988–89 to around 16,500 tonnes in 1997–98. The most depleted areas include the Chatham Rise, Challenger Plateau, Puysegur and the West Coast of the South Island.

The Orange Roughy Fishery, 1980–81 to 1996–97 seasons

Kermadec Is.

10

1

North-East Coast
910.4t 1996–7
910.4t 1996–7

Challenger Plateau
(outside EEZ)
253t 1996–7
7304t 1982–3

West Coast
55t 1996–7
55t 1996–7

2A

East Cape
2491t 1996–7
3437t 1993–4

Spawning Box
(northern slopes,
Chatham Rise)
1500t 1996–7
20200t 1986–7

Challenger Plateau
(inside EEZ)
1055t 1996–7
10555t 1986–7

7A

Ritchie Banks
1270t 1996–7
6329t 1991–2

Wairarapa
272t 1996–7
6685t 1983–4

2B

Chatham Is.

7B

Cook Canyon
425t 1996–7
1763t 1985–6

Kaikoura
580t 1996–7
4326t 1985–6

3A

North-West
Chatham Rise
1900t 1996–7
8400t 1980–1

East Chatham Rise
1700t 1996–7
12000t 1991–2

Puysegur
300t 1996–7
6950 t 1994–5

South Chatham Rise
2200t 1996–7
11000t 1989–90

Snares Is.

3B

Bounty Is.

Auckland Islands
100t 1996–7
1250t 1994–5

Auckland Is.

Antipodes
800t 1996–7
3100t 1995–6

Campbell I.

Arrow Plateau
200t 1996–7
850t 1994–5

Most recent ORH catch
tonnage and date

Highest ever ORH catch
tonnage and date

Annual Orange Roughy Catch

10,000 tonnes

3000 tonnes

1000 tonnes

200 tonnes

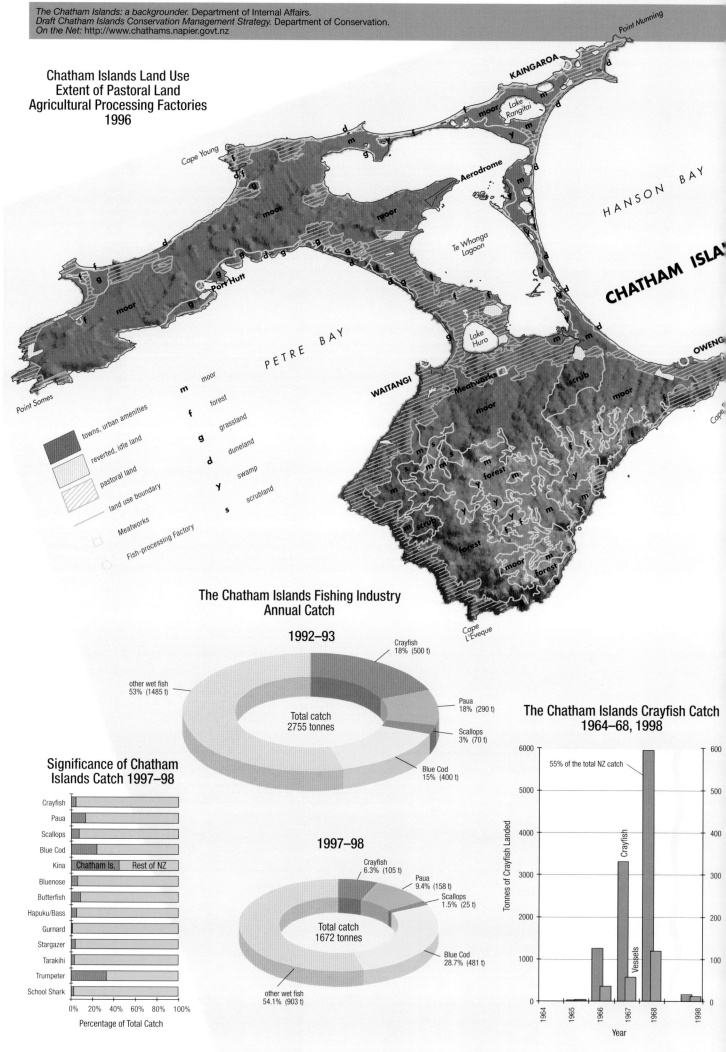

For more information...

The Chatham Islands: a backgrounder. Department of Internal Affairs.
Draft Chatham Islands Conservation Management Strategy. Department of Conservation.
On the Net: http://www.chathams.napier.govt.nz

Chatham Islands Land Use
Extent of Pastoral Land
Agricultural Processing Factories
1996

Legend:
- towns, urban amenities
- reverted, idle land
- pastoral land
- land use boundary
- Meatworks
- Fish-processing Factory

- m moor
- f forest
- g grassland
- d duneland
- y swamp
- s scrubland

Map labels: KAINGAROA, Point Munning, HANSON BAY, CHATHAM ISLA..., Cape Young, Aerodrome, Lake Rangitai, Te Whanga Lagoon, OWENG..., Point Somes, Port Hutt, PETRE BAY, Lake Huro, WAITANGI, Meatworks, scrub, moor, forest, Cape L'Eveque, Cape...

The Chatham Islands Fishing Industry
Annual Catch

1992–93

Total catch 2755 tonnes

- Crayfish 18% (500 t)
- Paua 18% (290 t)
- Scallops 3% (70 t)
- Blue Cod 15% (400 t)
- other wet fish 53% (1485 t)

1997–98

Total catch 1672 tonnes

- Crayfish 6.3% (105 t)
- Paua 9.4% (158 t)
- Scallops 1.5% (25 t)
- Blue Cod 28.7% (481 t)
- other wet fish 54.1% (903 t)

Significance of Chatham Islands Catch 1997–98

Chatham Is. | Rest of NZ

- Crayfish
- Paua
- Scallops
- Blue Cod
- Kina
- Bluenose
- Butterfish
- Hapuku/Bass
- Gurnard
- Stargazer
- Tarakihi
- Trumpeter
- School Shark

0% 20% 40% 60% 80% 100%
Percentage of Total Catch

The Chatham Islands Crayfish Catch
1964–68, 1998

55% of the total NZ catch

Tonnes of Crayfish Landed
Crayfish
Vessels

Year: 1964, 1965, 1966, 1967, 1968, 1998

Bateman Contemporary Atlas New Zealand

Land Use 1996
Chatham Islands and New Zealand compared

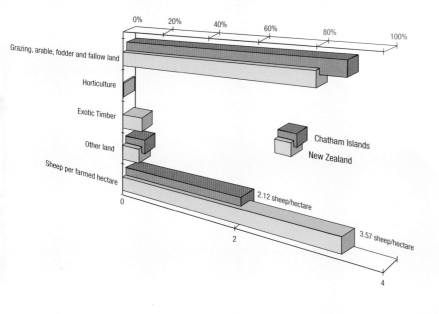

Chatham Islands Location
Exclusive Economic Zone

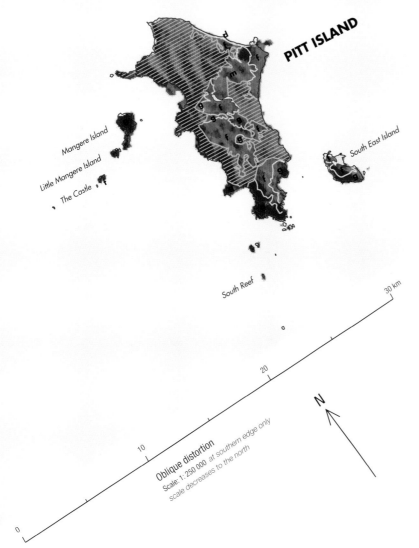

Rekohu (Chatham Islands) is about 800 km to the east of Banks Peninsula, approximately 90,000 hectares in size, and supports a permanent population of about 830, 50 of whom live on Pitt Island. The islands' people depend almost entirely on earnings from agriculture and fishing for their existence, which historically for some has been barely subsistence in nature.

Farming on the Chathams is almost exclusively pastoral, with the exception of about 6 ha of horticulture. The 41 farms (with about 65 farmers) run just over 100,000 sheep, 6500 cattle and a few hundred pigs, deer and goats. About 600,000 kg of wool is produced annually and sold at mainland markets, along with beef and sheepmeat products. The small meatworks processed 15,000 sheep and 600 cattle per annum in the 1980s, but numbers decreased in the early 1990s as more money was to be made by exporting livestock to the mainland. The meatworks were not opened in the 1993/4 season.

The Chatham Islands are generally low-lying and rolling rather than mountainous in nature, and around 90% of the land area is available for grazing, a higher figure than for New Zealand as a whole. However, due to the marginal nature of agricultural activity, most of this area remains undeveloped moorland, only lightly grazed. Poor pasture management, undersized farms, low stock prices and parasites affecting the stock all contributed to the marginality of farming in the middle years of the century, and some land has begun to revert to moorland, fernland, scrub and forest. The existence of sensitive ecosystems, including rare fauna, is further discouragement to agricultural development. The stock density, therefore, is little more than half that of mainland New Zealand.

While pastoral agriculture provides islanders with 16% of their GDP, fishing is the economy's mainstay (68% of GDP). About 65 fishing vessels operate out of Waitangi, Owenga, Port Hutt, Kaingaroa and Pitt Island. The four remaining factories are located at Waitangi, Kaingaroa, Port Hutt and Owenga. In 1910 large freezers were built at Kaingaroa and Owenga, enabling the export of frozen blue cod and groper (hapuka). The industry expanded steadily during the twentieth century, taking labourers from the stagnating farms, until in 1965 crayfish beds (rock lobster) were discovered off the coast of the Chatham Islands. Within a few years these beds were stripped, with up to 6000 tonnes per annum being taken. Because of this exploitation New Zealand was the second-largest producer of crayfish in the world by 1970, but stocks were quickly depleted. Eight factories were built between 1965 and 1968 to process the catch, and the sudden influx of revenue provided funds for the redevelopment of roading and wharf facilities.

Exotic Forests Major Owners 1996

- Carter Holt Harvey Forests
- City Forests Ltd.
- Ernslaw One Ltd.
- Fletcher Challenge Consortium
- Hawkes Bay Forests Ltd.
- Juken Nissho Ltd.
- Mangakahia Forest Ltd.
- Marlborough Forestry Corp.
- Ministry of Forestry
- Crown Forestry Management Ltd.
- Pan Pacific Forest Industries Ltd.
- Rayonier New Zealand Ltd.
- Selwyn Plantation Board Ltd.
- Tasman Forestry Ltd.
- Timberlands West Coast Ltd.
- Wenita Forest Products
- Winstone Pulp International Ltd.
- Other Major Forestry Owners

Mills, 1996

- △ Pulp Mill
- □ Paper Mill
- ○ Pulp and Paper Mill
- ☆ Panel Board Mill

Average Five-Yearly Timber Yield by Region

actual
estimated

000m³

4000
2000
0

1991–95
1996–00
2001–05
2006–10
2011–15

N.B. These are the Northland figures

Indigenous and Exo Timber Productio 1921–1997

Cubic Metres (000m³)

3500
3000
2500
2000
1500
1000
500
0

1921   1930   1940

Indigenou

Year er

Northland

4000
2000
0

Central North Island

10000
8000
6000
4000
2000
0

Auckland

2000
0

East Coa.

2000
0

Hawkes Bay

2000
0

Southern North Island

2000
0

Cape Reinga
Cape Maria van Diemen
North Cape
Parengarenga Harbour
Great Exhibition Bay
Karikari Peninsula
Doubtless Bay
Cavalli Is.
Bay of Islands
Cape Brett
Poor Knights Is.
Juken Nissho Ltd, Kaitaia
Tauroa Point
Hokianga Harbour
Maunganui Bluff
Bream Head
Whangarei Harbour
Bream Bay
Hen and Chickens
Mokohinau Is.
Little Barrier Island
Great Barrier Island
Cape Rodney
Kawau I.
Cape Colville
Kaipara Harbour
Mercury Is.
Mercury Bay
Rangitoto I.
Hauraki Gulf
Waiheke I.
Ponui I.
Firth of Thames
Slipper I.
Mayor I.
Fletcher Wood Panels, Kumeu
Carter Holt Harvey Timber Ltd., Mt. Eden
Fletcher Hardboard, Penrose
NZFP Pulp and Paper Ltd, Te Papapa
Manukau Harbour
Kopine Particle Board Ltd, Kopu
Matakana I.
Tauranga Harbour
Motiti I.
White I.
Cape Runaway
Raglan Harbour
Woody Head
H.T. Plywood Ltd.
Bay of Plenty
East Ca
Aotea Harbour
Caxton Paper Ltd.
NZFP Pulp and Paper Ltd., Whakatane
Kawhia Harbour
Albatross Point
Carter Holt Harvey Timber Ltd, Tokoroa
Tasman Pulp and Paper, Kawerau
NZFP Pulp and Paper Ltd, Kinleith
Gable End Foreland
Kaingaroa
Largest Radiata pine plantation in the world 281,000 ha
Fletcher Wood Panels, Taupo
Poverty Bay
Young Nicks Head
North Taranaki Bight
Mahia Peninsula
Sutherla
Bli
George S
Hawke Bay
Portland I.
Caswell Sound
Charles Sound
Nancy Sound
Thompson Sound
Secretary I.
Doubtful Sound
Cape Egmont
South Taranaki Bight
Winstone Pulp International Ltd., Karioi
Pan Pacific Forest Industries Ltd.
Dagg Sound
Breaksea Sound
Resolution I.
Dusky Sound
West Cape
Chalky Inlet
Preservation Inlet
Cape Turnagain
Cape Reinga
Kapiti I.
Juken Nissho Ltd, Masterton
Castle Point
Mana I.
SOUTH ISLAND
Cape Terawhiti
Wellington Harbour
Turakirae Head
Cook Strait
Palliser Bay
Cape Palliser
N.B. The Auckland Islands are approx. 400 km south of South Cape
Auckland Islands
Carnley Harbour
Adams I.
Solan

Bateman Contemporary Atlas New Zealand

Total Timber Production

Exotic

1970 1980 1990 1997

March

...bert Conformal Conic Projection

...e: 1: 3 000 000

0 20 30 40 50 60 70 80 90 100 km

- - - - regional boundaries

Cape Farewell
Farewell Spit
Golden Bay
Stephens I.
D'Urville I.
172° E   173° E   174° E
Kahurangi Point
Separation Point
Pelorus Sound
Forsyth I.
Cape Jackson
Queen Charlotte Sound
41° S   Tasman Bay   41° S
Karamea Bight
Arapawa I.
Nelson Pine Industries Ltd.
Cloudy Bay
Cook Strait

Cape Campbell

171° E Cape Foulwind

2000

42° S   42° S

4000

174° E
Kaikoura Peninsula

2000

0
West Coast

International Panel & Lumber Co Ltd., Gladstone

170° E

Nelson-Marlborough

43° S   43° S

Abut Head

N.B. The Chatham Islands are approx. 800 km east of Banks Peninsula

176° 30' W

169° E

Pegasus Bay

Canterbury Timber Products Ltd.
New Zealand Veneers Ltd., Christchurch
Lyttelton Harbour

Banks Peninsula

Cape Young

Petre Bay   Hanson Bay

168° E

Cascade Point
Jackson Bay

Akaroa Harbour

44° S   44° S
Chatham Island
Cape L'Eveque

...a Bay

Canterbury Bight

173° E

Pitt Island
Rangatira I.

172° E

2000

0
Canterbury

176° 30' W

45° S

Otago Harbour
Otago Peninsula
Cape Saunders

46° S

NZFP Pulp and Paper Ltd.
Mataura

171° E

...a Pt
...ntre I.

Nugget Point

2000

Foveaux Strait
Toetoes Bay
Waipapa Point
Ruapuke I.
Paterson Inlet

0
Otago-Southland

47° S

Stewart Island

169° E   170° E

South Cape

168° E

Nearly 30% (7.9 million hectares) of New Zealand's land area is forest-cloaked, of which 6.4 million hectares is indigenous, and 1.5 million hectares is exotic production forest. The forestry sector is the country's third largest export earner, accounts for over 6% of GDP and employs over 30,000 people.

The indigenous forest resource was heavily exploited until the 1960s, when the large exotic forests planted in the 1930s matured and became more economically viable than native timber. These large plantations, found on marginal and uneconomic farmlands such as the poor soils of the volcanic plateau, are 91% radiata pine (Pinus radiata). High planting levels in the late 1970s and early 1980s mean that further forests are now maturing, and the projected wood supply for the next 20 years is for large increases in output, almost all of which will be available for export.

New Zealand's indigenous forests are the remnants of a vast forest covering much of both islands, and is now largely confined to mountainous areas. The only extensive areas of lowland native forest are found on the South Island's West Coast. Because the Crown owns 77% of indigenous forests, it has been able to enact legislation affording some protection from further harvesting: less than 2% of total forest production is from indigenous forests.

Ownership of the cutting rights to exotic forests has moved to the private sector in a series of sales since 1989. New Zealand-owned and foreign companies alike have invested in this growing industry: 70% of the exotic forest estate is owned by ten major companies, while the remaining forest is owned by small companies, local government, Māori interests, joint ventures and thousands of farmers. These smaller investors planted 50% of the 60,000 hectares of new trees planted in 1995.

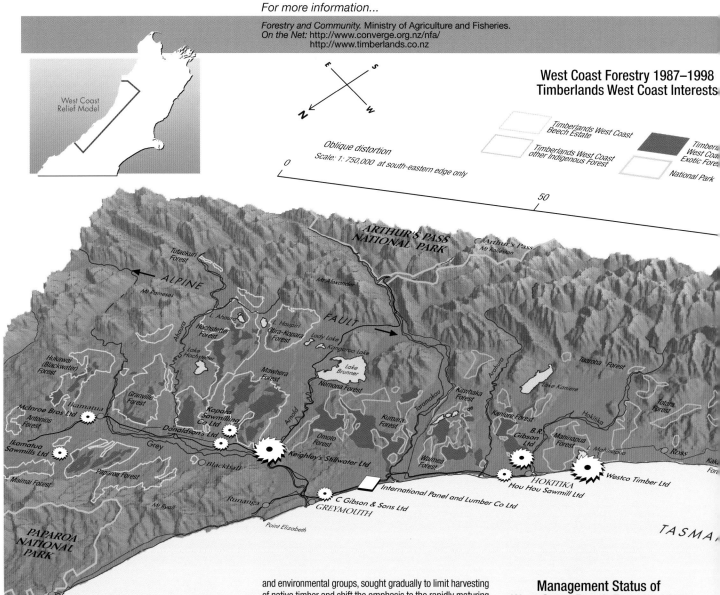

West Coast
Relief Model

E   S

N   W

Oblique distortion
Scale: 1: 750,000 at south-eastern edge only

0

50

West Coast Forestry 1987–1998
Timberlands West Coast Interests

Timberlands West Coast
Beech Estate

Timberlands West Coast
other Indigenous Forest

Timber
West Coas
Exotic Fore

National Park

ARTHUR'S PASS NATIONAL PARK

On the West Coast of the South Island lie the largest
remaining natural forests in New Zealand. Beech and mixed
beech-podocarp (mainly rimu) forests dominate to the north
and south, while in the centre between the Taramakau and
Karangarua Rivers a 'beech gap' leaves podocarps on their
own. Moving inland from the coast, lowland podocarps give
way to upland beech forest. This natural forest has historically
been subject to considerable logging, both to clear the land
for farming and for harvesting purposes — the first sawmill
opened in Hokitika in 1865. In recent years logging has been
severely limited by law: annual sawn timber production has
fallen from 140,000 m^3 in the late 1960s to 55,000 m^3 in
1993, and will reduce to 15,000 m^3 by 2006.

The first exotic plantings began at Mahinapua in 1928,
and were followed by more recent planting on the dissected
glacial outwash surfaces immediately to the west of the Alpine
Fault, filling the spaces between the beech stands. Overall
plantings, while substantial, leave the West Coast with less
exotic forest than any other New Zealand region. However,
as young trees mature the exotic harvest is likely to triple
from 140,000 m^3 in 1991–95 to 410,000 m^3 in 2001–05.

In the 1970s natural forests became increasingly
recognised for their conservation and scenic values, and
environmental lobby groups exerted pressure on the
government to limit the felling of trees that took hundreds of
years to grow. The increasing political awareness of
environmentalists saw them use the West Coast as a symbol
of their struggle, portraying the local residents as greedy,
interested only in short-term gain. In their turn, West Coast
residents viewed the timber industry as an essential (if small)
part of their local economy, and characterised environmentalists
as middle-class urban-dwellers seeking to block progress
(Scott, 1992).

The West Coast Accord, a 1989 agreement between the
government, the West Coast timber industry, local authorities

and environmental groups, sought gradually to limit harvesting
of native timber and shift the emphasis to the rapidly maturing
exotic crop. The most controversial part of this scheme was
the granting of rights to 'sustained-yield management' of
some indigenous forest, effectively allowing continued cutting
rights. This compromise satisfied neither the timber industry
nor the environmentalists. Among the casualties were local
interests — landowners and local councils among them —
whose desires were traded away in an attempt to attract
political support for the preservation of forests.

Meanwhile, the government restructured the forest
industry, selling off much of the State Forest asset (Roche,
1990). Timberlands West Coast Ltd., a State-Owned Enterprise,
was formed in 1990 to manage the Crown's West Coast non-
reserved indigenous and exotic forests.

The impact of the West Coast Accord on employment
was uneven. Harihari lost half its 54 state forestry staff by
1987, of whom one-third could find no full-time work.
Greymouth, however, was hardly affected. Though the Accord
provided $5 million for investment in local tourism, this did
not generate the expected revenue — even when, again
against local wishes, all the State-owned land south of the
Cook River was granted World Heritage status in 1990.

Land ownership on the West Coast further complicates
the issue. The State owns a far higher percentage of land on
the West Coast than in any other region. Government decisions
regarding the use of Crown land therefore have a greater
impact on the West Coast than anywhere else. As an example,
forested land owned by farmers, but legally unable to be
cleared, can be sold only at low prices to the Department of
Conservation. This further reduces the ratings base from
which local and regional councils derive their income, resulting
in direct economic loss to the region (Steng, 1990).

Controversy over the Accord erupted in 1998 when
Timberlands West Coast unveiled plans to 'sustainably' log
parts of their northern beech estate and their southern rimu
forests. The government appeared divided over the issue,
while environmental lobby groups mobilised for a political
and possibly legal confrontation.

Bateman Contemporary Atlas New Zealand

Management Status of
West Coast Beech Forests, 1998

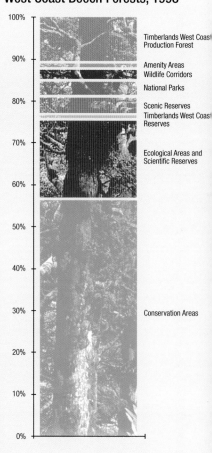

100%

Timberlands West Coast
Production Forest

90%

Amenity Areas
Wildlife Corridors

National Parks

80%

Scenic Reserves
Timberlands West Coast
Reserves

70%

Ecological Areas and
Scientific Reserves

60%

50%

40%

30%

Conservation Areas

20%

10%

0%

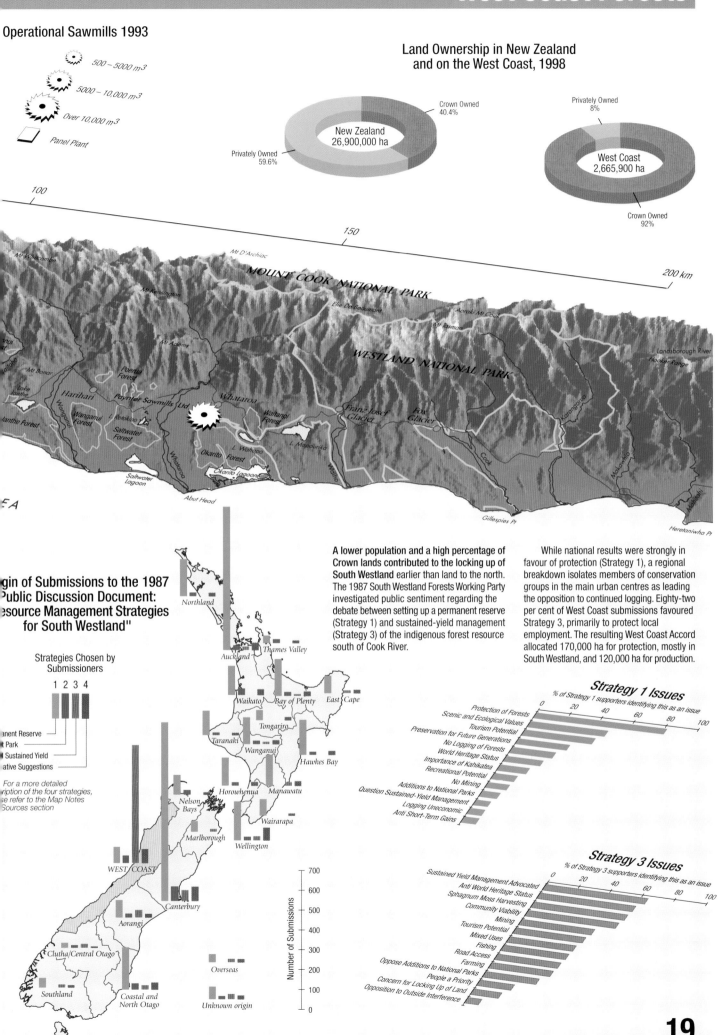

Operational Sawmills 1993

- 500 – 5000 m3
- 5000 – 10,000 m3
- Over 10,000 m3
- Panel Plant

Land Ownership in New Zealand and on the West Coast, 1998

New Zealand
26,900,000 ha

Crown Owned 40.4%

Privately Owned 59.6%

West Coast
2,665,900 ha

Privately Owned 8%

Crown Owned 92%

100

150

200 km

"Origin of Submissions to the 1987 Public Discussion Document: Resource Management Strategies for South Westland"

Strategies Chosen by Submissioners

1 2 3 4

- Permanent Reserve
- Park
- Sustained Yield
- Alternative Suggestions

For a more detailed description of the four strategies, please refer to the Map Notes and Sources section

A lower population and a high percentage of Crown lands contributed to the locking up of South Westland earlier than land to the north. The 1987 South Westland Forests Working Party investigated public sentiment regarding the debate between setting up a permanent reserve (Strategy 1) and sustained-yield management (Strategy 3) of the indigenous forest resource south of Cook River.

While national results were strongly in favour of protection (Strategy 1), a regional breakdown isolates members of conservation groups in the main urban centres as leading the opposition to continued logging. Eighty-two per cent of West Coast submissions favoured Strategy 3, primarily to protect local employment. The resulting West Coast Accord allocated 170,000 ha for protection, mostly in South Westland, and 120,000 ha for production.

Number of Submissions

700
600
500
400
300
200
100
0

Overseas

Unknown origin

Strategy 1 Issues
% of Strategy 1 supporters identifying this as an issue

0 20 40 60 80 100

- Protection of Forests
- Scenic and Ecological Values
- Tourism Potential
- Preservation for Future Generations
- No Logging of Forests
- World Heritage Status
- Importance of Kahikatea
- Recreational Potential
- No Mining
- Additions to National Parks
- Question Sustained-Yield Management
- Logging Uneconomic
- Anti Short-Term Gains

Strategy 3 Issues
% of Strategy 3 supporters identifying this as an issue

0 20 40 60 80 100

- Sustained Yield Management Advocated
- Anti World Heritage Status
- Sphagnum Moss Harvesting
- Community Viability
- Mining
- Tourism Potential
- Mixed Uses
- Fishing
- Road Access
- Farming
- Oppose Additions to National Parks
- People a Priority
- Concern for Locking Up of Land
- Opposition to Outside Interference

19

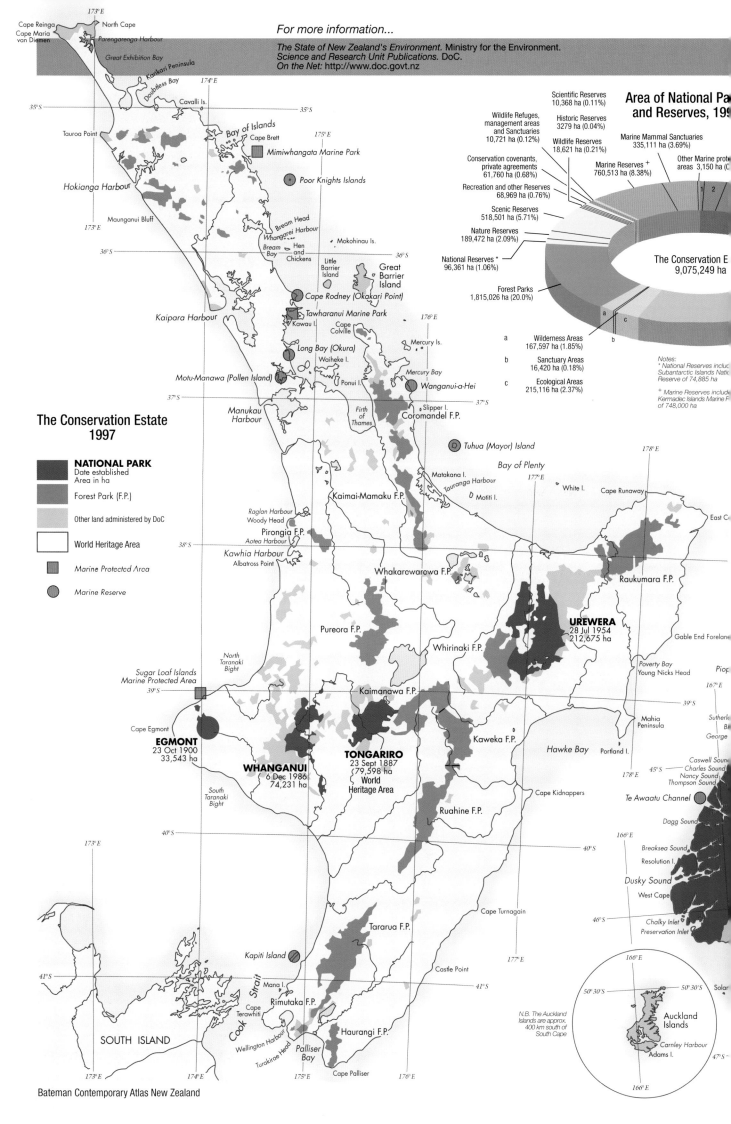

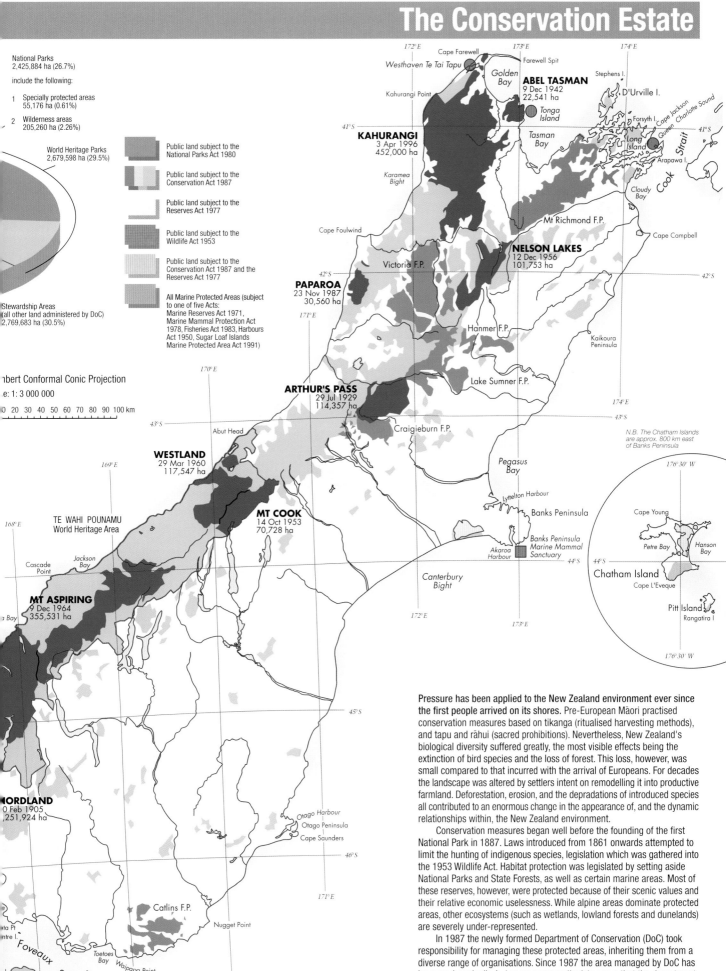

National Parks
2,425,884 ha (26.7%)

include the following:

1 Specially protected areas
55,176 ha (0.61%)

2 Wilderness areas
205,260 ha (2.26%)

World Heritage Parks
2,679,598 ha (29.5%)

Public land subject to the
National Parks Act 1980

Public land subject to the
Conservation Act 1987

Public land subject to the
Reserves Act 1977

Public land subject to the
Wildlife Act 1953

Public land subject to the
Conservation Act 1987 and the
Reserves Act 1977

All Marine Protected Areas (subject
to one of five Acts:
Marine Reserves Act 1971,
Marine Mammal Protection Act
1978, Fisheries Act 1983, Harbours
Act 1950, Sugar Loaf Islands
Marine Protected Area Act 1991)

Stewardship Areas
(all other land administered by DoC)
2,769,683 ha (30.5%)

Lambert Conformal Conic Projection
Scale: 1: 3 000 000

0 20 30 40 50 60 70 80 90 100 km

KAHURANGI
3 Apr 1996
452,000 ha

ABEL TASMAN
9 Dec 1942
22,541 ha

NELSON LAKES
12 Dec 1956
101,753 ha

PAPAROA
23 Nov 1987
30,560 ha

ARTHUR'S PASS
29 Jul 1929
114,357 ha

WESTLAND
29 Mar 1960
117,547 ha

MT COOK
14 Oct 1953
70,728 ha

TE WAHI POUNAMU
World Heritage Area

MT ASPIRING
9 Dec 1964
355,531 ha

FIORDLAND
10 Feb 1905
1,251,924 ha

Westhaven Te Tai Tapu
Cape Farewell
Farewell Spit
Golden Bay
Tonga Island
Kahurangi Point
Stephens I.
D'Urville I.
Forsyth I.
Tasman Bay
Long Island
Cape Jackson
Queen Charlotte Sound
Arapawa I.
Cook Strait
Cloudy Bay
Karamea Bight
Mt Richmond F.P.
Cape Campbell
Cape Foulwind
Victoria F.P.
Hanmer F.P.
Kaikoura Peninsula
Lake Sumner F.P.
Craigieburn F.P.
Abut Head
Pegasus Bay
Lyttelton Harbour
Banks Peninsula
Banks Peninsula Marine Mammal Sanctuary
Akaroa Harbour
Cascade Point
Jackson Bay
Canterbury Bight
Otago Harbour
Otago Peninsula
Cape Saunders
Catlins F.P.
Nugget Point
Toetoes Bay
Waipapa Point
Ruapuke I.
Paterson Inlet
Stewart Island
Foveaux Strait
South Cape

N.B. The Chatham Islands
are approx. 800 km east
of Banks Peninsula

Cape Young
Petre Bay
Hanson Bay
Chatham Island
Cape L'Eveque
Pitt Island
Rangatira I.

Pressure has been applied to the New Zealand environment ever since the first people arrived on its shores. Pre-European Māori practised conservation measures based on tikanga (ritualised harvesting methods), and tapu and rāhui (sacred prohibitions). Nevertheless, New Zealand's biological diversity suffered greatly, the most visible effects being the extinction of bird species and the loss of forest. This loss, however, was small compared to that incurred with the arrival of Europeans. For decades the landscape was altered by settlers intent on remodelling it into productive farmland. Deforestation, erosion, and the depredations of introduced species all contributed to an enormous change in the appearance of, and the dynamic relationships within, the New Zealand environment.

Conservation measures began well before the founding of the first National Park in 1887. Laws introduced from 1861 onwards attempted to limit the hunting of indigenous species, legislation which was gathered into the 1953 Wildlife Act. Habitat protection was legislated by setting aside National Parks and State Forests, as well as certain marine areas. Most of these reserves, however, were protected because of their scenic values and their relative economic uselessness. While alpine areas dominate protected areas, other ecosystems (such as wetlands, lowland forests and dunelands) are severely under-represented.

In 1987 the newly formed Department of Conservation (DoC) took responsibility for managing these protected areas, inheriting them from a diverse range of organisations. Since 1987 the area managed by DoC has increased markedly, but some conservationists argue that the department is under-resourced. Ten key Acts govern New Zealand's conservation strategies. Other organisations, representing recreationists, environmental groups, Maori interests, people seeking to preserve historic places, and others all have input into the management of the conservation estate.

For more information...

The State of New Zealand's Environment. Ministry for the Environment.
On the Net: http://www.mfe.govt.nz/issues/ozone.html
http://www.boprc.govt.nz

The Tarawera River ecosystem has been subjected to considerable pressure since the 1950s, when two large timber processing mills were built. Five to ten per cent of the river flow is extracted for the Caxton and the Tasman Pulp and Paper mills: the waste is returned at a much higher temperature and contains a number of pollutants. The pollution has led to the river being called the 'Black Drain'.

Overall reduced flow, partly caused by reafforestation, threatens to parch downstream wetlands, which are a small remnant (1.7%) of their original size. Most original wetlands were replaced by farmland, latterly by kiwifruit orchards. This 'fashion' farming will continue to place stress on the lower catchment area (Environment B.O.P., 1996).

A number of organisations have interests in the condition of the Tarawera River catchment, but the major responsibility lies with Environment B.O.P., (the Bay of Plenty Regional Council). The Resource Management Act 1991 requires Environment B.O.P. to prepare and administer a regional plan to reconcile the various interests of the catchment. This body must deal with the tension between the desire for a healthy environment (in a 1992 survey, 86% of respondents wanted improvement in the Tarawera River downstream of Kawerau) and the wish for continued employment opportunities. The Tasman operation alone employs 1300 people, and generated a billion dollars for New Zealand in 1992. Another 4500 are employed in 'flow-on' industries.

The Tasman and Caxton jobs are important to the region, which contains a disproportionate number of young, unskilled people. The population of the Tarawera River catchment is both much younger and contains a much higher proportion of Māori than the New Zealand population — 31% are under 15 years of age, compared to 23% for New Zealand, and 46% are Māori, compared to 13% for New Zealand.

The Resource Management Act requires planning authorities to consider the significant concerns of local iwi, in this case Ngāti Awa, Ngāti Rangitihi, Tuhourangi and Tūwharetoa ki Kawerau. Historical and current practices have caused great distress to the mauri (life force) of the Tarawera River, and traditional food sources have been destroyed. Improving the situation without threatening the jobs of local Māori is a difficult task.

The regional plan seeks continued reduction of discharge into the lower Tarawera River. Measures suggested include better water treatment, less water usage, increasing the level of dissolved oxygen by adding water supersaturated with oxygen, a combined mill treatment system, reduction of chlorine compounds in the bleaching processes, and land application of effluent. Because of Māori concerns it also needs to address the discharge of human effluent from Edgecumbe and the Caxton Mill. Some progress has been made, but the Tarawera River remains one of the country's most polluted.

Ozone Depletion
October 16, 1998

Dobson Units

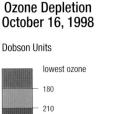

lowest ozone

- 180
- 210
- 240
- 270
- 300
- 330
- 360
- 390

highest ozone

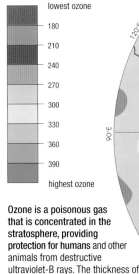

Ozone is a poisonous gas that is concentrated in the stratosphere, providing protection for humans and other animals from destructive ultraviolet-B rays. The thickness of the ozone layer fluctuates wildly, influenced by stratospheric winds and global circulation patterns.

Researchers have recorded a significant depletion of the ozone layer over the last twenty years, averaging about 5% per decade. This has happened as CFC (chlorofluorocarbon) molecules, which are used as coolants in refrigerators and air-conditioners and propellants in spray cans, have been released into the atmosphere. Twenty-five grams of CFCs can destroy a tonne of ozone.

Ozone depletion has been much more dramatic in the area around Antarctica. The 'hole' forms over Antarctica as strong air currents trap extremely cold air over the frozen continent, imprisoning ozone and chlorinated chemicals. The CFCs annihilate the ozone molecules when they are activated by the spring sun. This 'hole' does not directly affect New Zealand, but is of concern because it is evidence of a destructive side-effect of a supposedly 'safe' gas.

Developed nations acted quickly (but not quickly enough, according to some) to limit the use of CFCs and related gases. In 1986 New Zealand used 2300 tonnes of CFCs, a figure which fell to 1211 tonnes by 1989, and to 375 tonnes by 1994. It is estimated that it will take at least 50 years for the ozone layer to recover, and a century for atmospheric chlorine levels to return to near 'normal'.

Bateman Contemporary Atlas New Zealand

Average October Total Ozone, Halley Bay, Antarctica, 1960-1994

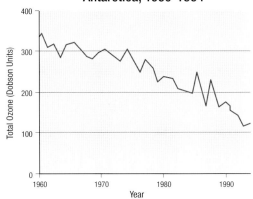

Potentially Contaminated S

416   number of sites per reg
Case Studies of contaminated si

- Iron/Steel Works
- Gas Works
- Explosives Industry
- Engine Works
- Electroplating and Heat Treatment
- Electrical Manufacturing (Transforme
- Dry Cleaning Establishments
- Drum Reconditioning Works
- Defence Works (Army, Navy and Air F
- Chemicals Manufacture and Formatic
- Asbestos Production and Disposal
- Airports (rural, domestic and internat
- Agricultural/ Horticultural Activities
- Acid/alkali manufacture and formatio

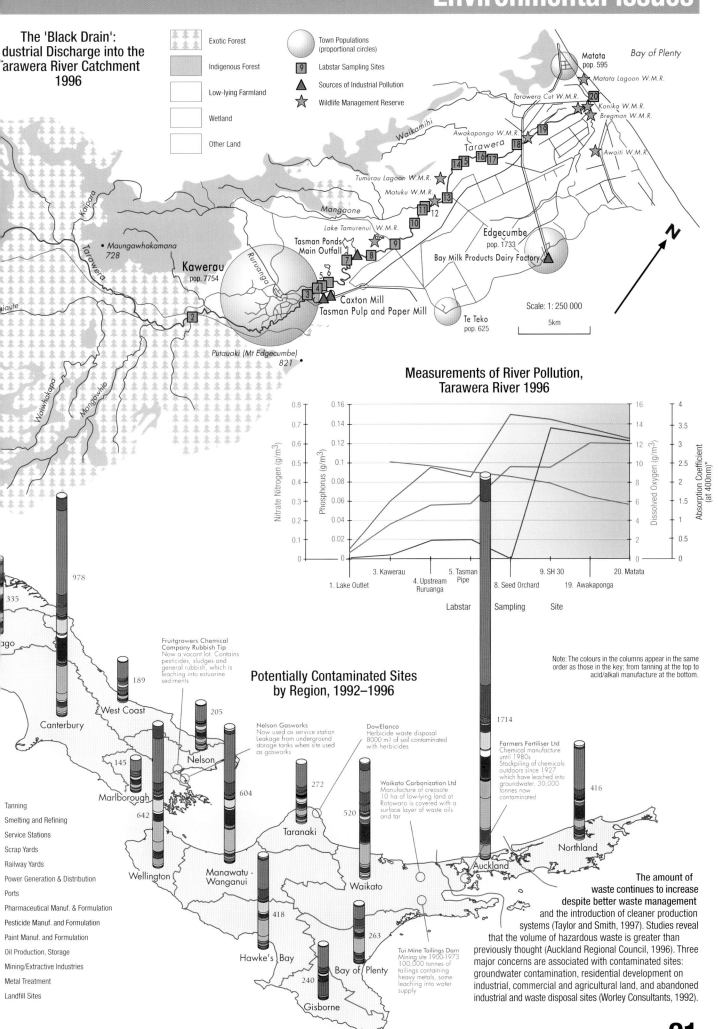

The 'Black Drain': Industrial Discharge into the Tarawera River Catchment 1996

Measurements of River Pollution, Tarawera River 1996

Potentially Contaminated Sites by Region, 1992–1996

The amount of waste continues to increase despite better waste management and the introduction of cleaner production systems (Taylor and Smith, 1997). Studies reveal that the volume of hazardous waste is greater than previously thought (Auckland Regional Council, 1996). Three major concerns are associated with contaminated sites: groundwater contamination, residential development on industrial, commercial and agricultural land, and abandoned industrial and waste disposal sites (Worley Consultants, 1992).

The 880 hectare Avon-Heathcote estuary formed about 450 years ago when the South Brighton Spit enclosed the outlets of Christchurch's two main rivers. It is unique among New Zealand estuaries in supporting a large and varied wildlife population within a heavily urbanised area.

The estuary supports a bird population of national and international importance. Over 1% of the world population of each of four species live there. It is the fifth largest estuary in New Zealand in terms of bird numbers, and is considerably smaller than those estuaries which have more birds, so is much more densely populated. Around 115 species use the estuary at some time during the year, including terns which migrate from the Arctic (S-J. Owen, 1992).

It is inevitable that such a system should come under pressure from humans. Early Māori settlers (Waitaha, Ngāti Māmoe and latterly Ngāi Tahu) used the estuary as a source of mahinga kai. To them the shallow waters of the estuary and the wetlands surrounding it were rich food reservoirs.

Soon after European settlers arrived, industrial pollution began affecting the estuary, originating from a concentration of heavy industry located at Woolston and Sydenham, within a few kilometres of the coast. This heavy industry included woollen mills, metal works and foundries, glue works, tanneries and the municipal gas works. By 1900 a quarter of New Zealand's manufacturing was located in this industrial belt — all drained by the Heathcote River into the estuary.

The Heathcote River acted as a conduit for toxic waste. In 1903, for example, 4.5 million litres of industrial effluent was discharged each day into the river. This pollution was exacerbated by sediment associated with urban development. The Avon and Heathcote Rivers brought down silt from urban clearance, as did the city's main outfall drain, which emptied into Heathcote Bay. The rivers and the estuary silted up rapidly. What was once navigable for vessels drawing eight metres became shallow and unnavigable. Many plants died as a consequence of this heavy silting: sample cores taken show layers of vegetation smothered by silt. River sweeping began in the 1920s in an attempt to clear river silting because of fears of flooding, shifting the problem to the estuary itself.

The effect of pollution, silting, draining and urban infill was to dramatically reduce the amount of wetland and therefore plant life, and to poison much of the shellfish. Bird numbers also suffered, though accurate records were not kept. Certain species were no longer seen at this location.

In 1956 land at Te Ihutai beside the estuary was taken from local Māori under the Public Works Act for the building of a sewage treatment works, which were to discharge treated effluent into the estuary. Ngāi Tahu objected strongly but were unable to halt the process, and the small amount paid in compensation still remains untouched by the iwi. Waste from

Idealised Sediment Core from the Estuary Over the Last 600 Years

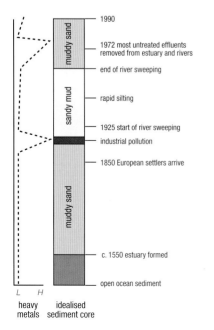

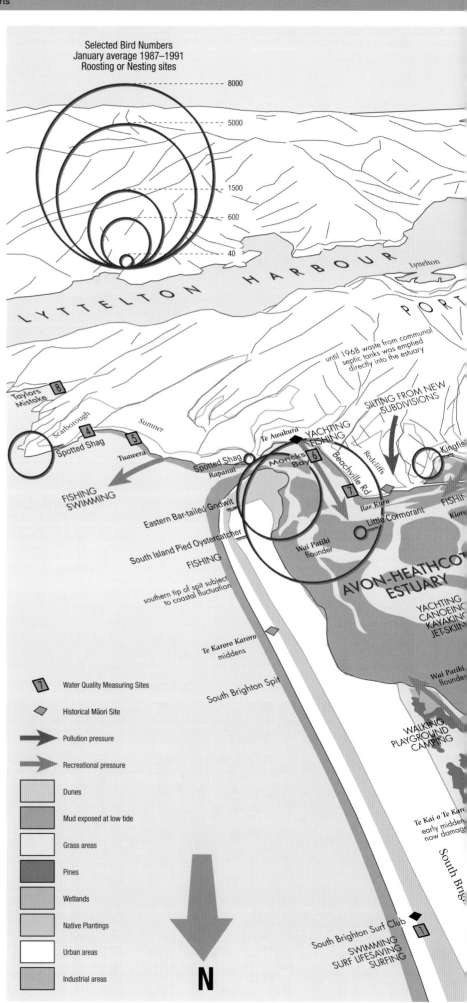

The Avon-Heathcote Estuary: Conflicting Uses of a Sensitive Ecological Area

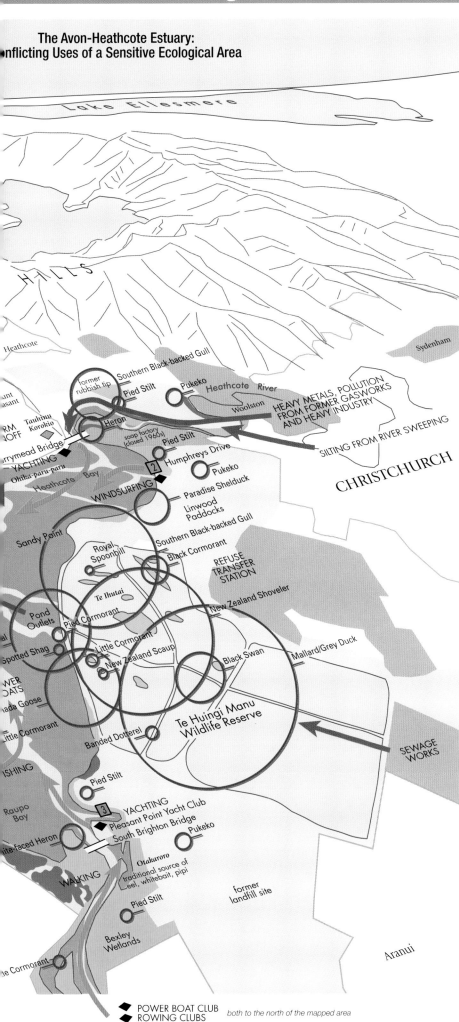

Compliance with Recreational Water Quality Guidelines 1996

Measuring Site	CFU/100ml[1]	%non-compliance[2]
1. South Brighton Surf Club	5	0
2. Humphreys Drive	180	25
3. Pleasant Point Yacht Club	120	37.5
4. Scarborough Beach	29	0
5. Sumner Beach	18.5	0
6. Moncks Bay	11	0
7. Beachville Road Jetty	25	0
8. Taylors Mistake	3.5	0

1. seasonal median concentration of colony-forming units per 100 millilitres of sample

2. percentage of medians of five consecutive samples that exceeded 200 faecal coliforms per 100 millilitres of sample

the main sewage works containing unacceptable levels of coliform bacteria made taking shellfish from the estuary hazardous. Equally deleterious was the practice by residents of the hill suburbs of dumping raw effluent into the estuary. In the late 1960s Sumner was connected to the city sewerage system, and the treatment works were upgraded to eliminate 99.9% of coliform. However, any human effluent discharge — irrespective of treatment levels — renders it culturally unacceptable for Māori to take shellfish from the estuary, even though molluscs in Moncks Bay are safe to eat. Ngāi Tahu have placed a rāhui (ban) on the estuary. Paradoxically, bird populations increased as a direct result of the sewage works. Birds made their homes in large numbers on the oxidation ponds (this was officially recognised when the ponds were made a wildlife reserve) and at the pond outlets where high levels of nutrients are available.

From the 1970s onwards pollution levels began to reduce. The major cause was the decline in profitability of manufacturing: almost all eastern Christchurch's heavy industry has closed or relocated. The gas works, a major source of pollution, finally closed in 1981. Industry has cleaned up its act, while other pollutants are now closely monitored.

Present-day pressures are more likely to come from recreationists taking advantage of this large expanse of calm water, making the estuary an urban playground. Three yachting clubs, a power boating club, jet skiers, fishers, canoeists, kayakers and windsurfers share the estuary with a wide range of birdlife and a wetland ecology. Recreationists are encouraged to be careful not to disturb the large bird and plant populations of the estuary and wetland margins.

Historically, the management of the Avon-Heathcote estuary has largely been done in an ad hoc fashion. The delicate balance between the desires of an urban population, the disposal of its refuse, the rights of the tangata whenua and the responses of a sensitive ecological area has swung back and forth without regulation. In the last two decades, however, first the Christchurch City Council and now the Canterbury Regional Council have taken greater responsibility in managing the estuary.

Since the 1991 Resource Management Act the exact boundaries of responsibility for the estuary and environs have not been clear. In July 1992 the Planning Tribunal sat in a hearing to determine this issue, and found that the landward boundary of the coastal marine area for the estuary is 200 metres landward of the Ferrymead Bridge and the South Brighton Bridge. The Canterbury Regional Council administers the area within this boundary and below the mean high water mark on behalf of the Department of Conservation; the rest is the responsibility of the Christchurch City Council.

These authorities are currently faced with difficulties regarding the outfall of the Sewage Works. The City Council's resource consent expires in 2001, and they are considering a proposal to spend $30 million over eight years to upgrade the Sewage Works. Attached to this is a suggestion that the outfall be piped 2 km offshore of the South Brighton Spit, at a cost of $47-57 million. Environmental impact studies are currently being undertaken to investigate outfall options. The Christchurch City Council will need resource consent for whichever outfall they decide upon: they will apply to the Canterbury Regional Council, but opinions differ as to whether the granting authority will be the Regional Council, an appointed commissioner or the Minister of Conservation.

For more information...

Natural Hazards: their Potential in the Pacific Southwest. Aust. Geological Survey Orgn.
Tephra 13 (1), May 1994. Civil Defence.
On the Net: http://www.mocd.govt.nz

New Zealand is at risk from a number of natural threats. These threats are classified as natural hazards only if they place human life and property at risk. The impact of many 'natural disasters' is exacerbated by unwisely situated human activity, such as on a floodplain or on the slopes of an active volcano. Thus it is possible to mitigate the seriousness of risk from some natural hazards by careful and conservative planning, and to construct warning systems for others — with varying degrees of success.

Natural hazards can be divided into two broad, though not mutually exclusive, categories: meteorological and geological. Volcanic and earthquake events are less frequent but more costly in terms of life and property. Should events of the scale of the 1855 Wellington earthquake or the 1886 Tarawera eruption occur today, they would cause immense, widespread damage and many thousands of fatalities. Landslides can be triggered by earthquakes, volcanic activity and, more commonly, heavy rainfall. Most of the geologically young landscape is threatened, particularly that on which ground cover is stressed by stock or has been removed entirely. The coastland is threatened by less obvious hazards: the ever-present threat of tsunami is not reflected in their historical absence from New Zealand shores, while those shores suffer regular incursion from coastal erosion.

180°E

VII

VIII

IX

VIII

170°E

Northland Volcanic Field

Omaha coast
1980s – erosion destroys houses

Tarawera eruption
1886 – 153 deaths

White Island eruption
1914 – 14 deaths

Edgecumbe earthquake
1987 – 5000 affected
$1100m losses

Auckland Volcanic Field

White
Island

Waikato River (1891)

IX

VII

Edgecumbe (1987)

Tarawera

Ohiwa harbour
1980s – erosion destroys houses

Taupo
Volcanic
Zone

Te Rapa landslide
1846 – 61 deaths

Pouawa Bay
1947 – locally-generated tsunami
destroys bridge on main highway

Tongariro
Ngauruhoe
Ruapehu

Taranaki

VII

IX

Hawke's Bay (1931)

Hawke's Bay
(1863)

Hawke's Bay earthquake
1931 – 256 deaths
11,000 evacuated

Tangiwai lahar
1953 – 151 deaths

40°S

Wanganui (1843)

Weber (1990)

Pahiatua (1934)

40

Wellington (c. 1460)

Murchison earthquake
1929 – 17 deaths

South Wairarapa (1942)

Inangahua earthquake
1968 – 3 deaths

Wairau (1848)

Wairarapa (1855)

Wairarapa earthquake
1855 – 5 deaths

Inangahua (1968)

Murchison (1929)

Wairau earthquake
1848 – 3 deaths

VIII

IX

VIII

Cheviot (1901)

Mt Cook landslide
1991 – mountain height reduced by 10m

VII

Motunau coast
1990 – cliff erosion destroys houses

Lambert Conformal Conic Projection

Scale: 1:8 800 000

0   50   100   150   200   250   300   350   400 km

180°E

Arica tsunami
1868 – from Chile: destroyed a settlement,
loss of life, wave travelled 6km inland

Chile tsunami
1960 – 3.5m high,
$130,000 damage in Lyttelton

Washdyke coast
1980s – coastal erosion and salt incursion
Pastoral land contaminated, industrial
estate threatened

Natural Hazards of Geological Origin

Oamaru (1876)

Waitaki coast
1970s – erosion destroys buildings and
land from Waitaki Boys High School

Landslide Potential

High	Areas of past landslide disasters where eruption products, mudrock outcrops, or earthquakes are likely to produce future landslides.
Moderate	Landslides common, or adjacent areas of similar terrain, lithology and exposure to seismicity or intense rains.

Historic Damaging Earthquakes

+ High
+ Moderate

Earthquake Potential (Modified Mercalli Scale)
10% chance of being equalled or exceeded in a 50-year period

Natural Disaster Event
○— Event, date, description

-VII- No damage to buildings of good design and construction. Slight to moderate damage in well-built ordinary structures. Damage considerable in poorly built or badly designed structures.

-VIII- No damage to specially designed structures, but damage can be considerable in ordinary substantial buildings, including partial collapse. Great damage in poorly built structures. Fall of walls, columns, monuments and factory stacks.

-IX- Damage great, including partial collapse of substantial buildings. Well-designed frame structures distorted. Unsecured buildings shifted off foundations. Ground cracked conspicuously. Underground pipes broken. Serious damage to reservoirs.

Volcanic Activity (last 700,000 years)

	Andesite
	Lahar
	Rhyolite
	Basalt
	Ignimbrite
▲	Active volcano

IX

Abbotsford landslide
1979 – 69 houses destroyed

VII

Reported Tsunami Events, 1840 – 1982 (per 50km of coast)

2 or less		6
3		7
4		8
5		9 or more

170°E

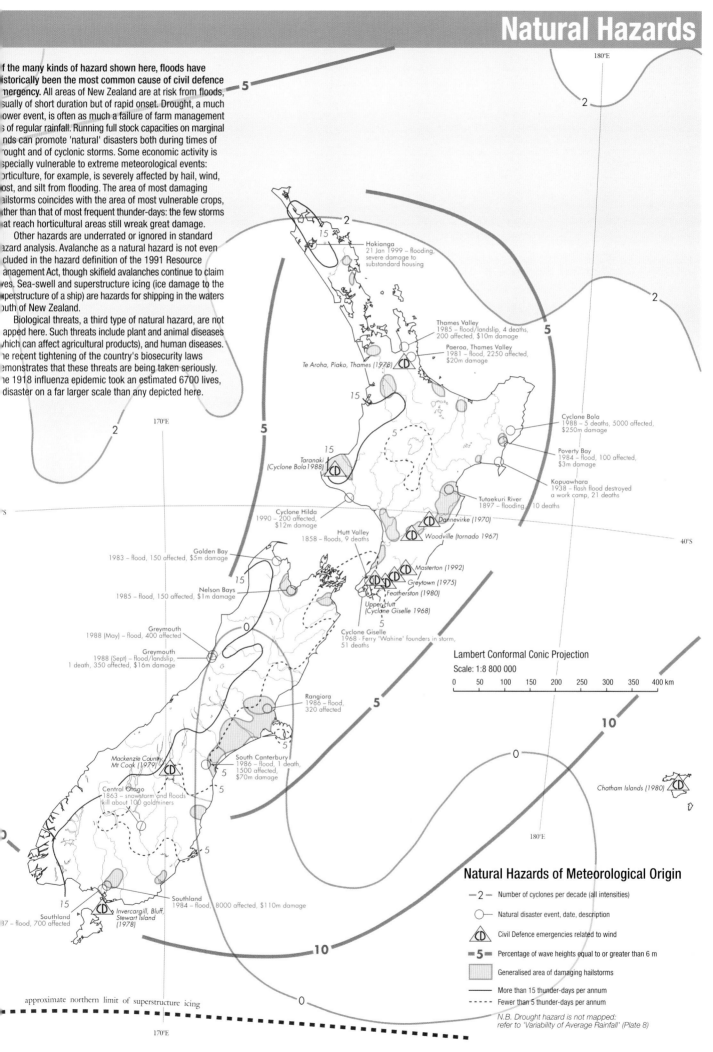

f the many kinds of hazard shown here, floods have
istorically been the most common cause of civil defence
mergency. All areas of New Zealand are at risk from floods,
sually of short duration but of rapid onset. Drought, a much
ower event, is often as much a failure of farm management
s of regular rainfall. Running full stock capacities on marginal
nds can promote 'natural' disasters both during times of
rought and of cyclonic storms. Some economic activity is
specially vulnerable to extreme meteorological events:
orticulture, for example, is severely affected by hail, wind,
ost, and silt from flooding. The area of most damaging
ailstorms coincides with the area of most vulnerable crops,
ather than that of most frequent thunder-days: the few storms
at reach horticultural areas still wreak great damage.

Other hazards are underrated or ignored in standard
azard analysis. Avalanche as a natural hazard is not even
cluded in the hazard definition of the 1991 Resource
anagement Act, though skifield avalanches continue to claim
es. Sea-swell and superstructure icing (ice damage to the
uperstructure of a ship) are hazards for shipping in the waters
outh of New Zealand.

Biological threats, a third type of natural hazard, are not
apped here. Such threats include plant and animal diseases
hich can affect agricultural products), and human diseases.
ne recent tightening of the country's biosecurity laws
emonstrates that these threats are being taken seriously.
ne 1918 influenza epidemic took an estimated 6700 lives,
disaster on a far larger scale than any depicted here.

Natural Hazards of Meteorological Origin

- 2 — Number of cyclones per decade (all intensities)
- Natural disaster event, date, description
- Civil Defence emergencies related to wind
- 5 — Percentage of wave heights equal to or greater than 6 m
- Generalised area of damaging hailstorms
- More than 15 thunder-days per annum
- Fewer than 5 thunder-days per annum

N.B. Drought hazard is not mapped:
refer to 'Variability of Average Rainfall' (Plate 8)

23

For more information...

Tephra 13 (1), May 1994. Civil Defence.
On the Net: http://www.gns.cri.nz/earthact/volcanoes/index.html
http://www.geo.mtu.edu/volcanoes/new.zealand/ruapehu

At about 250,000 years old, Ruapehu is the largest and most active of New Zealand's volcanoes. Its summit consists of several snow-covered craters with a central active vent filled by a lake which drains into the Whangaehu River. Ruapehu eruptions are initially phreatic (steam explosions) which quickly melt the permanent snow. This leads to the formation of lahars (volcanic mudflows) which travel swiftly down the mountainside using well-defined tracks. Other hazards include ejecta, lava flows, ash falls, and less common but deadly pyroclastic surges, which engulf everything in their path.

The lava plateau surrounding Ruapehu is used by two main highways (State Highways 1 and 4), the North Island Main Trunk Railway and major electricity transmission lines. The Tongariro Hydro-Electric Power Scheme is sited within 30 km of the mountain. The army holds exercises nearby. But most at risk are the three skifields on the mountain slopes (one of which is located in an active lahar track), and other activities, such as tramping, associated with the Tongariro National Park of which the mountain is a part. Although only 6500 people live within 30 km of the summit, that number can double on a ski weekend.

Ruapehu reminded New Zealanders of the risk of living and working near volcanoes by erupting in 1995 and again in 1996. The first phase (18 September to 14 October 1995) began with the largest lahar since 1975; then on 23 September a large explosion generated lahars that swept through Whakapapa skifield 57 minutes after it had closed for the day. An eight-hour eruption on 8 October emptied Crater Lake, bringing the phreatic eruptions to an end: subsequent activity produced much more ash. By mid-November Crater Lake had begun to refill, but at that time was less than 1% of its former volume.

The second eruption sequence began with volcanic tremors on 15 June 1996, which became a full-scale eruption two days later. Ashfall closed airports hundreds of kilometres away. Further eruptions, all producing massive ash clouds, took place on 15–17 July and 20–28 July. Activity had ceased by the end of September.

The latest eruptive phase (1995–6) caused no fatalities but has cost the local tourist industry dearly. In both 1995 and 1996 the ski season was severely curtailed as the slopes were declared off-limits, and local businesses struggled to survive. The Rangipo hydro-electric station was closed on 28 October 1995 as heavy rain sent ash into the Mangatoetoenui stream. The Desert Road (SH 1) was closed three times and air traffic was excluded from zones downwind of the volcano. The financial effect of the two eruptive phases is estimated at $46 million for 1995 and $98 million for 1996 (Statistics New Zealand, 1998).

Ruapehu Ash Cloud, 17 June 1996
image courtesy of Manaaki Whenua Landcare Research

Ruapehu Volcanic Hazard

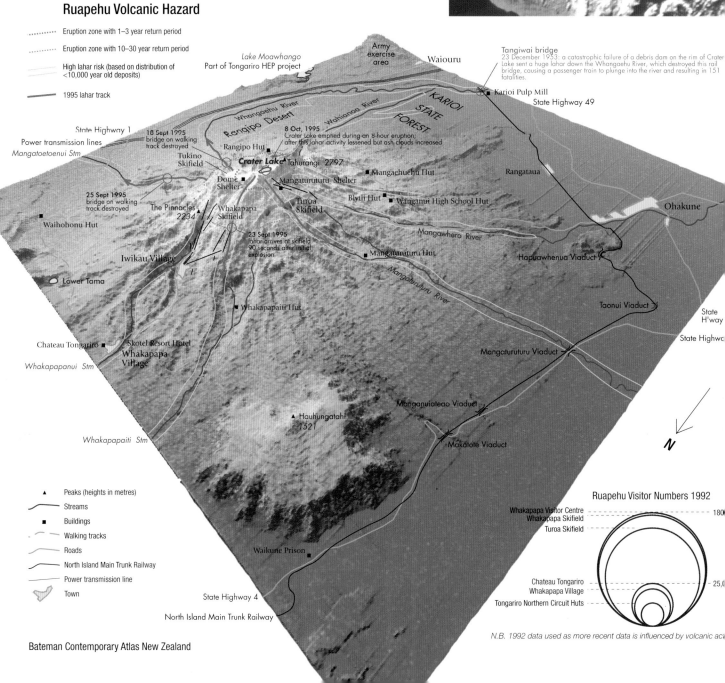

Bateman Contemporary Atlas New Zealand

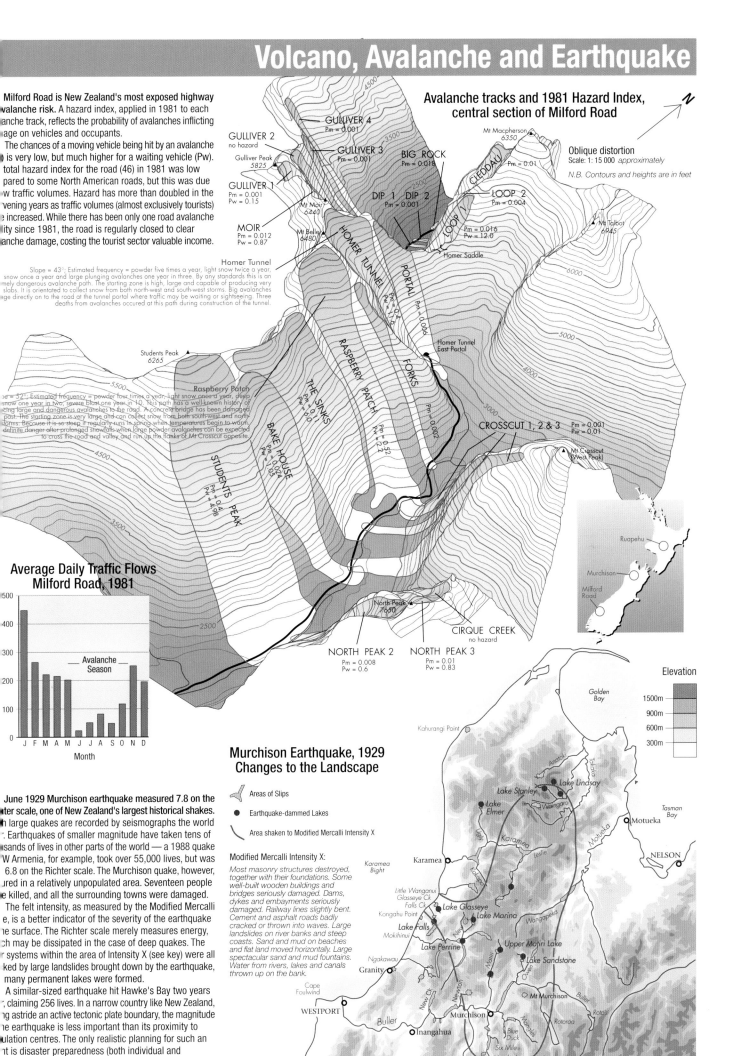

Milford Road is New Zealand's most exposed highway
[a]valanche risk. A hazard index, applied in 1981 to each
[ava]lanche track, reflects the probability of avalanches inflicting
[dam]age on vehicles and occupants.

The chances of a moving vehicle being hit by an avalanche
[(Pm)] is very low, but much higher for a waiting vehicle (Pw).
[The] total hazard index for the road (46) in 1981 was low
[com]pared to some North American roads, but this was due
[to lo]w traffic volumes. Hazard has more than doubled in the
[inter]vening years as traffic volumes (almost exclusively tourists)
[hav]e increased. While there has been only one road avalanche
[fatal]ity since 1981, the road is regularly closed to clear
[aval]anche damage, costing the tourist sector valuable income.

Slope = 43°; Estimated frequency = powder five times a year, light snow twice a year, large plunging avalanches one year in three. By any standards this is an [extr]emely dangerous avalanche path. The starting zone is high, large and capable of producing very [big] slabs. It is orientated to collect snow from both north-west and south-west storms. Big avalanches [plun]ge directly on to the road at the tunnel portal where traffic may be waiting or sightseeing. Three deaths from avalanches occured at this path during construction of the tunnel.

[Slo]pe = 52°. Estimated frequency = powder four times a year, light snow once a year, deep [snow] one year in two, severe blast one year in 10. This path has a well-known history of [produ]cing large and dangerous avalanches to the road. A concrete bridge has been damaged [in the] past. The starting zone is very large and can collect snow from both south-west and north-[west] storms. Because it is so steep it regularly runs in spring when temperatures begin to warm. [Take] definite danger after prolonged snowfalls when large powder avalanches can be expected [to] cross the road and valley and run up the flanks of Mt Crosscut opposite.

Average Daily Traffic Flows
Milford Road, 1981

Murchison Earthquake, 1929
Changes to the Landscape

[In] June 1929 Murchison earthquake measured 7.8 on the
[Rich]ter scale, one of New Zealand's largest historical shakes.
[Suc]h large quakes are recorded by seismographs the world
[ove]r. Earthquakes of smaller magnitude have taken tens of
[thou]sands of lives in other parts of the world — a 1988 quake
[in N]W Armenia, for example, took over 55,000 lives, but was
[only] 6.8 on the Richter scale. The Murchison quake, however,
[occur]red in a relatively unpopulated area. Seventeen people
[wer]e killed, and all the surrounding towns were damaged.

The felt intensity, as measured by the Modified Mercalli
[scal]e, is a better indicator of the severity of the earthquake
[at th]e surface. The Richter scale merely measures energy,
[whi]ch may be dissipated in the case of deep quakes. The
[rive]r systems within the area of Intensity X (see key) were all
[bloc]ked by large landslides brought down by the earthquake,
[and] many permanent lakes were formed.

A similar-sized earthquake hit Hawke's Bay two years
[late]r, claiming 256 lives. In a narrow country like New Zealand,
[lyin]g astride an active tectonic plate boundary, the magnitude
[of th]e earthquake is less important than its proximity to
[pop]ulation centres. The only realistic planning for such an
[even]t is disaster preparedness (both individual and
[gov]ernmental) and insurance cover.

Avalanche tracks and 1981 Hazard Index, central section of Milford Road

Oblique distortion
Scale: 1: 15 000 *approximately*

N.B. Contours and heights are in feet

Modified Mercalli Intensity X:

Most masonry structures destroyed, together with their foundations. Some well-built wooden buildings and bridges seriously damaged. Dams, dykes and embayments seriously damaged. Railway lines slightly bent. Cement and asphalt roads badly cracked or thrown into waves. Large landslides on river banks and steep coasts. Sand and mud on beaches and flat land moved horizontally. Large spectacular sand and mud fountains. Water from rivers, lakes and canals thrown up on the bank.

Areas of Slips

Earthquake-dammed Lakes

Area shaken to Modified Mercalli Intensity X

Elevation

1500m
900m
600m
300m

For more information...

Creating Flood Disasters. Neil Ericksen.
Newsletter. Meteorological Society of New Zealand.
On the Net: http://www.mocd.govt.nz/tephra/tephraindex.html

Hailstorms are a hazard to horticultural industry (fruit, market gardens and viticulture) and, on rare occasions, to houses and life. They may be generated above the Canterbury Plains when north-easterly sea breezes supply moisture to unstable south-westerly airflows. In other parts of the country hailstorms result from similar combinations of local conditions.

Storm tracks were documented as part of the 1980–83 Canterbury Hail Project. The Southern Oscillation, then in a strongly negative El Niño phase, contributed to persistent westerly to south-westerly air flows in 1982–3, and many of the storms shown here were embedded in the 'squall line' of south-westerly changes. Other storms were propagated from warm air above sun-facing slopes in the foothills of the Southern Alps (such as Mts Peel, Somers and Hutt).

The most severe storm of the period was on 19 January 1983. As a southerly change advanced across the Canterbury Plains, it merged with a humid sea breeze and the squall line intensified. Thunderstorms affected the southern part of Christchurch and adjacent areas, bringing a tornado and hailstones 50 mm in diameter. The funnel touched the ground in open fields a few kilometres south-west of Halswell, then moved erratically northwards, causing considerable damage to houses in Kinrara Place, Halswell. The path of destruction was about 200 m wide. Wind speeds of up to 150 km/h were reported as far away as 5 km from the tornado path. By the time the system had reached eastern Christchurch it had lost much of its power.

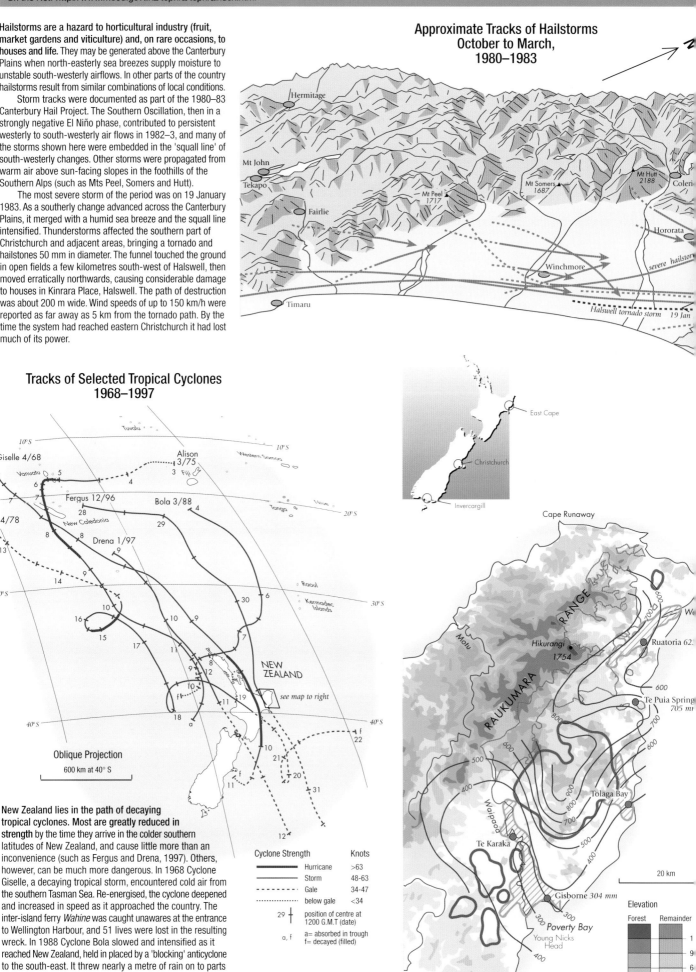

Approximate Tracks of Hailstorms
October to March, 1980–1983

Tracks of Selected Tropical Cyclones
1968–1997

Oblique Projection

600 km at 40° S

New Zealand lies in the path of decaying tropical cyclones. Most are greatly reduced in strength by the time they arrive in the colder southern latitudes of New Zealand, and cause little more than an inconvenience (such as Fergus and Drena, 1997). Others, however, can be much more dangerous. In 1968 Cyclone Giselle, a decaying tropical storm, encountered cold air from the southern Tasman Sea. Re-energised, the cyclone deepened and increased in speed as it approached the country. The inter-island ferry *Wahine* was caught unawares at the entrance to Wellington Harbour, and 51 lives were lost in the resulting wreck. In 1988 Cyclone Bola slowed and intensified as it reached New Zealand, held in placed by a 'blocking' anticyclone to the south-east. It threw nearly a metre of rain on to parts of the East Cape in three days, causing massive damage (see detail at right).

Cyclone Strength	Knots
Hurricane	>63
Storm	48-63
Gale	34-47
below gale	<34

29 ┼ position of centre at 1200 G.M.T (date)

a, f — a= absorbed in trough f= decayed (filled)

Elevation — Forest — Remainder

20 km

Bateman Contemporary Atlas New Zealand

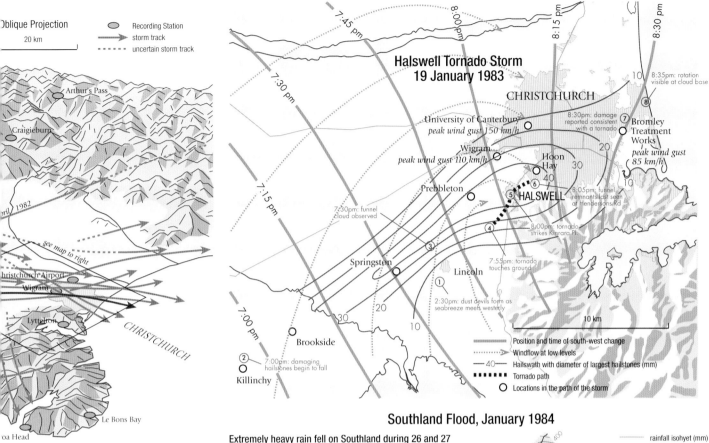

Oblique Projection
20 km

- Recording Station
- → storm track
- ⋯⋯ uncertain storm track

Arthur's Pass
Craigieburn
April 1982
see map to right
Christchurch Airport
Wigram
Lyttelton
CHRISTCHURCH
Le Bons Bay
oa Head

Halswell Tornado Storm
19 January 1983

CHRISTCHURCH

7:45 pm · 8:00 pm · 8:15 pm · 8:30 pm

8:35pm: rotation visible at cloud base

University of Canterbury
peak wind gust 150 km/h

8:30pm: damage reported consistent with a tornado

Bromley Treatment Works
peak wind gust 85 km/h

Wigram
peak wind gust 110 km/h

Hoon Hay

Prebbleton

HALSWELL

8:05pm: funnel remnants last seen at Hendersons Rd

7:30pm: funnel cloud observed

8:00pm: tornado strikes Kinrara Pl.

7:55pm: tornado touches ground

Springston

Lincoln

2:30pm: dust devils form as seabreeze meets westerly

7:15 pm · 7:00 pm

Brookside

7:00pm: damaging hailstones begin to fall

Killinchy

10 km

— Position and time of south-west change
⋯⋯ Windflow at low levels
—40— Hailswath with diameter of largest hailstones (mm)
▪▪▪▪ Tornado path
○ Locations in the path of the storm

Southland Flood, January 1984

Extremely heavy rain fell on Southland during 26 and 27 January 1984, resulting in serious flooding and causing at least $55 million in insured property losses. This was the third time in seven years that a major flood had affected the region.

Ericksen (1986) notes that "Flood disasters are essentially human creations." This was true of northern Invercargill, where two-thirds of the urban area flooded in 1984 was built after the passing of the 1953 Town and Country Planning Act. As the city grew out on to the floodplain, confident in the ability of stopbanks to protect them, the potential for disaster was increased, and was realised in 1984.

Cost to the community includes property damage, long-term dislocation of families and the resultant stress this causes. The full monetary cost, including income and production losses, of this flood may well have been $250 million, twice as expensive as the more widely remembered Cyclone Bola four years later.

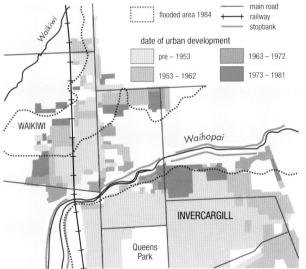

⋯⋯ rainfall isohyet (mm)

areas in which maximum 24-hour rainfall exceeded the 50-year return periods

— Jan 1984
— Jan 1980
— Oct 1978

Mataura
Oct 1978
Jan 1984
see map to left
Invercargill
Jan 1980

50 km

The Impact of Cyclone Bola
East Cape, 1988

Between 6 and 9 March Cyclone Bola delivered warm tropical air with up to [...] mm of rainfall to the East Cape region [of New] Zealand. This rain fell on land that [had] historically suffered severe natural [ero]sion, made worse by the removal of [the] protective forest cover as farmers tried [to] exploit marginal lands. This $110m [disa]ster was not unexpected, following [simi]lar events in 1938 and 1948.

A 1970 land use plan recommended [plan]ting exotic forests on over 100,000 [ha o]f critical headwaters to prevent erosion. [In 1]988, 75,000 ha of this land remained [in p]asture. Unfortunately, the erosion [pun]ished not only those who farmed the [hea]dwaters, but also those in the valleys, [who]se wineries and orchards were covered [by m]illions of tonnes of silt.

 'Critical Inland Area', 1970 land use plan.

'Strict control should be enforced to minimise erosion and flooding in major catchments. Large parts need reafforestation and are capable of supporting commercial forests.'

— Rainfall (mm) 6 - 9 March, 1988

Extensive flooding/silt, Bola flood, 1988

>20% earth movement, Bola flood, 1988

Flooded Area, Invercargill
North, January 1984

1 km

⋯⋯ flooded area 1984
—+— main road / railway
— stopbank

date of urban development
pre – 1953
1953 – 1962
1963 – 1972
1973 – 1981

Waikiwi
WAIKIWI
Waihopai
INVERCARGILL
Queens Park

Some individuals choose to relocate after such a flood — the Government supported 29 Invercargill families to acquire flood-free sections — but most push for further strengthening of flood protection measures. The pressure to protect post-disaster redevelopment is hard for councillors to resist. Within months of the 1984 flood the nearby Mataura Borough Council shortsightedly sought to allow housing in newly 'protected' areas, because they had just spent $100,000 on river control works.

Impediments remain to preventing flood disasters in New Zealand. Many towns were sited on rivers last century, and remain vulnerable. Residents may resist publicity about flood hazard, as it potentially lowers land values. But, most importantly, flood protection works perpetuate flood disasters by encouraging development behind their walls.

For more information...

The Prehistoric Exploration and Colonisation of the Pacific. Irwin, G.J.
In the Wake of Cook. Mackay, D.M.
New Zealand Historical Atlas. McKinnon, M.A. (ed).

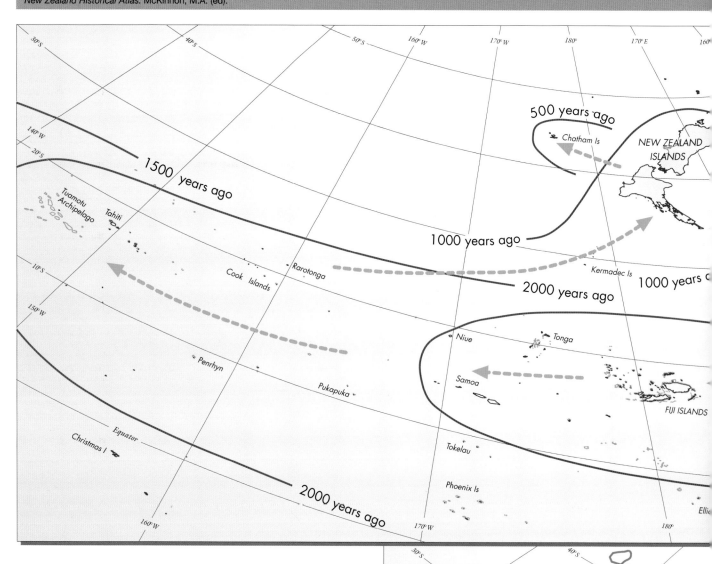

European Exploration of the Southern Pacific

Ferdinand Magellan's expedition, the first Europeans to sail the Pacific, passed more than a thousand kilometres north of the New Zealand islands in 1521. Mapmakers speculated about the exotic civilisations and fabulous riches which might exist in the blank space south of Magellan's route — some calling it 'Terra Australis', the southern land — but European interest was sufficiently low for 120 years to pass before Abel Tasman discovered land in the southern Pacific. The decline of Spanish and Portugese dominance coincided with this period. As they sought to protect their established interests against the rise of English and Dutch sea power, they had few resources to spare for exploration on the other side of the world.

Tasman's description of the land was sufficiently bleak to discourage systematic exploration of the area to the east of the New Zealand islands, an area larger than Europe. It would not be for a further 120 years or so that well-equipped expeditions, such as those led by Cook, du Fresne and de Surville in the late eighteenth century, charted New Zealand's coastline and resources. The three voyages made by James Cook (1769-1779) finally exploded the myth of Terra Australis, instead describing in meticulous detail a vast ocean sprinkled with tiny islands, the eastern coast of Australia and the outline of two modest sized New Zealand islands.

Having taken 250 years to discover the extent of these islands, European traders showed little interest in them. Further exploration by Bligh, Broughton, Vancouver and Malaspina refined Cook's work, though none of these men was primarily interested in the New Zealand islands. The resources of the Pacific Ocean encouraged whalers and sealers to southern shores, and the New Zealand islands were seen as one of many provisioning places. The British government decided that Australia was the best prospect for colonisation, though their attitude to their southern 'possessions' is summarised by the purpose of the first Australian settlement, a penal colony at Port Jackson in 1788. Contact between the New Zealand islands and the rest of the world increased after this, but their position in the flows of Pacific trade was marginal at best. The grand dream of a southern 'El Dorado' had finally been replaced by the reality of flax, timber, seals and whales.

While the systematic exploitation of the New Zealand islands was of little interest to Europe, the few Europeans to frequent these shores became of increasing importance to Māori. Relationships between early explorers and local Māori were characterised by much tolerance, some misunderstanding and sudden outbreaks of violence. This pattern continued throughout the late eighteenth and early nineteenth centuries, as Māori sought to adapt to the presence of increasing numbers of Europeans on their shores.

Bateman Contemporary Atlas New Zealand

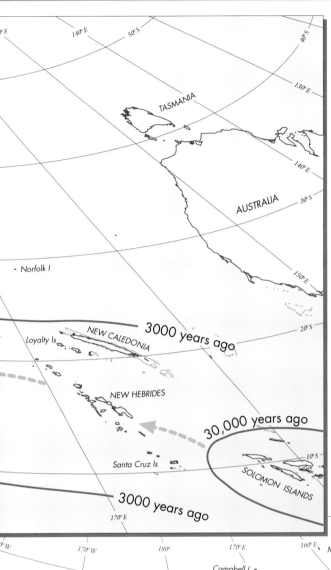

The Spread of Polynesian Settlement in the Southern Pacific

The ancestors of the Māori were Polynesian people who themselves originated from south-east Asia. Thirty thousand years ago, at about the time Australia was being colonised by its indigenous race, Polynesian forbears were living in the Bismarck Archipelago and the Solomon Islands. There they remained until about 3500 years ago when, for reasons that remain unclear to archaeologists, the nascent Polynesian culture began spreading eastwards.

Those who settled in the central southern Pacific began to develop a recognisable Polynesian culture. Colonisation of the Pacific continued to move eastwards, pushing past Tahiti at the same time as classical Greek culture expanded around the Mediterranean, but on a greater scale. It is almost certain that Polynesians reached South America, as the kūmara is a native of that continent. Then, in the centuries before European contact, voyaging declined and some previously colonised islands were abandoned.

For many years researchers were puzzled by the speed and direction of colonisation. The eastward expansion proceeded directly into the prevailing winds and currents, which would appear at first glance to be a hindrance. Scholars considered the voyages which discovered new islands in the vast ocean to be accidental, probably one-way colonisations. However, recent work with computer simulations has shown that if the upwind exploration is regarded as an advantage, the rapid colonisation is easily explained (Irwin, 1992). Explorers sailed upwind because this was the direction from which they could most easily return. These adventurers knew that if they turned back downwind with half of their provisions remaining, it was very likely that they would make landfall back at their starting point, or close to it. They also used 'island screens' — the area within which an island group can be detected — to enlarge their return target. Archaeologists now consider the colonisation of the Pacific to have been a deliberate, relatively risk-free two-way process.

The colonisation of the New Zealand islands was another matter. Once explorers had discovered all the island groups of the central Pacific, they began to search across and downwind. Hawaii and the New Zealand islands were discovered by this more risky method, their position delaying their settlement for a thousand years. The Cook Islands, and others in central Polynesia, were the likely previous homeland of the Māori. There is evidence of return voyaging at least part of the way from the New Zealand islands to Polynesia. Mayor Island obsidian, a stone which occurs naturally only off the coast of the North Island, has been found in a settlement site on the Kermadecs, on a direct return line to Rarotonga.

The New Zealand islands, the last major land mass to be settled by humans (except Antarctica), were unlike anything the Polynesian voyagers had previously encountered. Used to tiny islands scattered across a huge ocean, the discoverers of the New Zealand islands did not even have words for rivers (wai = water) or lakes (roto = lagoon). It is difficult to imagine how challenging it must have been to adapt to the new land, especially considering almost all the food the explorers brought with them would not grow in the cooler southern latitudes.

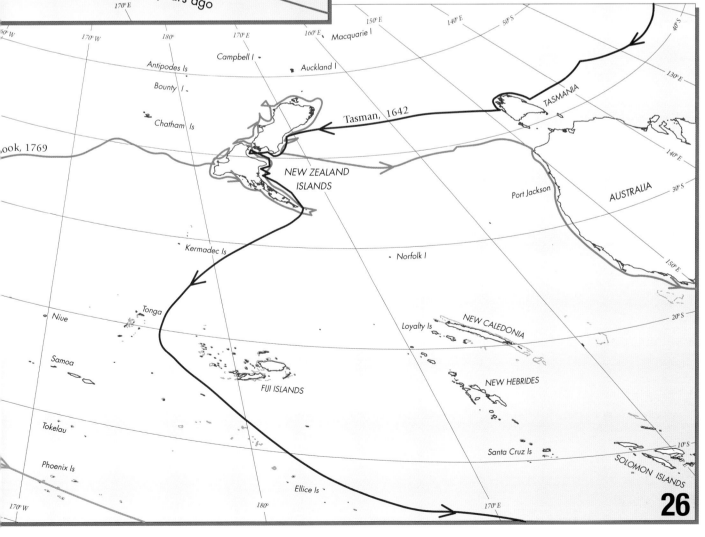

For more information...

The Prehistory of New Zealand. Davidson, J.
The Origins of the First New Zealanders. Sutton, D.G.
New Zealand Historical Atlas. McKinnon, M.A. (ed).

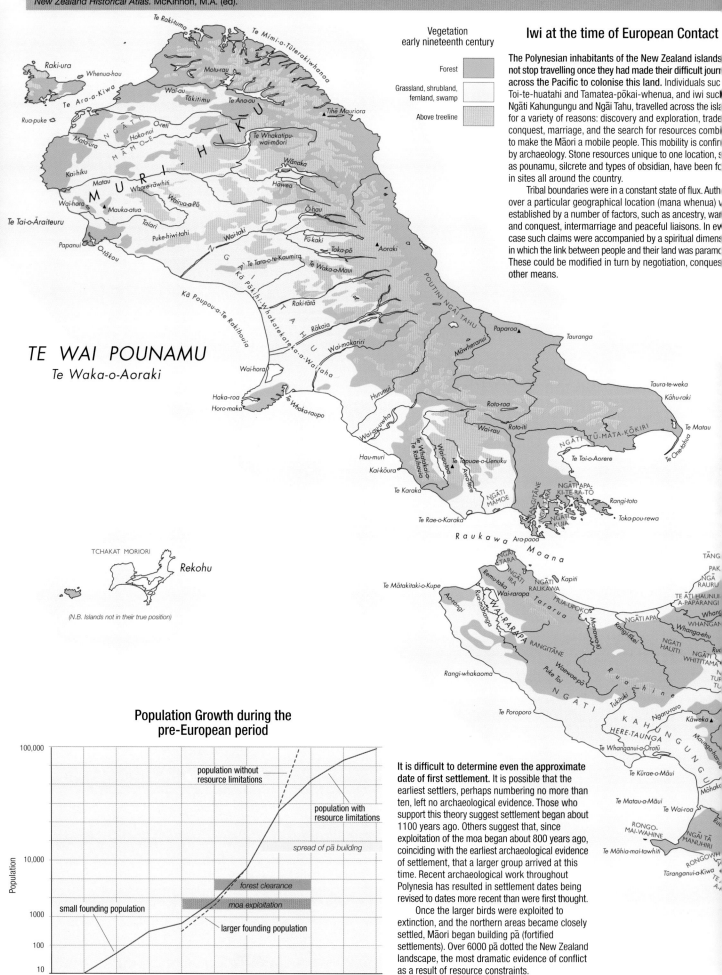

Vegetation
early nineteenth century

- Forest
- Grassland, shrubland, fernland, swamp
- Above treeline

Iwi at the time of European Contact

The Polynesian inhabitants of the New Zealand islands [did] not stop travelling once they had made their difficult journ[ey] across the Pacific to colonise this land. Individuals suc[h as] Toi-te-huatahi and Tamatea-pōkai-whenua, and iwi suc[h as] Ngāti Kahungunu and Ngāi Tahu, travelled across the isla[nds] for a variety of reasons: discovery and exploration, trade, conquest, marriage, and the search for resources combi[ned] to make the Māori a mobile people. This mobility is confir[med] by archaeology. Stone resources unique to one location, s[uch] as pounamu, silcrete and types of obsidian, have been fo[und] in sites all around the country.

Tribal boundaries were in a constant state of flux. Auth[ority] over a particular geographical location (mana whenua) w[as] established by a number of factors, such as ancestry, war[fare] and conquest, intermarriage and peaceful liaisons. In ev[ery] case such claims were accompanied by a spiritual dimens[ion] in which the link between people and their land was param[ount]. These could be modified in turn by negotiation, conques[t or] other means.

TE WAI POUNAMU

Te Waka-o-Aoraki

TCHAKAT MORIORI

Rekohu

(N.B. Islands not in their true position)

Population Growth during the pre-European period

It is difficult to determine even the approximate date of first settlement. It is possible that the earliest settlers, perhaps numbering no more than ten, left no archaeological evidence. Those who support this theory suggest settlement began about 1100 years ago. Others suggest that, since exploitation of the moa began about 800 years ago, coinciding with the earliest archaeological evidence of settlement, that a larger group arrived at this time. Recent archaeological work throughout Polynesia has resulted in settlement dates being revised to dates more recent than were first thought.

Once the larger birds were exploited to extinction, and the northern areas became closely settled, Māori began building pā (fortified settlements). Over 6000 pā dotted the New Zealand landscape, the most dramatic evidence of conflict as a result of resource constraints.

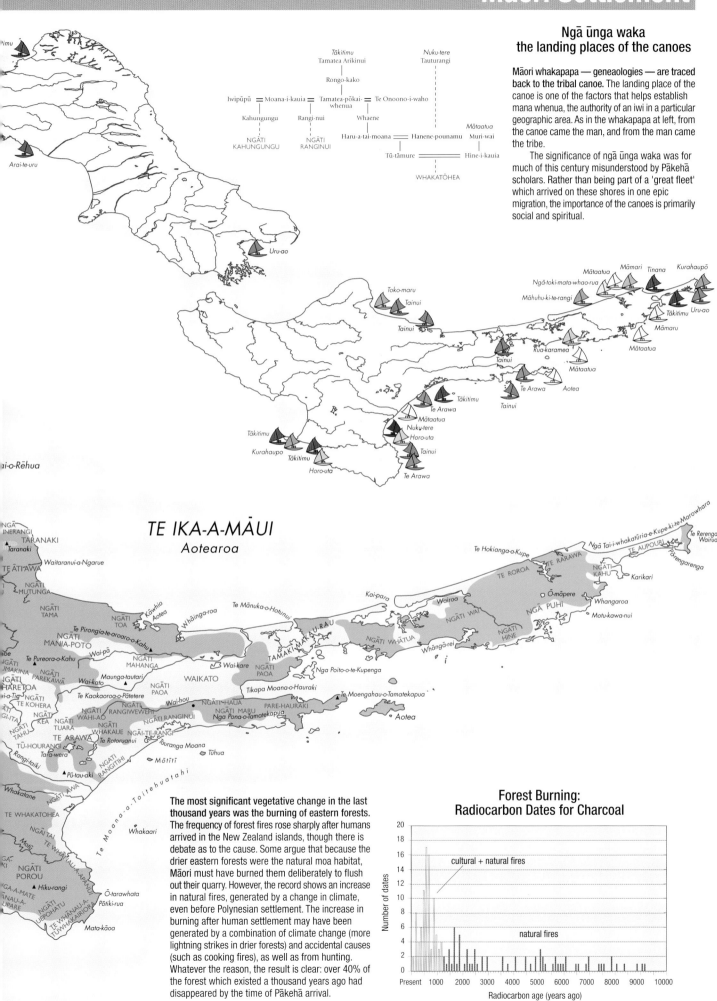

Ngā ūnga waka
the landing places of the canoes

Māori whakapapa — geneaologies — are traced back to the tribal canoe. The landing place of the canoe is one of the factors that helps establish mana whenua, the authority of an iwi in a particular geographic area. As in the whakapapa at left, from the canoe came the man, and from the man came the tribe.

The significance of ngā ūnga waka was for much of this century misunderstood by Pākehā scholars. Rather than being part of a 'great fleet' which arrived on these shores in one epic migration, the importance of the canoes is primarily social and spiritual.

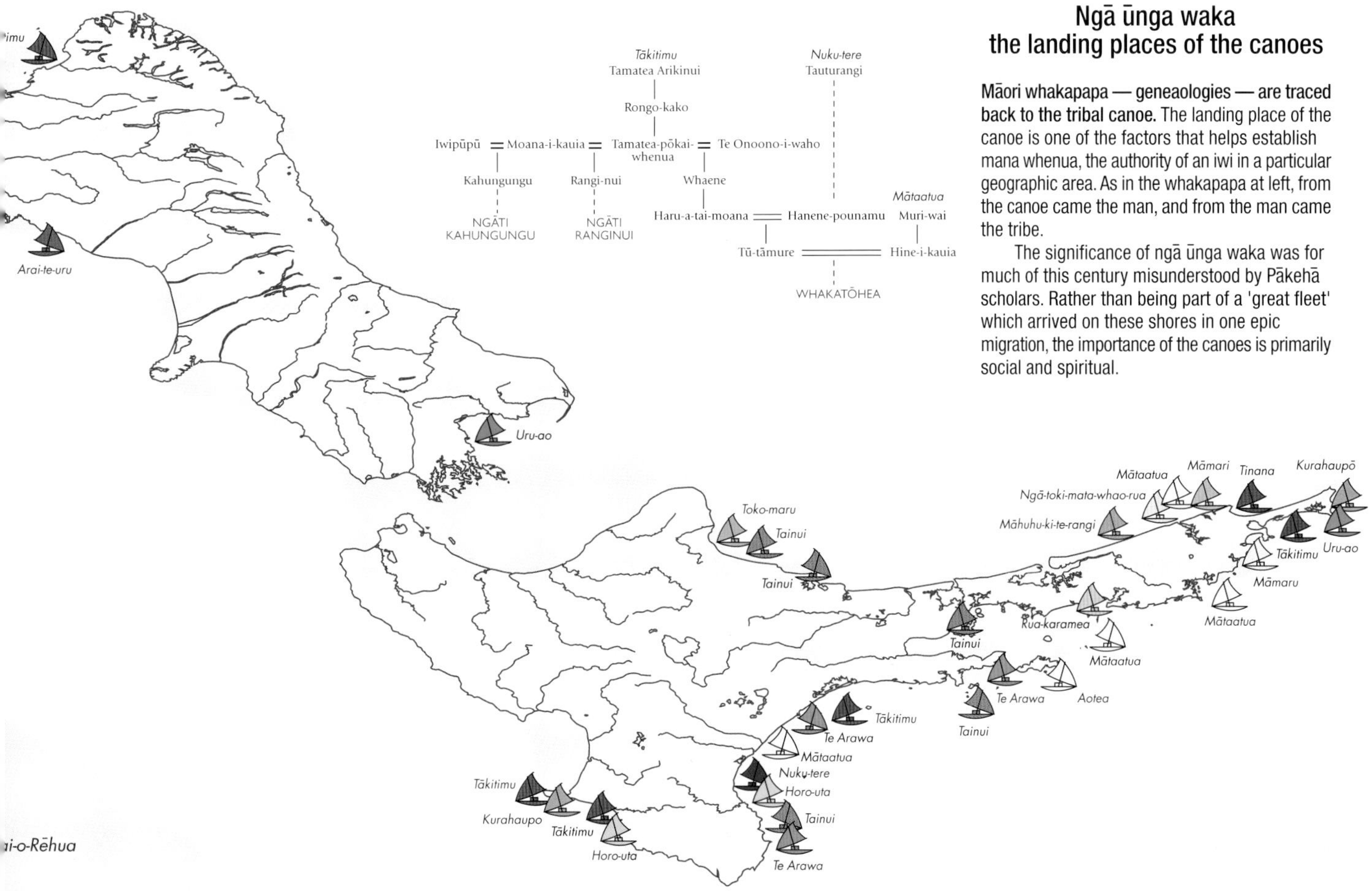
Tākitimu
Tamatea Arikinui
Rongo-kako
Iwipūpū = Moana-i-kauia = Tamatea-pōkai-whenua = Te Ononoo-i-waho
Kahungungu
NGĀTI KAHUNGUNGU
Rangi-nui
NGĀTI RANGINUI
Whaene
Haru-a-tai-moana = Hanene-pounamu
Nuku-tere
Tauturangi
Mātaatua
Muri-wai
Tū-tāmure = Hine-i-kauia
WHAKATŌHEA
Arai-te-uru
Uru-ao
Toko-maru
Tainui
Mātaatua
Māmari
Tinana
Kurahaupō
Ngā-toki-mata-whao-rua
Māhuhu-ki-te-rangi
Tākitimu
Uru-ao
Māmaru
Rua-karamea
Mātaatua
Te Arawa
Aotea
Tākitimu
Te Arawa
Nuku-tere
Horo-uta
Kurahaupo
Te Arawa

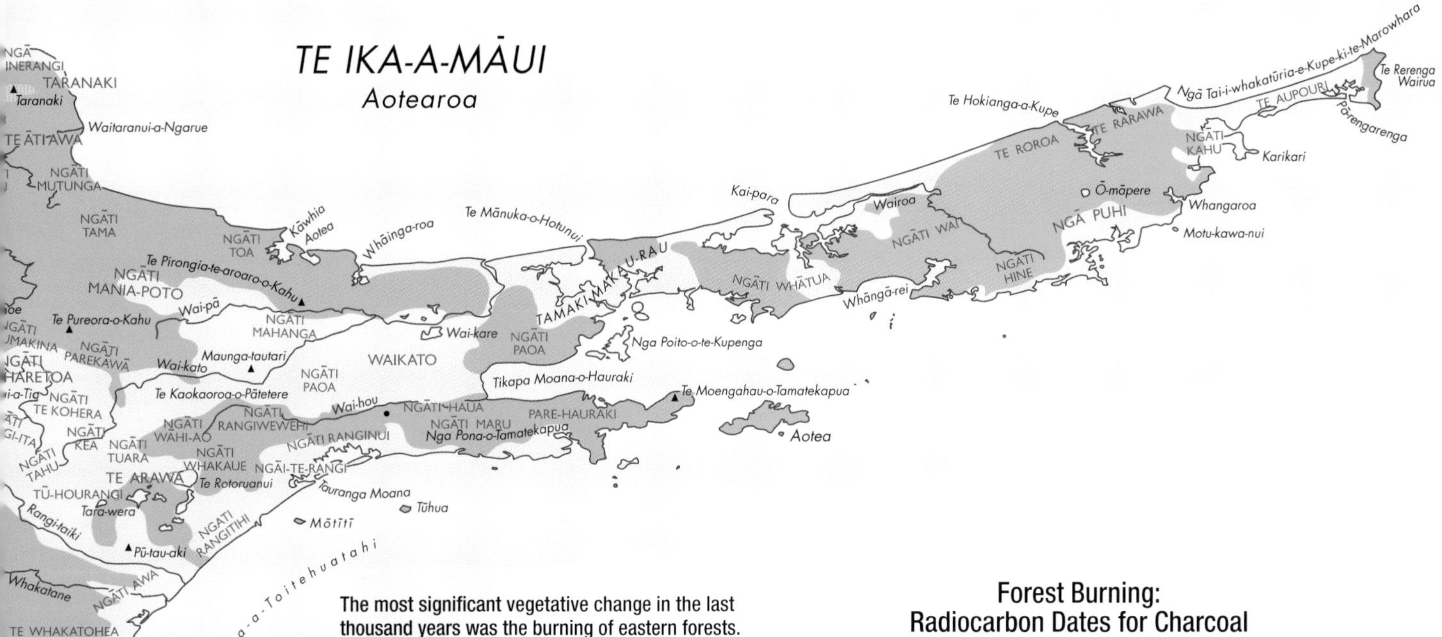
TE IKA-A-MĀUI
Aotearoa
TARANAKI
Taranaki
Waitaranui-a-Ngarue
TE ĀTI AWA
NGĀTI MUTUNGA
NGĀTI TAMA
NGĀTI TOA
Kāwhia
Aotea
Whāinga-roa
Te Pirongia-te-aroaro-o-Kahu
NGĀTI MANIA-POTO
Te Pureora-o-Kahu
Wai-pā
NGĀTI MAHANGA
NGĀTI PAREKAWĀ
Wai-kato
Maunga-tautari
WAIKATO
NGĀTI PAOA
Te Kaokaoroa-o-Pātetere
Wai-hou
NGĀTI RANGIWEWEHI
NGĀTI WAHI-AO
NGĀTI WHAKAUE
NGĀI-TE-RANGI
NGĀTI RANGINUI
Te Rotoruanui
TE ARAWA
TŪ-HOURANGI
Tara-wera
Rangi-taiki
Pū-tau-aki
NGĀTI RANGITIHI
Tauranga Moana
Tūhua
Mōtītī
Te Moana-a-Toitehuatahi
Whakatane
NGĀTI AWA
TE WHAKATOHEA
NGĀI TAI
TE WHĀNAU-A-APANUI
Whakaari
NGĀTI POROU
Hiku-rangi
Ō-tarawhata
Pōtiki-rua
Mata-kāoa
Te Mānuka-o-Hotunui
Kai-para
TAMAKI MAKAU-RAU
NGĀTI WHĀTUA
Wai-kare
NGĀTI PAOA
Nga Poito-o-te-Kupenga
Tikapa Moana-o-Hauraki
Te Moengahau-o-Tamatekapua
NGĀTI MARU
PARE-HAURAKI
Nga Pona-o-Tamatekapua
Aotea
Whāngā-rei
NGĀTI WAI
NGĀTI HINE
NGĀ PUHI
Wairoa
TE ROROA
Te Hokianga-a-Kupe
TE RARAWA
Ō-māpere
Whangaroa
Motu-kawa-nui
NGĀTI KAHU
Karikari
TE AUPOURI
Ngā Tai-i-whakatūria-e-Kupe-ki-te-Marowhara
Te Rerenga Wairua
Pārengarenga

The most significant vegetative change in the last thousand years was the burning of eastern forests. The frequency of forest fires rose sharply after humans arrived in the New Zealand islands, though there is debate as to the cause. Some argue that because the drier eastern forests were the natural moa habitat, Māori must have burned them deliberately to flush out their quarry. However, the record shows an increase in natural fires, generated by a change in climate, even before Polynesian settlement. The increase in burning after human settlement may have been generated by a combination of climate change (more lightning strikes in drier forests) and accidental causes (such as cooking fires), as well as from hunting. Whatever the reason, the result is clear: over 40% of the forest which existed a thousand years ago had disappeared by the time of Pākehā arrival.

Forest Burning: Radiocarbon Dates for Charcoal

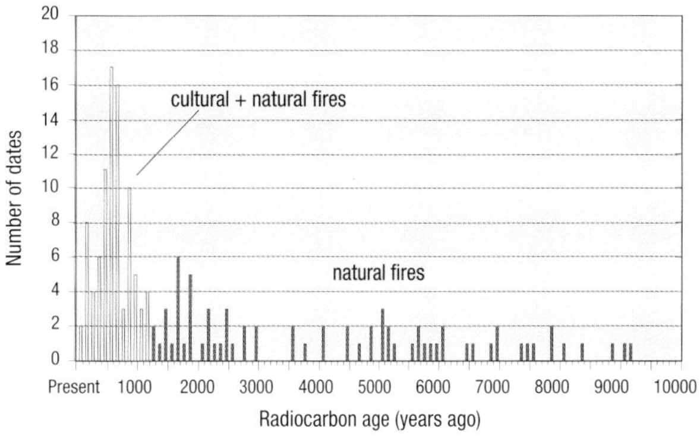
Number of dates
0
2
4
6
8
10
12
14
16
18
20
cultural + natural fires
natural fires
Present
1000
2000
3000
4000
5000
6000
7000
8000
9000
10000
Radiocarbon age (years ago)

For more information...

The New Zealand Wars. Belich, J.
New Zealand's Burning. Arnold, R.
New Zealand Historical Atlas. McKinnon, M.A. (ed).

European exploitation of New Zealand's relatively meagre resources began as sealers and whalers hunted their prey off the coast of the southern islands, and flax-cutters and foresters began to harvest in the early nineteenth century. Small towns, such as Kororāreka in the Bay of Islands, sprang up to provision them, barely clinging to survival and dependent on local Māori.

The discovery of gold was perhaps the single greatest factor influencing the colonial economy. Within three years of the first substantial discoveries in 1861 the non-Māori population of the colony had doubled. Christchurch, Auckland and Dunedin benefited most from the gold rushes, the latter remaining New Zealand's largest town until late in the century.

The first live sheep were imported in 1834, and by the 1860s the eastern tussock grasslands of both islands were divided up into hundreds of large sheep runs. After the first refrigerated meat shipment from New Zealand in 1882 the focus of pastoralists shifted from wool alone to encompass frozen meat, butter and cheese.

In order to facilitate the spread of farming, and to take advantage of readily accessible timber, much of the central and southern North Island bush was cleared between 1870 and 1910. Settlers who improved land by clearing the bush, sowing pasture and building a house could gain title to the land more cheaply, so by 1910 most of the bush in the southern North Island had been replaced by pasture.

The dry grasslands of the Canterbury Plains were eminently suited to the growing of grain, and ten years after the planned settlement of Christchurch, the province was exporting wheat. The wheat 'boom' of the late nineteenth century was actually three peaks of production separated by periods of lower prices. The most dramatic effect of the wheat boom was a much more closely settled eastern plainland.

The huge kauri tree of Northland and the Coromandel fell to the harvester in the decades either side of 1900. Both the timber and the gum from the tree proved valuable, and the industry provided Auckland with an impetus of growth which led to it becoming our largest city.

Resource Exploitation 1800–1910

- ■ Whaling stations, late 1830s
- ○ Gold rush site
- □ Area opened up by prospectors, 1852–1880
- --- Wheat-growing area, 1886
- • Property with at least 5000 sheep, 1879
- Kauri Gumfields, 1880–1910
- Bush area 1880
- Bush area 1910

Te Tiriti o Waitangi — The Treaty of Waitangi — was offered to a hui of northern Māori at Waitangi on 6 February 1840. Missionaries in New Zealand and members of the Aboriginal Protection Society in England had sought to persuade Māori and the British government respectively that such a treaty would be a good idea. During the rest of 1840 the document was taken around the country and signed by many more, but by no means all, influential chiefs. While Britain believed that it had obtained sovereignty over New Zealand, Māori understood the treaty differently, as expressed in the Māori-language version.

Mission Stations and Te Tiriti o Waitangi

Number of Signatories to Te Tiriti o Waitangi

- 70
- 35
- 10
- 2

Place of Treaty Signing

Mission Stations 1845

- ▲ Anglican
- ▲ Catholic
- ▲ Wesleyan
- △ Other (named)

Lambert Conformal Conic Projection
Scale: 1: 8 300 000

0   50   100   150   200   250

Bateman Contemporary Atlas New Zealand

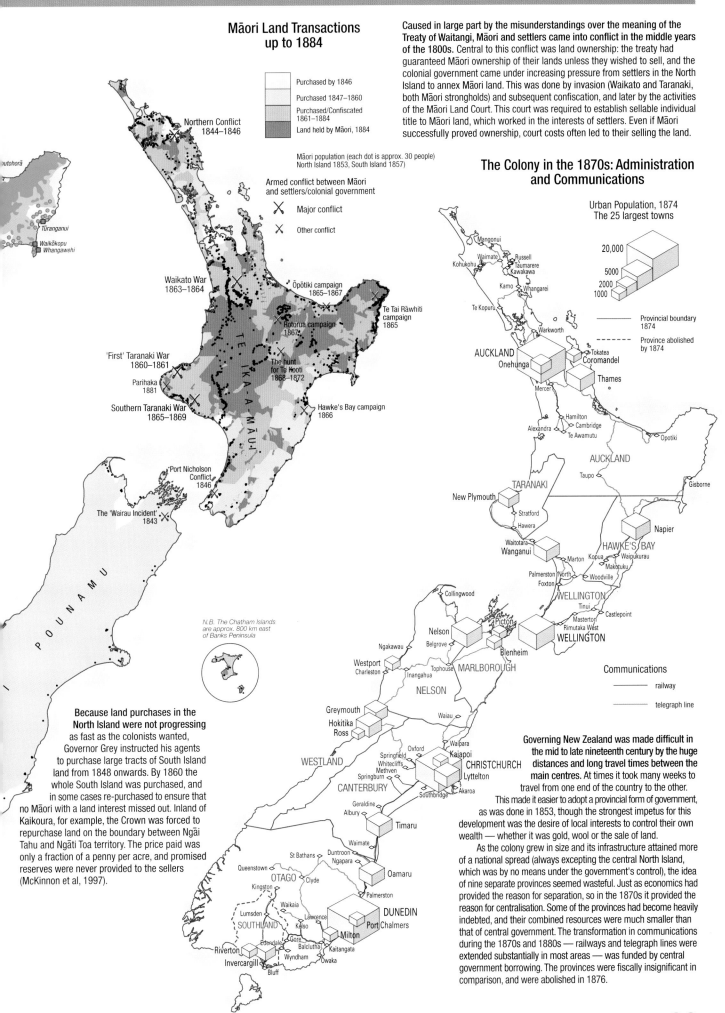

Māori Land Transactions up to 1884

Purchased by 1846
Purchased 1847–1860
Purchased/Confiscated 1861–1884
Land held by Māori, 1884

Māori population (each dot is approx. 30 people)
North Island 1853, South Island 1857)

Armed conflict between Māori and settlers/colonial government

✕ Major conflict

✕ Other conflict

Caused in large part by the misunderstandings over the meaning of the Treaty of Waitangi, Māori and settlers came into conflict in the middle years of the 1800s. Central to this conflict was land ownership: the treaty had guaranteed Māori ownership of their lands unless they wished to sell, and the colonial government came under increasing pressure from settlers in the North Island to annex Māori land. This was done by invasion (Waikato and Taranaki, both Māori strongholds) and subsequent confiscation, and later by the activities of the Māori Land Court. This court was required to establish sellable individual title to Māori land, which worked in the interests of settlers. Even if Māori successfully proved ownership, court costs often led to their selling the land.

The Colony in the 1870s: Administration and Communications

Urban Population, 1874
The 25 largest towns

20,000
5000
2000
1000

Provincial boundary 1874

Province abolished by 1874

Communications

—— railway

—— telegraph line

Northern Conflict 1844–1846

Waikato War 1863–1864

Ōpōtiki campaign 1865–1867

Te Tai Rāwhiti campaign 1865

Rotorua campaign 1867

'First' Taranaki War 1860–1861

The hunt for Te Kooti 1868–1872

Parihaka 1881

Southern Taranaki War 1865–1869

Hawke's Bay campaign 1866

Port Nicholson Conflict 1846

The 'Wairau Incident' 1843

TE IKA-A-MĀUI

POUNAMU

N.B. The Chatham Islands are approx. 800 km east of Banks Peninsula

Because land purchases in the North Island were not progressing as fast as the colonists wanted, Governor Grey instructed his agents to purchase large tracts of South Island land from 1848 onwards. By 1860 the whole South Island was purchased, and in some cases re-purchased to ensure that no Māori with a land interest missed out. Inland of Kaikoura, for example, the Crown was forced to repurchase land on the boundary between Ngāi Tahu and Ngāti Toa territory. The price paid was only a fraction of a penny per acre, and promised reserves were never provided to the sellers (McKinnon et al, 1997).

Governing New Zealand was made difficult in the mid to late nineteenth century by the huge distances and long travel times between the main centres. At times it took many weeks to travel from one end of the country to the other. This made it easier to adopt a provincial form of government, as was done in 1853, though the strongest impetus for this development was the desire of local interests to control their own wealth — whether it was gold, wool or the sale of land.

As the colony grew in size and its infrastructure attained more of a national spread (always excepting the central North Island, which was by no means under the government's control), the idea of nine separate provinces seemed wasteful. Just as economics had provided the reason for separation, so in the 1870s it provided the reason for centralisation. Some of the provinces had become heavily indebted, and their combined resources were much smaller than that of central government. The transformation in communications during the 1870s and 1880s — railways and telegraph lines were extended substantially in most areas — was funded by central government borrowing. The provinces were fiscally insignificant in comparison, and were abolished in 1876.

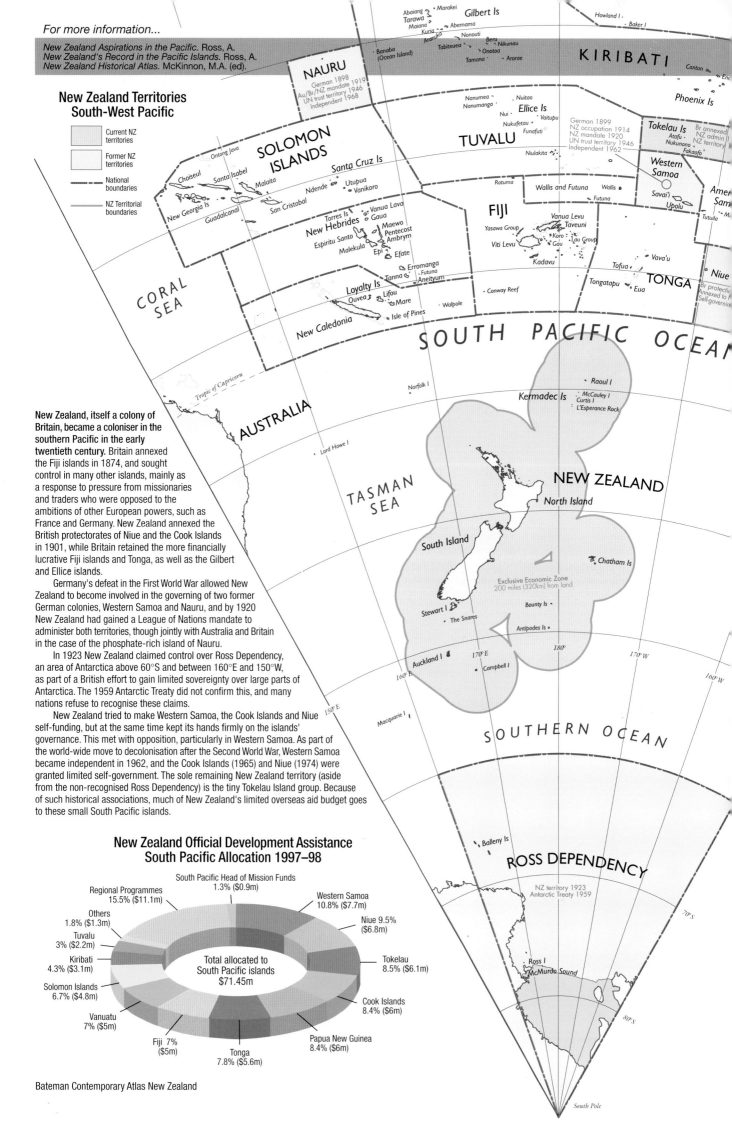

New Zealand Aspirations in the Pacific. Ross, A.
New Zealand's Record in the Pacific Islands. Ross, A.
New Zealand Historical Atlas. McKinnon, M.A. (ed).

New Zealand Territories
South-West Pacific

Current NZ territories

Former NZ territories

National boundaries

NZ Territorial boundaries

NAURU
German 1898
Au/Br/NZ mandate 1919
UN trust territory 1946
Independent 1968

Abaiang · Marakei · Gilbert Is
Tarawa
Maiana · Abemama
Kuria · Nonouti
Aranuka · Tabiteuea · Nikunau
Banaba · Beru · Onotoa
(Ocean Island) · Tamana · Arorae
Howland I. · Baker I.

KIRIBATI

Canton · Enc

Phoenix Is

SOLOMON ISLANDS

Ontong Java

Choiseul · Santa Isabel
New Georgia Is · Malaita
Guadalcanal · San Cristobal
Ndende · Santa Cruz Is
Utupua · Vanikoro

Nanumea · Nuitao
Nanumanga
Nui · Vaitupu
Nukufetau
Funafuti
TUVALU
Niulakita

German 1899
NZ occupation 1914
NZ mandate 1920
UN trust territory 1946
Independent 1962

Tokelau Is
Atafu
Nukunono
Fakaofo

Br annexed
NZ admin
NZ territory

Western Samoa
Savai'i
Upolu

Amer
Sam
Tutuila · M

Rotuma

Wallis and Futuna · Wallis
Futuna

Vanua Levu
Taveuni
Yasawa Group · Koro · Lau Group
Viti Levu · Gau
Kadavu

FIJI

New Hebrides
Torres Is · Vanua Lava
Gaua
Espiritu Santo · Maewo
Pentecost
Malekula · Ambrym
Epi · Efate
Erromanga
Tanna · Futuna
Aneityum

Loyalty Is
Ouvea · Lifou
Mare
Isle of Pines
New Caledonia

Conway Reef

Walpole

Tofua · Vava'u

Tongatapu · Eua
TONGA

Niue
Br protectio
Annexed to t
Self-governin

CORAL SEA

SOUTH PACIFIC OCEAN

New Zealand, itself a colony of Britain, became a coloniser in the southern Pacific in the early twentieth century. Britain annexed the Fiji islands in 1874, and sought control in many other islands, mainly as a response to pressure from missionaries and traders who were opposed to the ambitions of other European powers, such as France and Germany. New Zealand annexed the British protectorates of Niue and the Cook Islands in 1901, while Britain retained the more financially lucrative Fiji islands and Tonga, as well as the Gilbert and Ellice islands.

Germany's defeat in the First World War allowed New Zealand to become involved in the governing of two former German colonies, Western Samoa and Nauru, and by 1920 New Zealand had gained a League of Nations mandate to administer both territories, though jointly with Australia and Britain in the case of the phosphate-rich island of Nauru.

In 1923 New Zealand claimed control over Ross Dependency, an area of Antarctica above 60°S and between 160°E and 150°W, as part of a British effort to gain limited sovereignty over large parts of Antarctica. The 1959 Antarctic Treaty did not confirm this, and many nations refuse to recognise these claims.

New Zealand tried to make Western Samoa, the Cook Islands and Niue self-funding, but at the same time kept its hands firmly on the islands' governance. This met with opposition, particularly in Western Samoa. As part of the world-wide move to decolonisation after the Second World War, Western Samoa became independent in 1962, and the Cook Islands (1965) and Niue (1974) were granted limited self-government. The sole remaining New Zealand territory (aside from the non-recognised Ross Dependency) is the tiny Tokelau Island group. Because of such historical associations, much of New Zealand's limited overseas aid budget goes to these small South Pacific islands.

AUSTRALIA

Norfolk I.

Kermadec Is · Raoul I.
· McCauley I.
Curtis I.
L'Esperance Rock

Lord Howe I.

TASMAN SEA

NEW ZEALAND
North Island

South Island

Chatham Is

Exclusive Economic Zone
200 miles (320km) from land

Stewart I.
The Snares

Bounty Is

Antipodes Is

Auckland I. · 170°E
Campbell I.

160°E · 180° · 170°W · 160°W

Macquarie I.

SOUTHERN OCEAN

Balleny Is

ROSS DEPENDENCY
NZ territory 1923
Antarctic Treaty 1959

70°S

Ross I.
McMurdo Sound

80°S

South Pole

New Zealand Official Development Assistance
South Pacific Allocation 1997–98

South Pacific Head of Mission Funds
1.3% ($0.9m)

Regional Programmes
15.5% ($11.1m)

Western Samoa
10.8% ($7.7m)

Others
1.8% ($1.3m)

Niue 9.5%
($6.8m)

Tuvalu
3% ($2.2m)

Kiribati
4.3% ($3.1m)

Total allocated to
South Pacific islands
$71.45m

Tokelau
8.5% ($6.1m)

Solomon Islands
6.7% ($4.8m)

Vanuatu
7% ($5m)

Cook Islands
8.4% ($6m)

Fiji 7%
($5m)

Papua New Guinea
8.4% ($6m)

Tonga
7.8% ($5.6m)

Tropic of Capricorn

150°E

Bateman Contemporary Atlas New Zealand

Nauru, the world's smallest republic, has over the last century been devastated by the exploitation of phosphate resources by Australia, New Zealand and Britain, and latterly by the Nauruans themselves. Mining in the central plateau has left a moon-like barren terrain of 20-metre-high coral pinnacles over 80% of the land area.

Under the 1886 Anglo-German Convention, Nauru was allocated to Germany. Ten years later phosphate — a mixture of guano and coral rock — was discovered, and by 1906 an international company began to exploit the 18 km^2 of reserves. At the outbreak of the First World War (1914), Australian forces captured the island, ending Germany's involvement with Nauru. In 1920 the League of Nations granted Australia, New Zealand and Britain a Trustee Mandate to govern the island. These three countries took over the rights to phosphate mining.

The fertility of New Zealand pastures was enhanced by the application of phosphate, which was used extensively from the 1920s onwards. New Zealand profited greatly from cheap phosphate imports from Nauru, purchasing the product for as little as one-third of the world price. It was occupied by the Japanese (1942-45) and, after the Second World War, the island was designated a UN Trust Territory administered by Australia. Though not formally involved in the government of Nauru, New Zealand continued to benefit from cheap phosphate.

By 1961 the Nauruans were becoming uncomfortable with the degradation of their small island, despite the relatively high standard of living the phosphate brought them. Plans for resettlement were mooted, but rejected by the islanders. By 1970 control of the phosphate mining passed to the Nauruans themselves, who continued extracting the phosphate. Nevertheless, Nauru took Australia and its mining partners to the International Court of Justice, winning in 1993 an out-of-court settlement for compensation for the ecological damage caused. New Zealand pledged a US$8m contribution. Money won was invested to provide future income for the islanders, as the phosphate reserves ran out in 1998. A feasibility study estimates the cost of environmental rehabilitation at US$133 million.

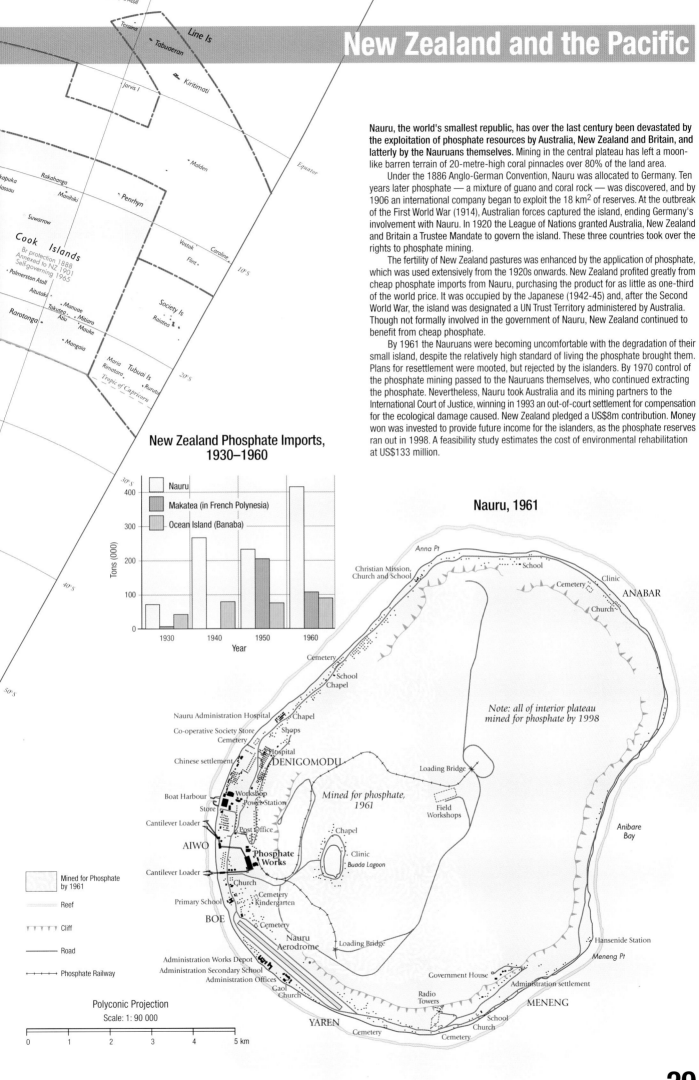

New Zealand Phosphate Imports, 1930–1960

Nauru
Makatea (in French Polynesia)
Ocean Island (Banaba)

Tons (000)

Nauru, 1961

Note: all of interior plateau mined for phosphate by 1998

Mined for phosphate, 1961

Polyconic Projection
Scale: 1: 90 000

0 1 2 3 4 5 km

Mined for Phosphate by 1961
Reef
Cliff
Road
Phosphate Railway

For more information...

Key Statistics. Statistics New Zealand (monthly).
New Zealand Official Yearbook. Statistics New Zealand.
On the Net: http://www.stats.govt.nz

Lambert Conformal Conic Projection
Scale: 1: 5 640 000

0   50   100   150   200   250   300 km

Population Density, 1996

Persons per km²

1
10

New Zealand Population
1891–2031

1994: base year for projection

Projection assumes 'medium' fertility and 'medium' mortality with long-term annual immigration of 5000 per annum.

Population (000)

4500
4000
3500
3000
2500
2000
1500
1000
500
0

1891 1901 1911 1921 1931 1941 1951 1961 1971 1981 1991 2001 2011 2021 2031

Year ended 31 December

Age/Sex Structure
1996 Census

Age

85+
80–84
75–79
70–74
65–69
60–64
55–59
50–54
45–49
40–44
35–39
30–34
25–29
20–24
15–19
10–14
5–9
0–4

% 4 3 2 1 0   0 1 2 3 4 %

Male   Female

N.B. The Chatham Islands are approx. 800 km east of Banks Peninsula

Population of New Zealand,
North Island and South Island
1874–1996

North Island

South Island

New Zealand

Census Year

Population (000)

4000 3500 3000 2500 2000 1500 1000 500 0

Bateman Contemporary Atlas New Zealand

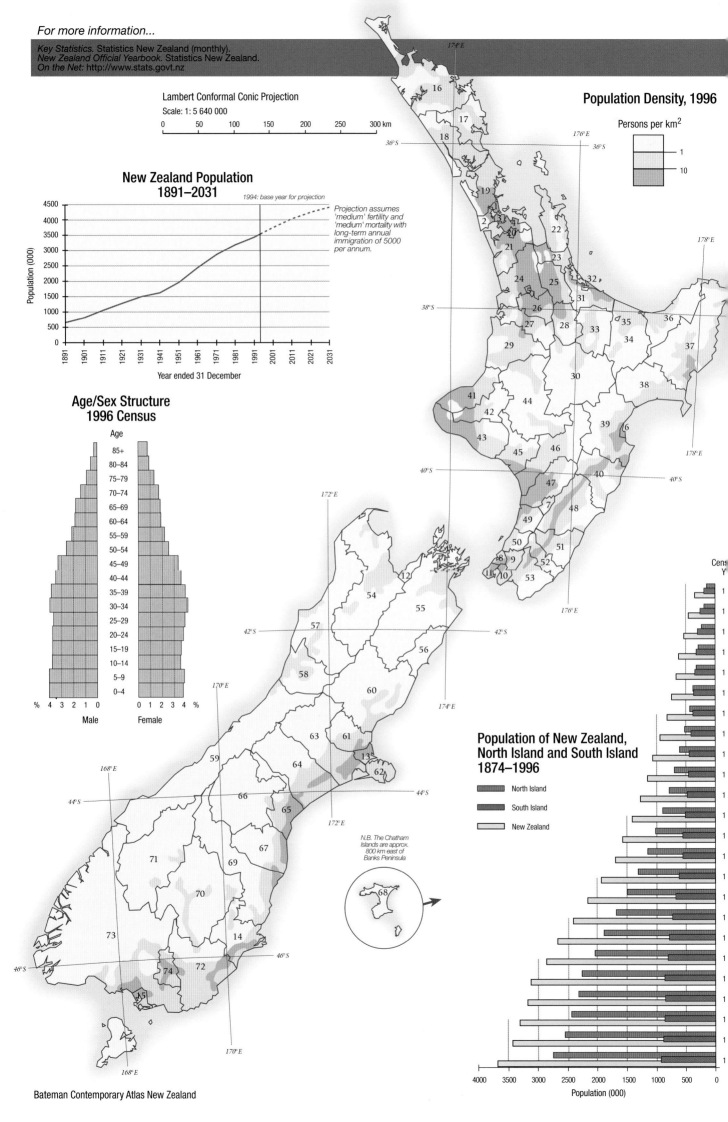

Population of Territorial Local Authorities (TLAs) and Urban Areas, 1996 census
(usually resident population)

The demography of New Zealand has changed radically in the last hundred years. The population has increased five-fold; become highly urbanised; drifted north, and the average age is much higher. The average family size is 50% smaller, the divorce rate has soared, the birth rate, death rate and rate of natural increase have decreased, and most minority populations have grown at rates faster than the population as a whole.

This map shows the comparative populations of Territorial Local Authorities (TLAs) and urban areas from the 1996 census. It does so in the form of a cartogram, using as its scale the population figures themselves: thus, the larger the population, the larger the size of the TLA or urban area.

The dominance of the North Island over the South Island (total populations of 2,718,170 and 899,384 respectively) is perhaps the map's main feature, and the dominance of the main urban areas (Auckland in the north, Christchurch in the south) is also shown clearly. In 1926 15% of New Zealanders lived in Auckland; by 1996 this figure had increased to 26%. Over two-thirds of the population live in places with more than 30,000 people.

Cities
1 North Shore
2 Waitakere
3 Auckland
4 Manukau
5 Hamilton
6 Napier
7 Palmerston North
8 Porirua
9 Upper Hutt
10 Lower Hutt
11 Wellington
12 Nelson
13 Christchurch
14 Dunedin
15 Invercargill

Districts
16 Far North
17 Whangarei
18 Kaipara
19 Rodney
20 Papakura
21 Franklin
22 Thames-Coromandel
23 Hauraki
24 Waikato
25 Matamata-Piako
26 Waipa
27 Otorohanga
28 South Waikato
29 Waitomo
30 Taupo
31 Western Bay of Plenty
32 Tauranga
33 Rotorua
34 Whakatane
35 Kawerau
36 Opotiki
37 Gisborne
38 Wairoa
39 Hastings
40 Central Hawke's Bay
41 New Plymouth
42 Stratford
43 South Taranaki
44 Ruapehu
45 Wanganui
46 Rangitikei
47 Manawatu
48 Tararua
49 Horowhenua
50 Kapiti Coast
51 Masterton
52 Carterton
53 South Wairarapa
54 Tasman
55 Marlborough
56 Kaikoura
57 Buller
58 Grey
59 Westland
60 Hurunui
61 Waimakariri
62 Banks Peninsula
63 Selwyn
64 Ashburton
65 Timaru
66 Mackenzie
67 Waimate
68 Chatham Islands
69 Waitaki
70 Central Otago
71 Queenstown-Lakes
72 Clutha
73 Southland
74 Gore

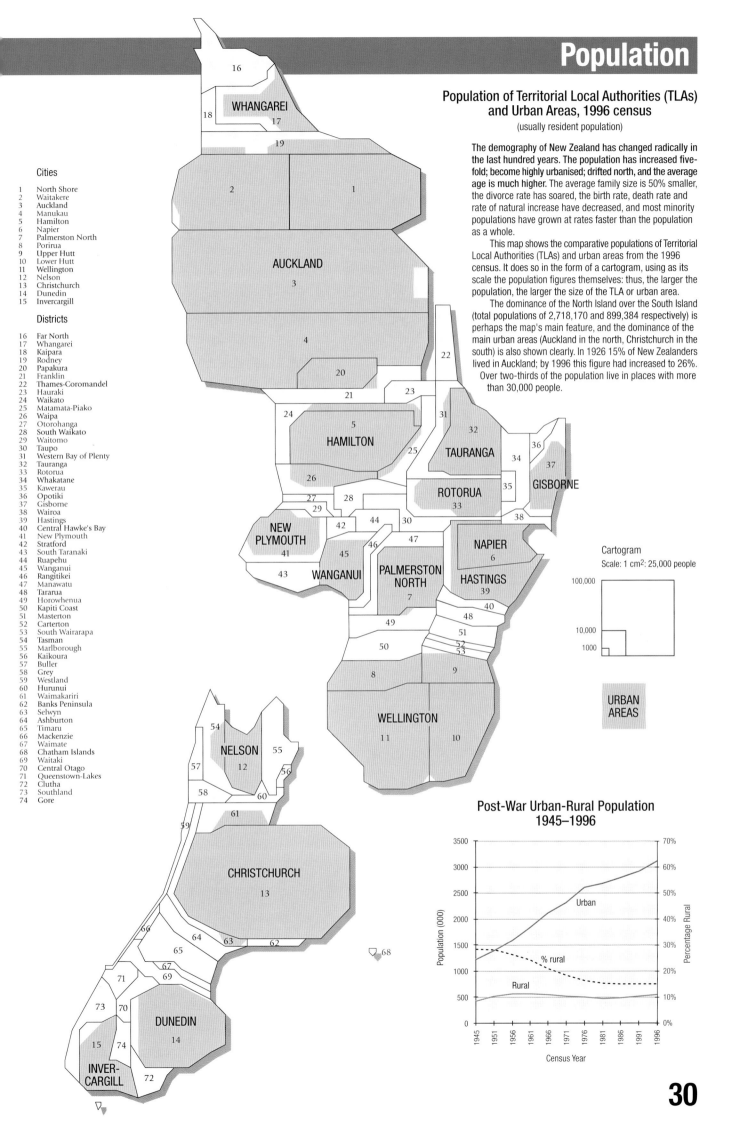

Cartogram
Scale: 1 cm² : 25,000 people

100,000

10,000

1000

URBAN AREAS

Post-War Urban-Rural Population 1945–1996

For more information...

Key Statistics. Statistics New Zealand (monthly).
New Zealand Official Yearbook. Statistics New Zealand.
On the Net: http://www.stats.govt.nz

Average Age of New Mothers
Total Fertility Rate
1945–1995

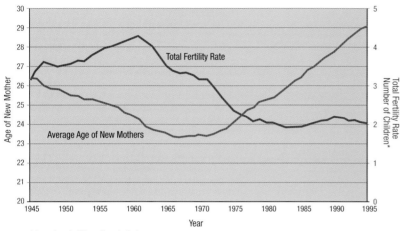

* based on fertility pattern in that year.
Total Fertility Rate is defined as the average number of births a woman would have during her
reproductive life if she was exposed to the fertility rates experienced during that year.

N.B. Statistics New Zealand is converting many of the rates on this page from figures based on
de facto population to a new resident population concept. The revised rates for 1991–1995, and
the new rates for 1996 and beyond will be published in the year 2000. These graphs are therefore
based on de facto population, and are limited to 1995 data as the most recent.

Birth and Death Rates
1960–1995

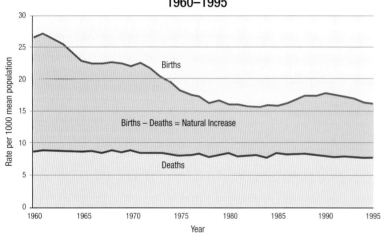

Urban Population,
1886, 1936 and 1996 censuses
of the 20 largest urban areas, 1996 census

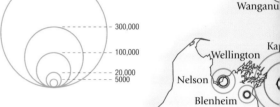
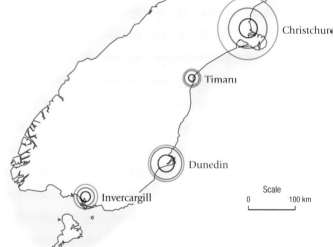

Average Age at Death
1945–1995

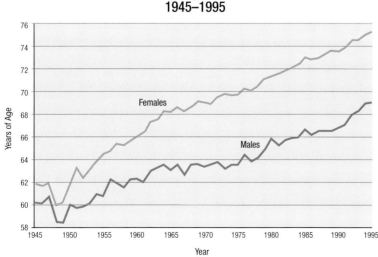

Components of Population Grow
Natural Increase and Net Migrat
1945–1995

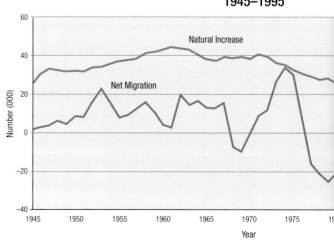

Bateman Contemporary Atlas New Zealand

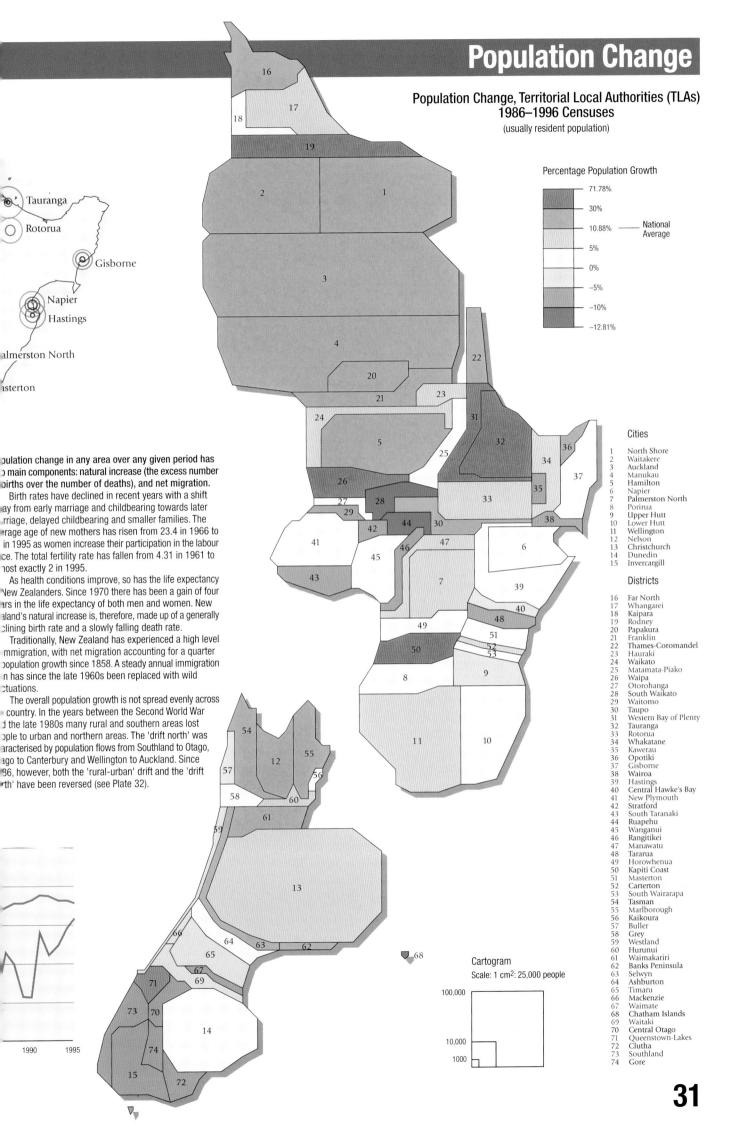

Population Change, Territorial Local Authorities (TLAs)
1986–1996 Censuses
(usually resident population)

Percentage Population Growth

	71.78%
	30%
	10.88% — National Average
	5%
	0%
	−5%
	−10%
	−12.81%

Tauranga
Rotorua
Gisborne
Napier
Hastings
almerston North
sterton

pulation change in any area over any given period has
main components: natural increase (the excess number
births over the number of deaths), and net migration.

Birth rates have declined in recent years with a shift
ay from early marriage and childbearing towards later
rriage, delayed childbearing and smaller families. The
rage age of new mothers has risen from 23.4 in 1966 to
in 1995 as women increase their participation in the labour
ce. The total fertility rate has fallen from 4.31 in 1961 to
ost exactly 2 in 1995.

As health conditions improve, so has the life expectancy
New Zealanders. Since 1970 there has been a gain of four
rs in the life expectancy of both men and women. New
aland's natural increase is, therefore, made up of a generally
clining birth rate and a slowly falling death rate.

Traditionally, New Zealand has experienced a high level
immigration, with net migration accounting for a quarter
opulation growth since 1858. A steady annual immigration
n since the late 1960s been replaced with wild
ctuations.

The overall population growth is not spread evenly across
country. In the years between the Second World War
I the late 1980s many rural and southern areas lost
ople to urban and northern areas. The 'drift north' was
aracterised by population flows from Southland to Otago,
ago to Canterbury and Wellington to Auckland. Since
36, however, both the 'rural-urban' drift and the 'drift
rth' have been reversed (see Plate 32).

Cities

1 North Shore
2 Waitakere
3 Auckland
4 Manukau
5 Hamilton
6 Napier
7 Palmerston North
8 Porirua
9 Upper Hutt
10 Lower Hutt
11 Wellington
12 Nelson
13 Christchurch
14 Dunedin
15 Invercargill

Districts

16 Far North
17 Whangarei
18 Kaipara
19 Rodney
20 Papakura
21 Franklin
22 Thames-Coromandel
23 Hauraki
24 Waikato
25 Matamata-Piako
26 Waipa
27 Otorohanga
28 South Waikato
29 Waitomo
30 Taupo
31 Western Bay of Plenty
32 Tauranga
33 Rotorua
34 Whakatane
35 Kawerau
36 Opotiki
37 Gisborne
38 Wairoa
39 Hastings
40 Central Hawke's Bay
41 New Plymouth
42 Stratford
43 South Taranaki
44 Ruapehu
45 Wanganui
46 Rangitikei
47 Manawatu
48 Tararua
49 Horowhenua
50 Kapiti Coast
51 Masterton
52 Carterton
53 South Wairarapa
54 Tasman
55 Marlborough
56 Kaikoura
57 Buller
58 Grey
59 Westland
60 Hurunui
61 Waimakariri
62 Banks Peninsula
63 Selwyn
64 Ashburton
65 Timaru
66 Mackenzie
67 Waimate
68 Chatham Islands
69 Waitaki
70 Central Otago
71 Queenstown-Lakes
72 Clutha
73 Southland
74 Gore

Cartogram

Scale: 1 cm² : 25,000 people

100,000

10,000

1000

1990   1995

31

For more information...

Discussion Papers. Population Studies Centre.
New Zealand Official Yearbook. Statistics New Zealand.
On the Net: http://www.stats.govt.nz

Inter-regional Migration 1991–19[9]
Major Net Flows

- net flow over 2000
- net flow 1001–2000
- net flow 500–1000

New Zealanders continue to be a mobile people. More than half the population aged five years and over lived at a different address in 1996 than in 1991. While immigration in particular has occupied public interest, it is migration within New Zealand — both inter-regional and within regions — which continues to be larger than international flows.

About ten per cent of New Zealanders moved between regions in the five-year period ending census night 1996. They moved for a number of reasons: young people seeking education or employment, Māori returning to rural areas, or older people moving to 'sunshine' areas for retirement. The most mobile age group between regions is the 20–24 year age, 21.6% of whom moved to a new region. Māori are moving to rural areas in increasing numbers: Auckland, in particular, continues to lose large numbers to Northland.

The regional patterns are varied. Some regions gain from most others, especially Auckland, Bay of Plenty, Nelson, Canterbury and Otago. Others, with weaker economies, lose to most regions (Northland, Gisborne, Taranaki, West Coast, Southland). The 'pull' of Auckland, long considered a fact, is more of a myth: Auckland is the major first port of call for immigrants, but Auckland's only net inter-regional gains are from the 15–29 year age group. The overall trend is northward movement within each island, but a net southward movement between the islands: for the second census in a row the long-established 'northward drift' was reversed. The net gain to the south since 1991 (4965 people) is the largest this century (Goodwin and Bedford, 1997).

Migration into Palmerston North
1991–1996

- O main urban area
- o secondary urban area

Numbers of Migrants

- 800
- 400
- 200
- 100
- 20

Source of Migrants

N.B. Width of line proportional to migration; all flows are into Palmerston North

- from overseas
- from rural areas
- from minor urban areas
- from main and secondary urban areas

Bateman Contemporary Atlas New Zealand

Where Palmerston Nor[th]
People Lived on Censu[s]
Night 1991

1991 Location

Age/Sex Structure
Migrants to Palmerston North from
within New Zealand, 1996 census

Age
65+
60-64
55-59
50-54
45-49
40-44
35-39
30-34
25-29
20-24
15-19
10-14
5-9

% 9 8 7 6 5 4 3 2 1 0   0 1 2 3 4 5 6 7 8 9 %
Male   Female

Palmerston North, with a population of ab[out] 74,000, maintains a large university (Massey) which attracts students from [all] over the country, but particularly from th[e] lower North Island. This can be seen whe[n] comparing the inter-urban migration patt[ern] (1991–1996) with the age-sex structure [of] the migrants. Significantly, the inflow of o[ver] 4500 20–24 year olds from elsewhere in N[ew] Zealand was 26.2% of its total inflow, wh[ile] 20–24 year olds comprised 19.8% of Cen[tral] Auckland's inflow, only 10.9% of that to[?] Napier and 9.3% of that to Tauranga. Tw[o] other similar-sized cities to Palmerston No[rth,] both with universities, also attract large numbers of 20–24 year olds: they make [?] 27.8% of Dunedin's inflow and 21.1% of [the] inflow to Hamilton.

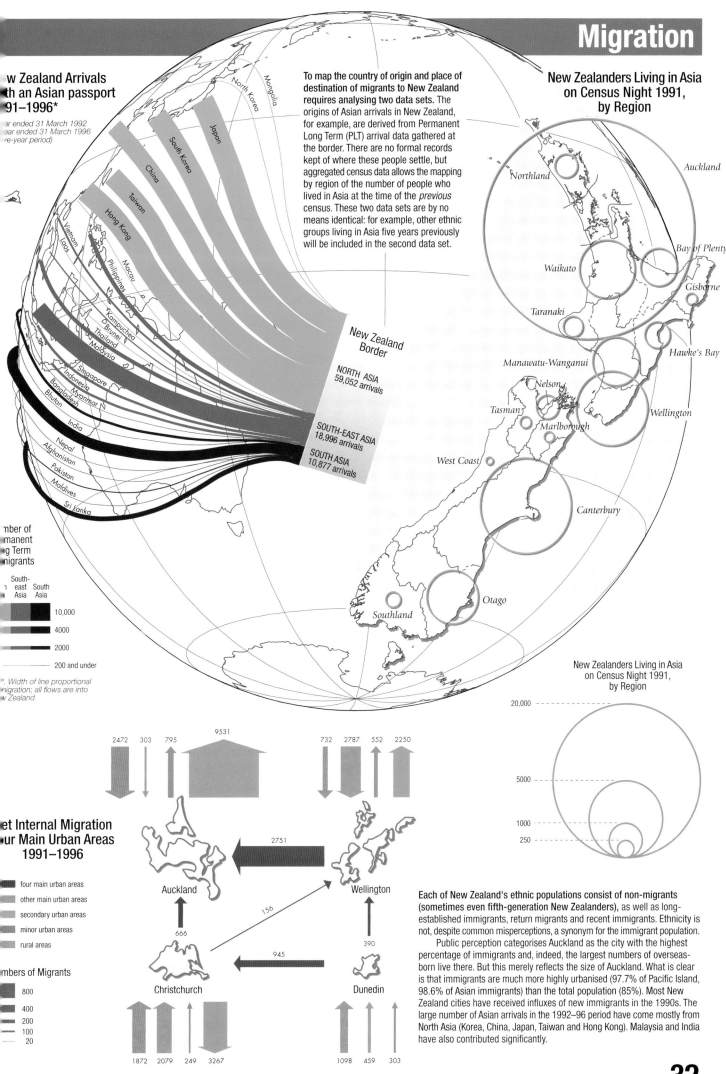

New Zealand Arrivals with an Asian passport 1991–1996*

*Year ended 31 March 1992
Year ended 31 March 1996
(five-year period)

To map the country of origin and place of destination of migrants to New Zealand requires analysing two data sets. The origins of Asian arrivals in New Zealand, for example, are derived from Permanent Long Term (PLT) arrival data gathered at the border. There are no formal records kept of where these people settle, but aggregated census data allows the mapping by region of the number of people who lived in Asia at the time of the *previous* census. These two data sets are by no means identical: for example, other ethnic groups living in Asia five years previously will be included in the second data set.

New Zealanders Living in Asia on Census Night 1991, by Region

New Zealand Border

NORTH ASIA
59,052 arrivals

SOUTH-EAST ASIA
18,996 arrivals

SOUTH ASIA
10,877 arrivals

Number of Permanent Long Term Migrants

South-east Asia | South Asia

10,000
4000
2000
200 and under

*. Width of line proportional to migration; all flows are into New Zealand

New Zealanders Living in Asia on Census Night 1991, by Region

20,000
5000
1000
250

Net Internal Migration Four Main Urban Areas 1991–1996

four main urban areas
other main urban areas
secondary urban areas
minor urban areas
rural areas

Numbers of Migrants

800
400
200
100
20

2472 303 795 9531

732 2787 552 2250

2751

Auckland

Wellington

156

666

390

945

Christchurch

Dunedin

1872 2079 249 3267

1098 459 303

Each of New Zealand's ethnic populations consist of non-migrants (sometimes even fifth-generation New Zealanders), as well as long-established immigrants, return migrants and recent immigrants. Ethnicity is not, despite common misperceptions, a synonym for the immigrant population.

Public perception categorises Auckland as the city with the highest percentage of immigrants and, indeed, the largest numbers of overseas-born live there. But this merely reflects the size of Auckland. What is clear is that immigrants are much more highly urbanised (97.7% of Pacific Island, 98.6% of Asian immigrants) than the total population (85%). Most New Zealand cities have received influxes of new immigrants in the 1990s. The large number of Asian arrivals in the 1992–96 period have come mostly from North Asia (Korea, China, Japan, Taiwan and Hong Kong). Malaysia and India have also contributed significantly.

32

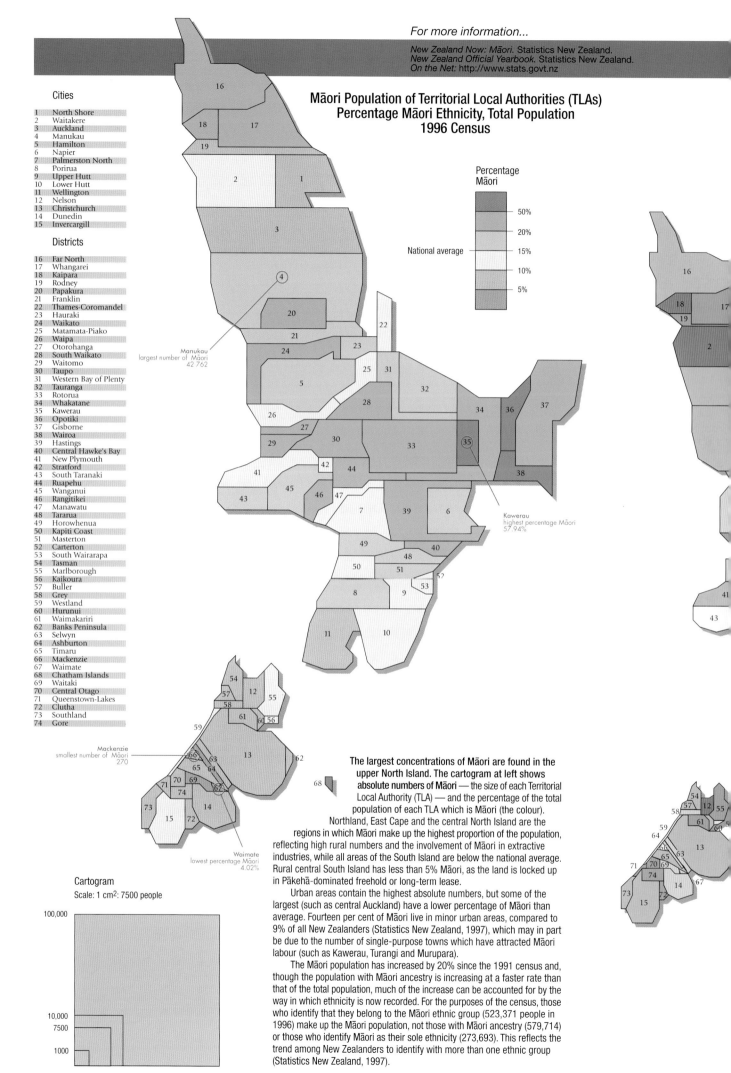

Cities

1 North Shore
2 Waitakere
3 Auckland
4 Manukau
5 Hamilton
6 Napier
7 Palmerston North
8 Porirua
9 Upper Hutt
10 Lower Hutt
11 Wellington
12 Nelson
13 Christchurch
14 Dunedin
15 Invercargill

Districts

16 Far North
17 Whangarei
18 Kaipara
19 Rodney
20 Papakura
21 Franklin
22 Thames-Coromandel
23 Hauraki
24 Waikato
25 Matamata-Piako
26 Waipa
27 Otorohanga
28 South Waikato
29 Waitomo
30 Taupo
31 Western Bay of Plenty
32 Tauranga
33 Rotorua
34 Whakatane
35 Kawerau
36 Opotiki
37 Gisborne
38 Wairoa
39 Hastings
40 Central Hawke's Bay
41 New Plymouth
42 Stratford
43 South Taranaki
44 Ruapehu
45 Wanganui
46 Rangitikei
47 Manawatu
48 Tararua
49 Horowhenua
50 Kapiti Coast
51 Masterton
52 Carterton
53 South Wairarapa
54 Tasman
55 Marlborough
56 Kaikoura
57 Buller
58 Grey
59 Westland
60 Hurunui
61 Waimakariri
62 Banks Peninsula
63 Selwyn
64 Ashburton
65 Timaru
66 Mackenzie
67 Waimate
68 Chatham Islands
69 Waitaki
70 Central Otago
71 Queenstown-Lakes
72 Clutha
73 Southland
74 Gore

Māori Population of Territorial Local Authorities (TLAs)
Percentage Māori Ethnicity, Total Population
1996 Census

Percentage Māori

50%
20%
National average   15%
10%
5%

Manukau
largest number of Māori
42 762

Kawerau
highest percentage Māori
57.94%

Mackenzie
smallest number of Māori
270

Waimate
lowest percentage Māori
4.02%

The largest concentrations of Māori are found in the upper North Island. The cartogram at left shows absolute numbers of Māori — the size of each Territorial Local Authority (TLA) — and the percentage of the total population of each TLA which is Māori (the colour). Northland, East Cape and the central North Island are the regions in which Māori make up the highest proportion of the population, reflecting high rural numbers and the involvement of Māori in extractive industries, while all areas of the South Island are below the national average. Rural central South Island has less than 5% Māori, as the land is locked up in Pākehā-dominated freehold or long-term lease.

Urban areas contain the highest absolute numbers, but some of the largest (such as central Auckland) have a lower percentage of Māori than average. Fourteen per cent of Māori live in minor urban areas, compared to 9% of all New Zealanders (Statistics New Zealand, 1997), which may in part be due to the number of single-purpose towns which have attracted Māori labour (such as Kawerau, Turangi and Murupara).

The Māori population has increased by 20% since the 1991 census and, though the population with Māori ancestry is increasing at a faster rate than that of the total population, much of the increase can be accounted for by the way in which ethnicity is now recorded. For the purposes of the census, those who identify that they belong to the Māori ethnic group (523,371 people in 1996) make up the Māori population, not those with Māori ancestry (579,714) or those who identify Māori as their sole ethnicity (273,693). This reflects the trend among New Zealanders to identify with more than one ethnic group (Statistics New Zealand, 1997).

Cartogram
Scale: 1 cm² : 7500 people

100,000

10,000
7500

1000

One of the most pressing issues facing the Māori population is **unemployment**. In 1996 Māori "comprised 27.7 percent of all unemployed people but only 12.3 percent of the total working-age population" (Statistics New Zealand, 1998: 68). Since 1986 the gap between Māori and non-Māori has widened: between 1986 and 1991 the unemployment rate for Māori increased from 14.9% to 24.2% (the equivalent rates for non-Māori were 5.8% and 9%).

A rapid rise in unemployment among Māori males between 1986 and 1991, particularly among those who had worked in the manufacturing sector, is expressed regionally in the areas where these people lived (such as Papakura, Waitakere and Nelson). These same areas, even more than the country as a whole, recovered quickly in the better economic conditions of the 1991 to 1996 period.

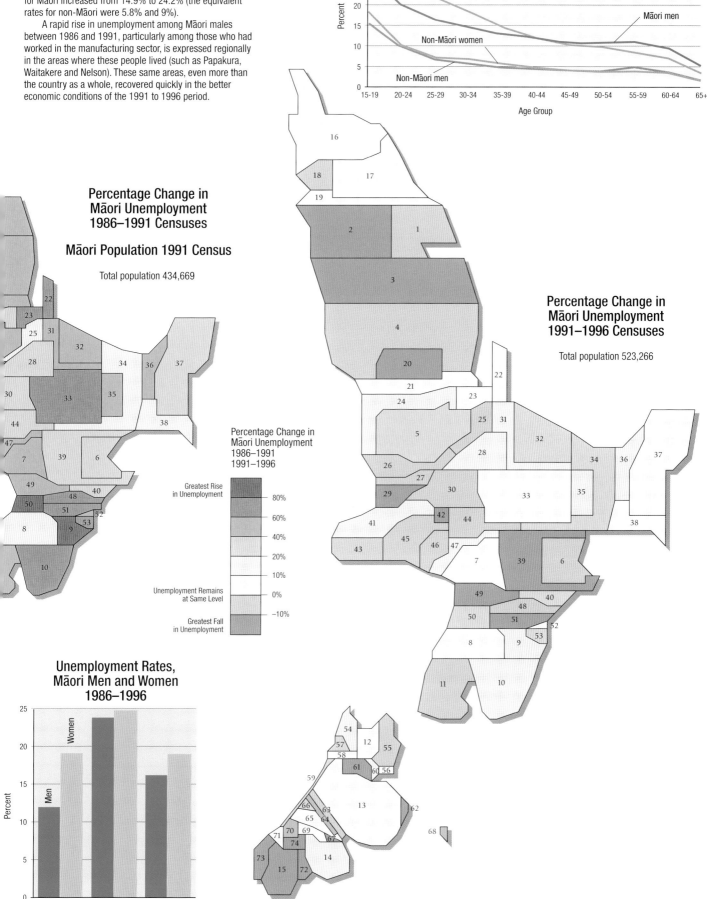

Unemployment Rates, Māori/Non-Māori Men and Women 1996

Percentage Change in Māori Unemployment 1986–1991 Censuses

Māori Population 1991 Census

Total population 434,669

Percentage Change in Māori Unemployment 1991–1996 Censuses

Total population 523,266

Percentage Change in Māori Unemployment 1986–1991 1991–1996

Greatest Rise in Unemployment — 80%
— 60%
— 40%
— 20%
— 10%
Unemployment Remains at Same Level — 0%
— −10%
Greatest Fall in Unemployment

Unemployment Rates, Māori Men and Women 1986–1996

33

New Zealand's population history reflects the thousand-year exclusivity of Polynesian society, then 140 years of European dominance. This second period threatened to swamp Māori cultural heritage, but in recent decades an indigenous cultural renaissance has convinced most New Zealanders that they now live in a multicultural society.

The numbers, however, reflect Pākehā dominance. About 80% of New Zealanders are of European origin, with those who call themselves Māori making up 14.5% of the population. Pacific Islanders are the third largest ethnic group (5.6% of the 1996 census).

The myth of racial harmony was maintained in the early and middle years of the twentieth century as Pākehā and Māori inhabited different worlds. The first strain on this myth was the migration of Māori to the cities, and then in the 1970s a large influx of Pacific Islanders into northen urban areas (and subsequent publicity about overstayers) heightened racial tension. In the last few years political posturing in opposition to increasing numbers of non-European immigrants (primarily Asian) has sharpened ideological divisions.

One area in which these cultures collide is the South Auckland urban area. In crude terms this urban area is divided socio-economically into a richer north and a poorer south by the East Tamaki industrial area. One would expect, therefore, that the Asian distribution would reflect the notion that Asian immigrants, who are required to bring wealth with them, would settle primarily in the more affluent suburbs of Howick and Pakuranga, while the Māori and Pacific Islanders, with fewer resources on average, would make their homes in the southern suburbs. However, there are a number of reasons why the cultural geography of South Auckland does not reflect these expectations.

The map of Asian ethnicity shows the location of all who call themselves Asians, not just recent immigrants. Some may be fourth or fifth generation New Zealanders, but the socio-economic expectation that they live in affluent areas is influenced by the perception that most Asians are recent immigrants.

As the Māori population grows as a percentage of total population, it takes on more of the total population's characteristics. Māori have begun to penetrate the more affluent suburbs, and have spread out from Mangere and Manurewa, where traditionally they have lived. The Pacific Island population is more recent, however, and so is more concentrated, having had less time to spread from Otara and Mangere.

Percentage Asian Ethnicity, South Auckland Urban Area 1996 Census

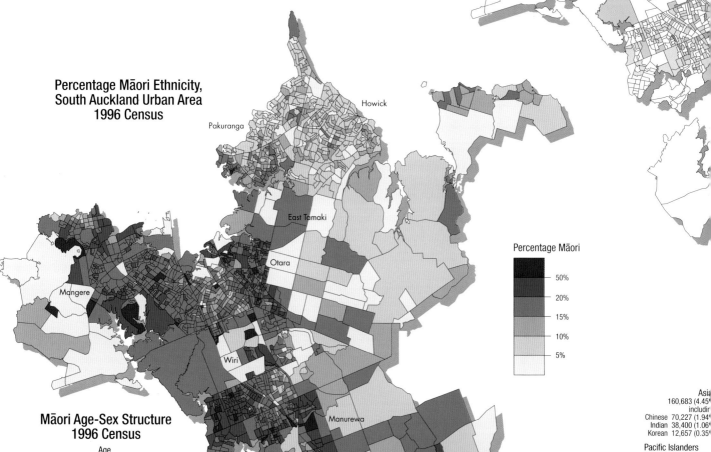

Percentage Māori Ethnicity, South Auckland Urban Area 1996 Census

Percentage Māori

- 50%
- 20%
- 15%
- 10%
- 5%

Asia
160,683 (4.45%)
includir
Chinese 70,227 (1.94%)
Indian 38,400 (1.06%)
Korean 12,657 (0.35%)

Pacific Islanders
173,178 (4.77%)
including:
Samoan 83,715 (2.31%)
Cook Islander 34,167 (0.94%)
Tongan 26,061 (0.72%)
Niuean 14,709 (0.41%)

Māori
523,374 (14.46%)

Other European
156,801 (4.34%)
including:
Dutch 40,284 (1.11%)
Australian 45,774 (1.27%)
German 8946 (0.25%)
South Slav 7440 (0.21%)

British/Ir
321,552 (8.89

Māori Age-Sex Structure 1996 Census

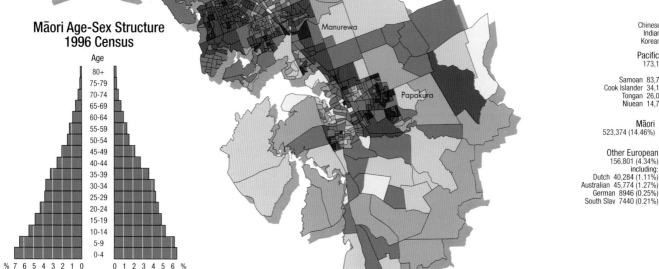

Bateman Contemporary Atlas New Zealand

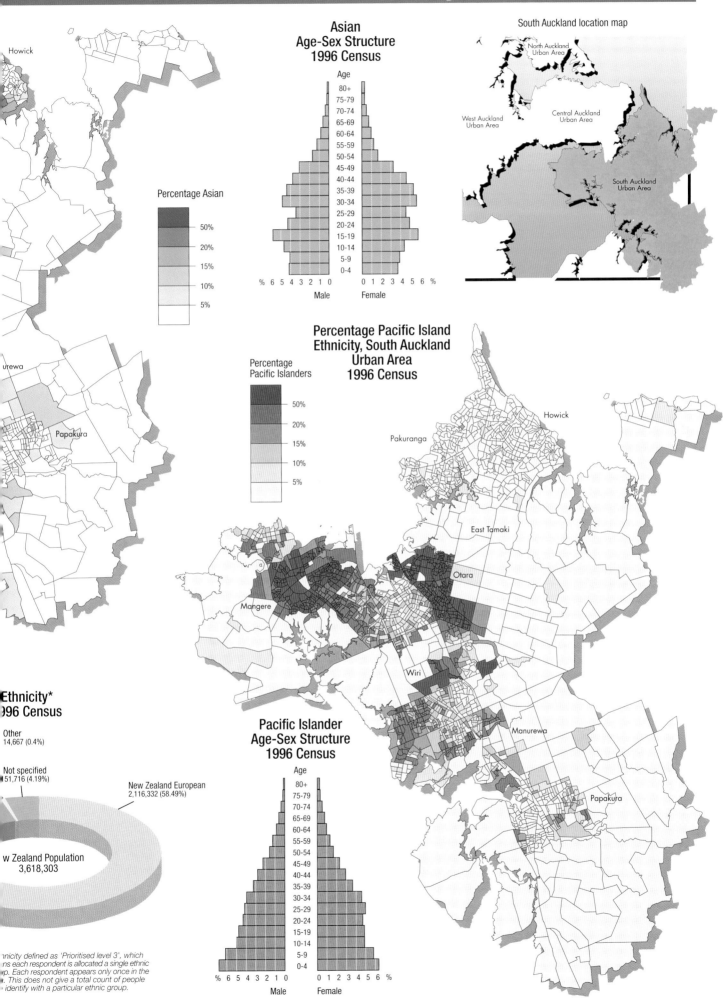

Asian Age-Sex Structure 1996 Census

South Auckland location map

North Auckland Urban Area

West Auckland Urban Area

Central Auckland Urban Area

South Auckland Urban Area

Percentage Asian

- 50%
- 20%
- 15%
- 10%
- 5%

Age

80+
75-79
70-74
65-69
60-64
55-59
50-54
45-49
40-44
35-39
30-34
25-29
20-24
15-19
10-14
5-9
0-4

% 6 5 4 3 2 1 0   0 1 2 3 4 5 6 %

Male   Female

Howick

Percentage Pacific Island Ethnicity, South Auckland Urban Area 1996 Census

Percentage Pacific Islanders

- 50%
- 20%
- 15%
- 10%
- 5%

Howick

Pakuranga

East Tamaki

Otara

Mangere

Wiri

Manurewa

Papakura

Papakura

Pacific Islander Age-Sex Structure 1996 Census

Age

80+
75-79
70-74
65-69
60-64
55-59
50-54
45-49
40-44
35-39
30-34
25-29
20-24
15-19
10-14
5-9
0-4

% 6 5 4 3 2 1 0   0 1 2 3 4 5 6 %

Male   Female

Ethnicity*
996 Census

Other
14,667 (0.4%)

Not specified
51,716 (4.19%)

New Zealand European
2,116,332 (58.49%)

w Zealand Population
3,618,303

nicity defined as 'Prioritised level 3', which
ns each respondent is allocated a single ethnic
p. Each respondent appears only once in the
. This does not give a total count of people
identify with a particular ethnic group.

34

In October 1996 New Zealand conducted its first MMP election, fulfilling the wishes of the people as expressed in a referendum on proportional representation. Boundaries for the 1999 election are similar, with most changes in the northern half of the North Island.

Electoral boundaries are revised by the Representation Commission following each five-yearly population census. As part of their terms of reference this commission may consider making changes based upon the following discretionary criteria: the requirement for the South Island to have 16 general electorates; the total number of Parliamentary seats (currently fixed at 120); topography; communications links; existing electoral boundaries; related communities of interest; and any projected variation in the population of these electorates. These discretionary criteria can only be applied within the limits of the one mandatory requirement, that all electorates must have the same total population, within a plus or minus five per cent tolerance level.

Māori electorates were first established in 1867. The number of Māori electorates is determined on the same basis as the General electorates so that all electorates, Māori and General, are approximately the same size in terms of their total population. In 1997 a campaign to encourage enrolment on the Māori electoral roll resulted in the addition of an extra seat, which came into force at the 1999 election.

Every effort is made to keep the process of setting electoral boundaries free from corruption. The manipulation of boundaries by politicians and parties in order to retain power (gerrymandering) is prevented by a Representation Commission that determines provisional boundaries, which are then open to objection and counter-objection. Final boundaries are then published.

General Electorates
1999 MMP Election

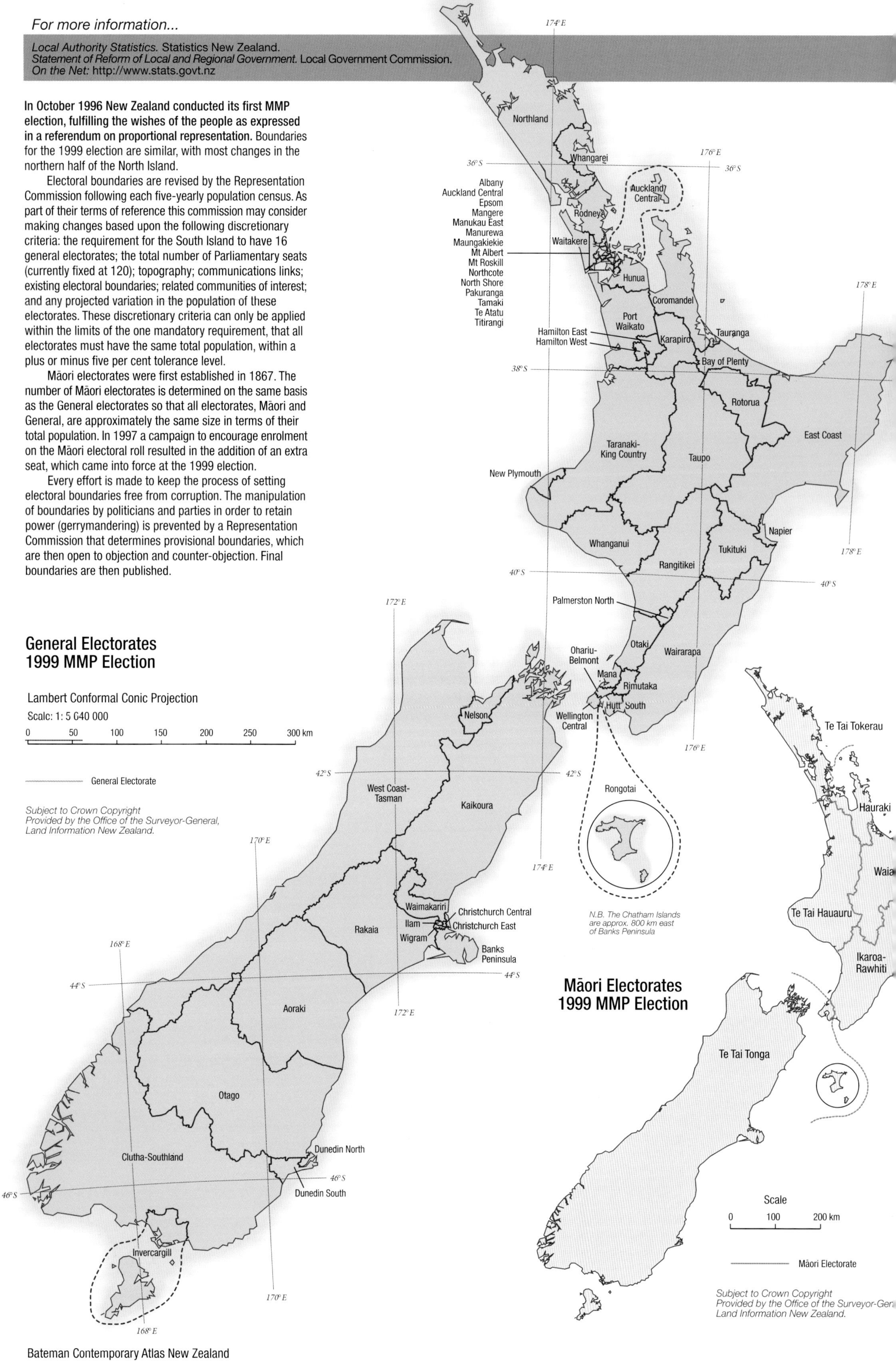

Lambert Conformal Conic Projection

Scale: 1: 5 640 000

| 0 | 50 | 100 | 150 | 200 | 250 | 300 km |

——————— General Electorate

Subject to Crown Copyright
Provided by the Office of the Surveyor-General,
Land Information New Zealand.

Māori Electorates
1999 MMP Election

N.B. The Chatham Islands
are approx. 800 km east
of Banks Peninsula

Scale

| 0 | 100 | 200 km |

——————— Māori Electorate

Subject to Crown Copyright
Provided by the Office of the Surveyor-Gen
Land Information New Zealand.

Bateman Contemporary Atlas New Zealand

l authorities were restructured in November 1989. The
ber of authorities was reduced to 86, and ad hoc
orities such as harbour boards and pest control boards
absorbed into regional, district and city councils.

There are two main types of local authority: regional and
orial. There are now 12 regional councils, 74 territorial
orities, 154 community boards and 6 special authorities.
Local authorities raise the majority of their revenue by
cising their power to levy rates. They then administer
al crucial pieces of legislation for the benefit of their
tituents, such as the Resource Management Act 1991,
ransit New Zealand Act 1989 and the Building Act 1991.
heir interpretations of acts such as these that influence
orm and size, rural development and conservation, and
infrastructure, amongst other things.

Regional councils have fewer functions than territorial
orities, but exercise them over much larger areas. This
s them to co-ordinate the control of pests, pollution,
port planning, civil defence, soil conservation and resource
agement.

Territorial authorities have a wide range of functions
ding land use consents, noise control, litter control,
ing, water supply, sewage reticulation and disposal,
ish collection and disposal, parks and reserves, libraries,
subdivision, pensioner housing, health inspection, building
ent, parking controls and civil defence.

Councils have been encouraged to separate their activities
hose with a regulatory function and those which can be
ated as businesses. Council-run business units compete
other businesses for council contracts. Councils may
have majority shareholdings in companies which operate
s, airports, public transport and electricity supply.

al Government Boundaries
th effect from 1 July 1992

bert Conformal Conic Projection
e: 1: 5 640 000

| 50 | 100 | 150 | 200 | 250 | 300 km |

———————— Territorial Local Authority (TLA)

━━━━━━━━ Regional Council

----------- Regional Council boundary
which runs through a TLA

N.B. The Chatham Islands
are approx. 800 km east
of Banks Peninsula

Local Authority Income
Non-Trading Activities
1996

N.B. All figures are
provisional.

Investment Income
7.8% ($245.9m)

Sales and other Income
19.8% ($622.7m)

Fees and Fines
4.8% ($149.9m)

Grants, Subsidies
and Levies 10.3%
($322.3m)

Petrol Tax 1.1%
($33.1m)

Rates 56.3%
($1769m)

Total Non-Trading Income
$3142.9m

35

For more information...

New Zealand Business Activity Statistics. Statistics New Zealand.
Annual Reports. Fletcher Challenge.
On the Net: http://www.stats.govt.nz

Selected Fletcher Challenge Overseas Assets, 1997–1998

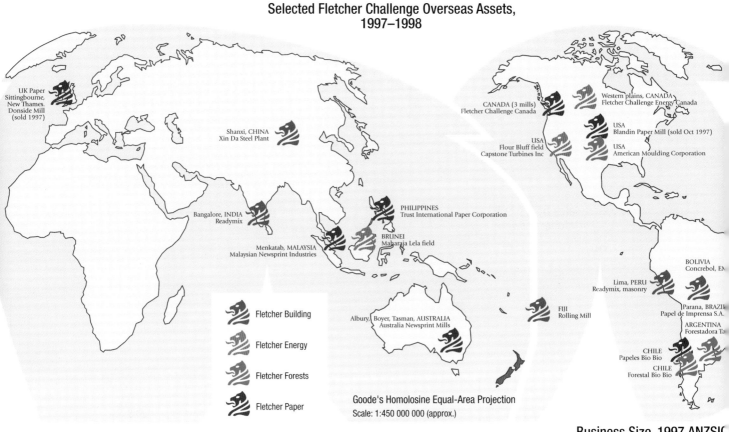

UK Paper
Sittingbourne,
New Thames.
Donside Mill
(sold 1997)

Shanxi, CHINA
Xin Da Steel Plant

Bangalore, INDIA
Readymix

Menkatab, MALAYSIA
Malaysian Newsprint Industries

PHILIPPINES
Trust International Paper Corporation

BRUNEI
Maharaja Lela field

Albury, Boyer, Tasman, AUSTRALIA
Australia Newsprint Mills

CANADA (3 mills)
Fletcher Challenge Canada

Western plains, CANADA
Fletcher Challenge Energy Canada

USA
Flour Bluff field
Capstone Turbines Inc

USA
Blandin Paper Mill (sold Oct 1997)

USA
American Moulding Corporation

BOLIVIA
Concrebol, EN

Lima, PERU
Readymix, masonry

FIJI
Rolling Mill

Parana, BRAZIL
Papel de Imprensa S.A.

ARGENTINA
Forestadora Ta

CHILE
Papeles Bio Bio

CHILE
Forestal Bio Bio

Fletcher Building
Fletcher Energy
Fletcher Forests
Fletcher Paper

Goode's Homolosine Equal-Area Projection
Scale: 1:450 000 000 (approx.)

Fletcher Challenge, New Zealand's largest multinational company and the only one to make the Fortune 500 list, owns overseas assets located primarily on the Pacific Rim. The company utilises low-wage countries such as Chile, Argentina, Malaysia and China to produce primary and manufactured goods, undercutting the prices of its competition. At present it is downsizing many of its investments in developed countries, such as Canada and the UK.

Fletcher Challenge was created in 1981 by the merger of three large agricultural-based companies. In 1992 it was split into four linked divisions: building, energy, forests and paper. While Fletcher Challenge has expanded internationally, New Zealand remains the core of its asset base and, at least in the case of Fletcher Building and Fletcher Energy, of its market.

Business Size, 1997 ANZSI(
Return on Assets, 1995–6 ANZS

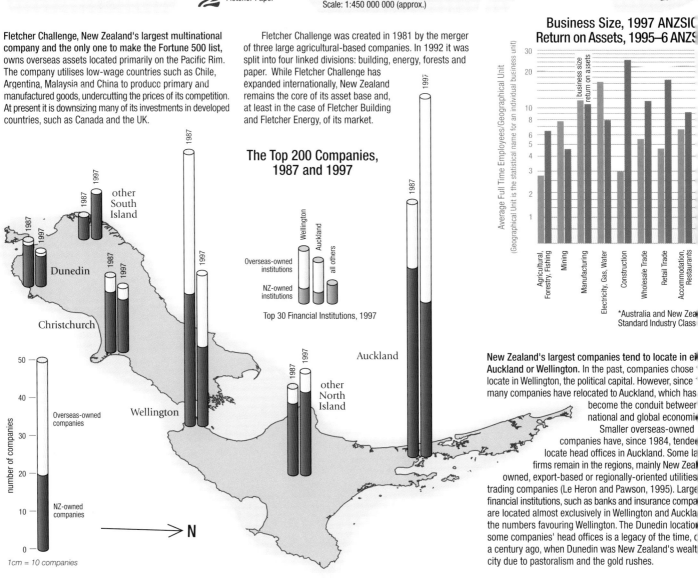

Average Full Time Employees/Geographical Unit
(Geographical Unit is the statistical name for an individual business unit)

business size
return on assets

Agricultural, Forestry, Fishing
Mining
Manufacturing
Electricity, Gas, Water
Construction
Wholesale Trade
Retail Trade
Accommodation, Restaurants

*Australia and New Zea
Standard Industry Class

The Top 200 Companies, 1987 and 1997

other South Island

Dunedin

Christchurch

Wellington

Overseas-owned institutions
NZ-owned institutions

Wellington
Auckland
all others

Top 30 Financial Institutions, 1997

Auckland

other North Island

number of companies

Overseas-owned companies

NZ-owned companies

1cm = 10 companies

New Zealand's largest companies tend to locate in e
Auckland or Wellington. In the past, companies chose
locate in Wellington, the political capital. However, since
many companies have relocated to Auckland, which has
become the conduit betweer
national and global economi
Smaller overseas-owned
companies have, since 1984, tende
locate head offices in Auckland. Some la
firms remain in the regions, mainly New Zeal
owned, export-based or regionally-oriented utilities
trading companies (Le Heron and Pawson, 1995). Large
financial institutions, such as banks and insurance compa
are located almost exclusively in Wellington and Auckla
the numbers favouring Wellington. The Dunedin location
some companies' head offices is a legacy of the time, c
a century ago, when Dunedin was New Zealand's wealt
city due to pastoralism and the gold rushes.

Bateman Contemporary Atlas New Zealand

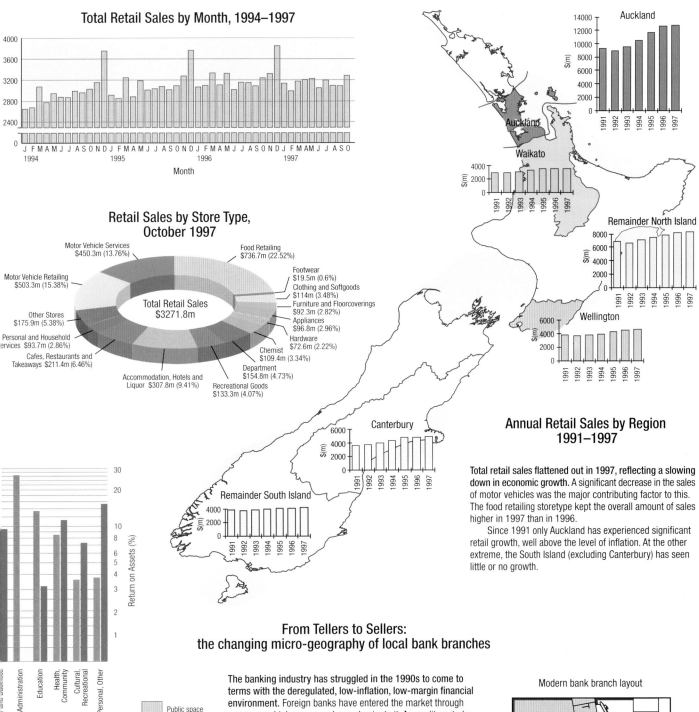

Total Retail Sales by Month, 1994–1997

Month

Retail Sales by Store Type, October 1997

Total Retail Sales $3271.8m

- Motor Vehicle Services $450.3m (13.76%)
- Food Retailing $736.7m (22.52%)
- Footwear $19.5m (0.6%)
- Clothing and Softgoods $114m (3.48%)
- Furniture and Floorcoverings $92.3m (2.82%)
- Appliances $96.8m (2.96%)
- Hardware $72.6m (2.22%)
- Chemist $109.4m (3.34%)
- Department $154.8m (4.73%)
- Recreational Goods $133.3m (4.07%)
- Accommodation, Hotels and Liquor $307.8m (9.41%)
- Cafes, Restaurants and Takeaways $211.4m (6.46%)
- Personal and Household Services $93.7m (2.86%)
- Other Stores $175.9m (5.38%)
- Motor Vehicle Retailing $503.3m (15.38%)

Return on Assets (%)

- Govt Administration
- Education
- Health, Community
- Cultural, Recreational
- Personal, Other

Public space
Staff only

Auckland

Waikato

Remainder North Island

Wellington

Canterbury

Remainder South Island

Annual Retail Sales by Region 1991–1997

Total retail sales flattened out in 1997, reflecting a slowing down in economic growth. A significant decrease in the sales of motor vehicles was the major contributing factor to this. The food retailing storetype kept the overall amount of sales higher in 1997 than in 1996.

Since 1991 only Auckland has experienced significant retail growth, well above the level of inflation. At the other extreme, the South Island (excluding Canterbury) has seen little or no growth.

From Tellers to Sellers: the changing micro-geography of local bank branches

The banking industry has struggled in the 1990s to come to terms with the deregulated, low-inflation, low-margin financial environment. Foreign banks have entered the market through mergers and takeovers, and now dominate it. As credit controls placed on banks by central government were lifted in the mid-1980s, banks went on a frenzy of lending, trying to maintain market share, but were punished for this strategy by the 1987 sharemarket crash. As the level of inflation fell below interest rates, banks needed to adopt conservative strategies, cutting costs and improving efficiency as interest margins declined (Flux, 1994).

This has had a profound effect on the 'micro-geography' of local bank branches. Formerly regarded as 'cost centres', transaction-oriented and often opaque to the customer, local branches have been transformed into 'profit centres'. This has been done by transferring much of the processing functions from local branches to regional processing centres, then turning the branch into a selling environment for all manner of bank products (credit cards, fee-based accounts, insurance etc). Automation has reduced the need for tellers: many customers are using telephone, Internet and ATM banking in preference to dealing with tellers. As processing functions have been centralised, new branch layouts have devoted much more floor space to customers, and while staff numbers are reduced, the customer has access to a much higher level of service. Tellers are often placed at the rear of the outlet, ensuring that the customers are exposed to advertising and sales staff on their way to conduct transactions.

Traditional bank branch layout

- Manager
- Accountant
- TELLERS
- Back-line Staff
- Enquiries

Modern bank branch layout

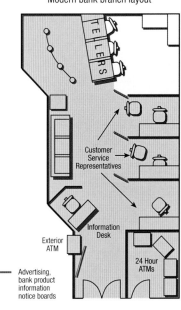

- TELLERS
- Customer Service Representatives
- Information Desk
- Exterior ATM
- 24 Hour ATMs
- Advertising, bank product information notice boards

36

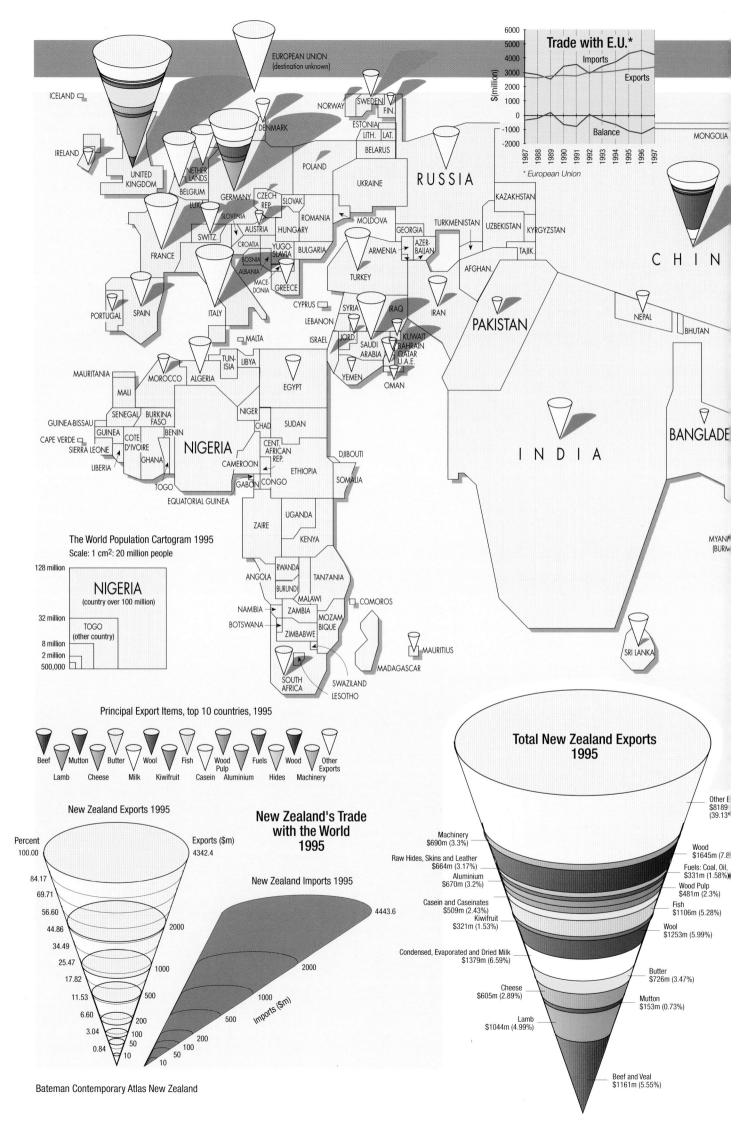

Trade with E.U.*

Imports
Exports
Balance

* European Union

EUROPEAN UNION
(destination unknown)

ICELAND
IRELAND
UNITED KINGDOM
NETHERLANDS
BELGIUM
LUX.
GERMANY
CZECH REP.
SLOVAK.
FRANCE
SWITZ.
AUSTRIA
SLOVENIA
CROATIA
BOSNIA
ALBANIA
MACE-DONIA
ITALY
PORTUGAL
SPAIN
GREECE
NORWAY
SWEDEN
FIN.
DENMARK
ESTONIA
LITH.
LAT.
BELARUS
POLAND
UKRAINE
ROMANIA
MOLDOVA
HUNGARY
YUGO-SLAVIA
BULGARIA
RUSSIA
GEORGIA
AZER-BAIJAN
ARMENIA
TURKEY
CYPRUS
MONGOLIA
KAZAKHSTAN
TURKMENISTAN
UZBEKISTAN
KYRGYZSTAN
TAJIK.
AFGHAN.
C H I N
SYRIA
LEBANON
ISRAEL
JORD.
SAUDI ARABIA
IRAQ
IRAN
PAKISTAN
NEPAL
BHUTAN
KUWAIT
BAHRAIN
QATAR
U.A.E.
OMAN
YEMEN
BANGLADE
MALTA
TUN-ISIA
LIBYA
EGYPT
INDIA
MAURITANIA
MALI
MOROCCO
ALGERIA
NIGER
CHAD
SUDAN
GUINEA-BISSAU
SENEGAL
BURKINA FASO
BENIN
GUINEA
CAPE VERDE
SIERRA LEONE
COTE D'IVOIRE
GHANA
LIBERIA
TOGO
NIGERIA
CENT. AFRICAN REP.
CAMEROON
GABON
CONGO
EQUATORIAL GUINEA
ETHIOPIA
DJIBOUTI
SOMALIA
ZAIRE
UGANDA
KENYA
ANGOLA
RWANDA
BURUNDI
TAN7ANIA
MALAWI
COMOROS
NAMIBIA
ZAMBIA
MOZAM-BIQUE
BOTSWANA
ZIMBABWE
MAURITIUS
MADAGASCAR
SOUTH AFRICA
SWAZILAND
LESOTHO
SRI LANKA
MYAN
(BURM

The World Population Cartogram 1995
Scale: 1 cm² : 20 million people

128 million

NIGERIA
(country over 100 million)

32 million

TOGO
(other country)

8 million
2 million
500,000

Principal Export Items, top 10 countries, 1995

Beef | Mutton | Butter | Wool | Fish | Wood Pulp | Fuels | Wood | Other Exports
Lamb | Cheese | Milk | Kiwifruit | Casein | Aluminium | Hides | Machinery

New Zealand Exports 1995

Percent
100.00
84.17
69.71
56.60
44.86
34.49
25.47
17.82
11.53
6.60
3.04
0.84

Exports ($m)
4342.4

2000
1000
500
200
100
50
10

New Zealand's Trade with the World 1995

New Zealand Imports 1995

4443.6

2000
1000
500
200
100
50
10
Imports ($m)

Bateman Contemporary Atlas New Zealand

Total New Zealand Exports 1995

Other E
$8189
(39.13

Machinery
$690m (3.3%)

Raw Hides, Skins and Leather
$664m (3.17%)

Aluminium
$670m (3.2%)

Casein and Caseinates
$509m (2.43%)

Kiwifruit
$321m (1.53%)

Condensed, Evaporated and Dried Milk
$1379m (6.59%)

Cheese
$605m (2.89%)

Lamb
$1044m (4.99%)

Wood
$1645m (7.8

Fuels: Coal, Oil,
$331m (1.58%)

Wood Pulp
$481m (2.3%)

Fish
$1106m (5.28%)

Wool
$1253m (5.99%)

Butter
$726m (3.47%)

Mutton
$153m (0.73%)

Beef and Veal
$1161m (5.55%)

Overseas Trade

For more information...

New Zealand Official Yearbook. Statistics New Zealand.
On the Net: http://www.tradenz.govt.nz/index2.html
http://www.mft.govt.nz

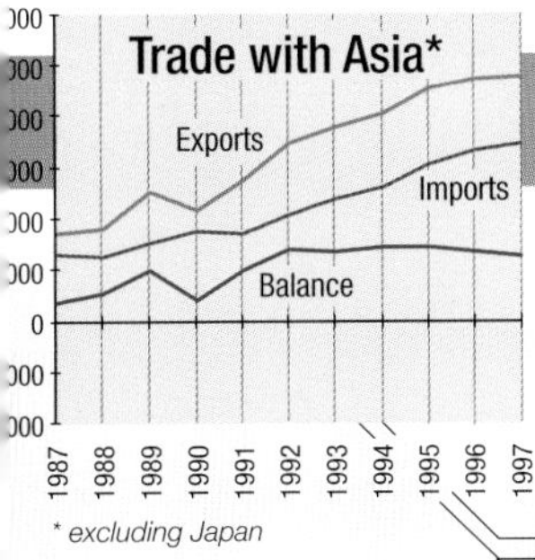

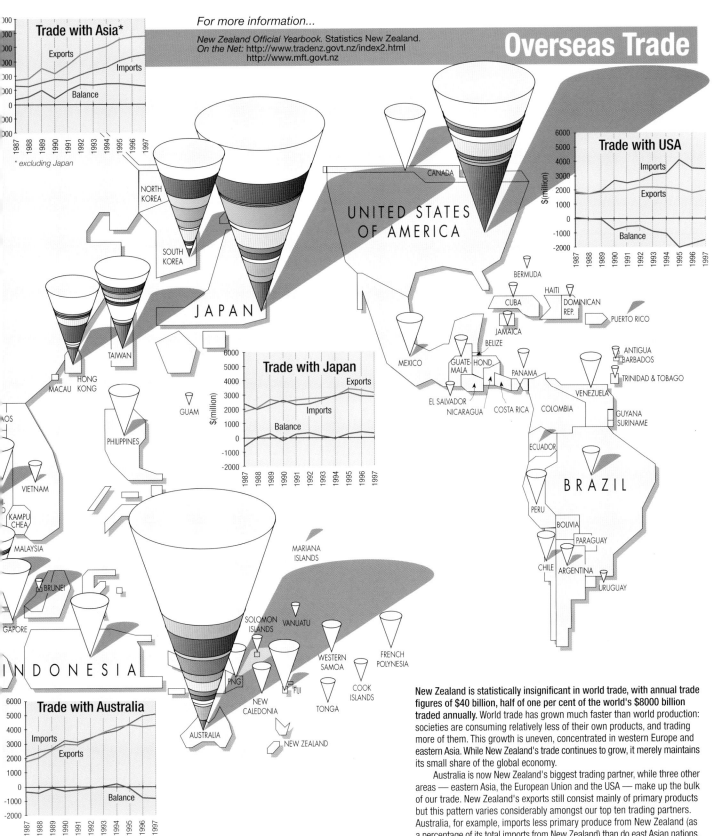

Trade with Asia*
Exports
Imports
Balance
0
1987
1988
1989
1990
1991
1992
1993
1994
1995
1996
1997
* excluding Japan

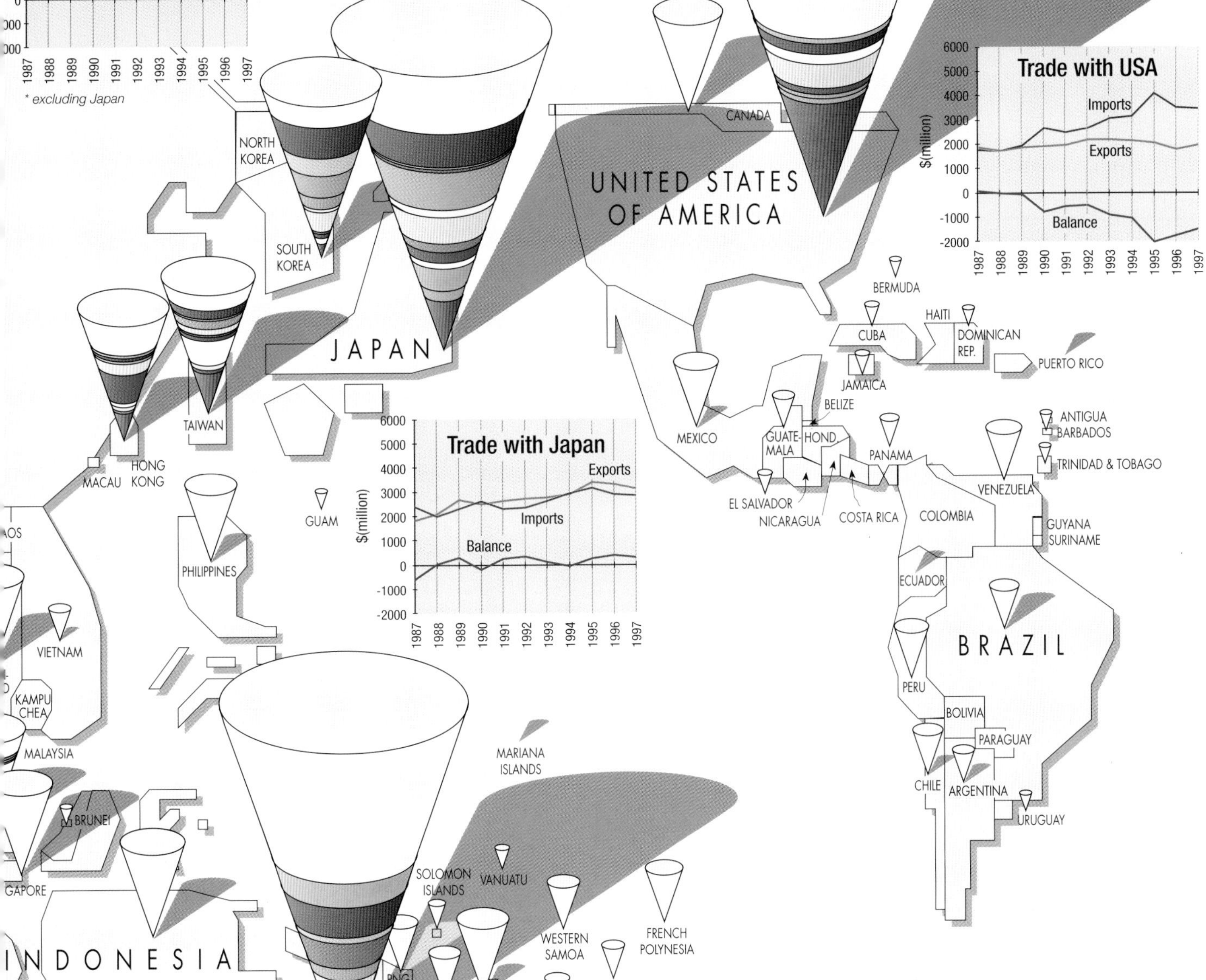

NORTH KOREA
SOUTH KOREA
JAPAN
TAIWAN
HONG KONG
MACAU
GUAM
PHILIPPINES
VIETNAM
KAMPUCHEA
MALAYSIA
BRUNEI
INDONESIA
CANADA
UNITED STATES OF AMERICA
BERMUDA
CUBA
HAITI
DOMINICAN REP.
PUERTO RICO
JAMAICA
BELIZE
MEXICO
GUATEMALA
HOND.
EL SALVADOR
NICARAGUA
COSTA RICA
PANAMA
ANTIGUA
BARBADOS
TRINIDAD & TOBAGO
VENEZUELA
COLOMBIA
GUYANA
SURINAME
ECUADOR
BRAZIL
PERU
BOLIVIA
PARAGUAY
CHILE
ARGENTINA
URUGUAY
MARIANA ISLANDS
SOLOMON ISLANDS
VANUATU
PNG
Trade with USA
Imports
Exports
Balance
$(million)
6000
5000
4000
3000
2000
1000
0
-1000
-2000
1987
1988
1989
1990
1991
1992
1993
1994
1995
1996
1997
Trade with Japan
Exports
Imports
Balance

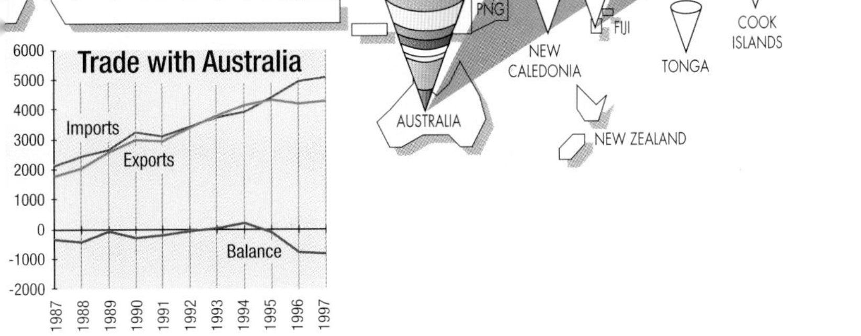

WESTERN SAMOA
FRENCH POLYNESIA
NEW CALEDONIA
FIJI
TONGA
COOK ISLANDS
AUSTRALIA
NEW ZEALAND
Trade with Australia
Imports
Exports
Balance
6000
5000
4000
3000
2000
1000
0
-1000
-2000
1987
1988
1989
1990
1991
1992
1993
1994
1995
1996
1997

Destination of Exports, 1920–1997

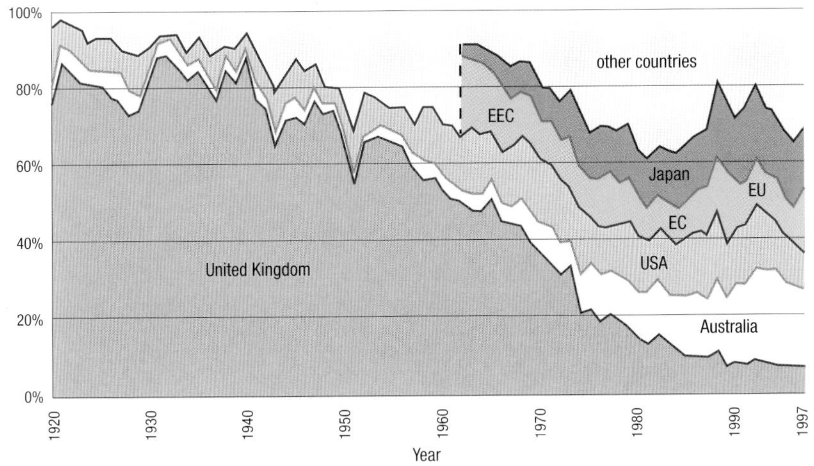

100%
80%
60%
40%
20%
0%
other countries
EEC
Japan
EU
EC
USA
United Kingdom
Australia
1920
1930
1940
1950
1960
1970
1980
1990
1997
Year

New Zealand is statistically insignificant in world trade, with annual trade figures of $40 billion, half of one per cent of the world's $8000 billion traded annually. World trade has grown much faster than world production: societies are consuming relatively less of their own products, and trading more of them. This growth is uneven, concentrated in western Europe and eastern Asia. While New Zealand's trade continues to grow, it merely maintains its small share of the global economy.

Australia is now New Zealand's biggest trading partner, while three other areas — eastern Asia, the European Union and the USA — make up the bulk of our trade. New Zealand's exports still consist mainly of primary products but this pattern varies considerably amongst our top ten trading partners. Australia, for example, imports less primary produce from New Zealand (as a percentage of its total imports from New Zealand) than do east Asian nations. New Zealand is a net exporter to Pacific Island nations and other third world economies, but a net importer from the European Union.

Patterns of trade have changed markedly since the regulated post-war decades of the 1940s to the 1960s. Then, the government encouraged export of primary produce to politically preserved markets (mostly the UK), and fostered tariff-protected import substitution to maintain a healthy balance of trade. The 1970s saw a loss of export markets, while import costs rose as a result of the 'oil shocks'. More sophisticated consumer tastes and widening demand saw a steadily worsening balance of payments problem which the regulatory governments of the time could not deal with. Massive restructuring in the 1980s opened the way for the integration of the New Zealand economy into a globalising market, characterised by more international investment, and higher vulnerability to regional downturns.

The trade market is not entirely free, however. In New Zealand tariffs and other trade barriers have been replaced by new restrictions, such as environmental law and intellectual property rights. In the 1990s other earners of foreign exchange such as tourism and education, less quantifiable than lamb or apples, contributed greatly to export earnings.

New Zealand International Visitors Survey. New Zealand Tourism Board.
Tourism in New Zealand: Facts and Forecasts. NZTB and NZTIA.
On the Net: http://www.nztb.govt.nz

Country of Origin 1996–97

1 square: 1%

Asia	Australia	North America
Japan		U.S.A.
South Korea	Europe	Canada
Taiwan	United Kingdom	
Hong Kong	Germany	Oceania
Thailand	Switzerland	Africa
Singapore	Netherlands	Central/South America
Malaysia	other Europe	former U.S.S.R.
other Asia		

New Zealand attracts tourists mainly from developed countries, which can be grouped in four main regions: Australia, Asia, Europe and North America. In the 1990s the Asian region became much more significant to the New Zealand tourist industry, both in terms of visitor numbers and the amount spent in the country, which meant that the Asian economic downturn at the end of 1997 impacted heavily on this industry. The 1997 year saw a 2 per cent decrease in visitor arrivals over 1996 (Statistics New Zealand, 1998), visitor arrivals totalling 1.497 million. Though the tourist industry faces difficulties with its markets, the long-term expectation is that tourism will remain the country's top foreign exchange earner (New Zealand Tourism Board, 1999).

Spatial Analysis Facility
University of Auckland

The assistance of the Spatial Analysis Facility in the preparation of this plate is gratefully acknowledged.

Tourist Destinations: the first month in New Zeala 1996–97

Days Weeks

Very few people visit Kaitaia at about the two-week mark on their journey.

Few tourists come to Kaitaia in the first two days of their New Zealand stay. However, Kaitaia receives its largest daily percentage of visitors on their third day in New Zealand.

Kaitaia

N.B. these data are mirrored for greater clarity. Percentages do not add up to 100% as many tourists stay longer than 28 days in New Zeala

Once tourists have entered the country they pursue many different kinds itineraries. The 1996–97 International Visitor Survey records their destinatio and this map shows how many days/weeks it takes tourists to get to each loca

A number of examples serve to demonstrate the concept. Methven attra most of its tourists early in their New Zealand stay, as do the gateway cities Auckland and Christchurch. Their graphs are 'bottom heavy'. Other destinatio somewhat removed from the package tour circuit, receive the bulk of their international visitors later in their New Zealand stay (Stewart Island, for exam which is 'top heavy'). Northland tourist destinations have few first-night travel — see the Kaitaia example above — except for Whangarei (those who stay i Whangarei their first night in New Zealand have presumably driven/flown no from Auckland). Rotorua receives a large proportion of tourists who are betw 4 and 8 days into their New Zealand stay.

Bateman Contemporary Atlas New Zealand

aspects of the tourism industry, including accommodation and associated food and entertainment industries, are labour-intensive. und 90,000 people are employed in 16,500 tourist businesses (New and Tourism Board, 1996). An increasing percentage of these people Maori, many of whom are moving away from the traditional 'concert and gi' tourism product towards an authentic marae-based cultural tourist erience, particularly in Northland and the central North Island.

The amount of tourist accommodation varies considerably between regions: mparison between this cartogram and the population cartogram (Plate 30) ws many regions have developed comparatively little tourism. Some parts of the ntry — central North Island, Otago and the three largest cities — have large numbers eds and high numbers of tourism employees, while others, notably Northland, have ewer employees relative to the accommodation available. This difference is a ction of the number or people employed in tourism work other than accommodation.

Conferences are a lucrative source of revenue for the industry in urban areas. In 1996 year 226,758 people (23,898 of them international visitors) attended 2874 erences. Another 'market angle' is Event Tourism, which encourages international ors to attend significant events such as the 1998 World Cup of Golf, the APEC mit in 1999, and the millennium celebrations and America's Cup in 2000. Such -profile events attract high levels of sponsorship and government assistance, in ectation of a 'flow-on' effect of visitors spending more time and money in New and. Whatever the 'flow-on' effects, the events themselves are not always successful: 1998 World Cup of Golf ran at a loss, costing the government $700,000.

Tourist Accommodation 1996–97
Bed Units in Territorial Local Authorities (TLAs)

Cartogram
Scale: 1cm² = 1500 beds

N.B. The number in each TLA corresponds to its name. For the names of the TLAs please refer to Plate 30.

Length of Visit, 1996–97
number of days tourists stay in New Zealand by country of origin

Employment in the Tourist Industry 1996–97
number of employees as a percentage of bed units

High employment per bed-unit — 60%, 25%, 16.7%, 12.5%, 8.3%, 3.6% Low employment per bed-unit

International Tourists' Choice of Accommodation, 1996
person-nights spent in New Zealand

Private Homes 36% · Motels 13% · Rented Homes 7% · Homestay 6% · Luxury Hotels 4% · Backpacker 11.5% · Camping Grounds/Campervans/Tents 6.5% · Hotels 5% · Other Accommodation 11%

New Zealand offers a wide range of tourist accommodation. Two issues are of particular concern to accommodation providers: oversupply of beds in some centres, and the underutilisation of accommodation at certain times of the year. This seasonal use of accommodation affects campground operators in particular.

38

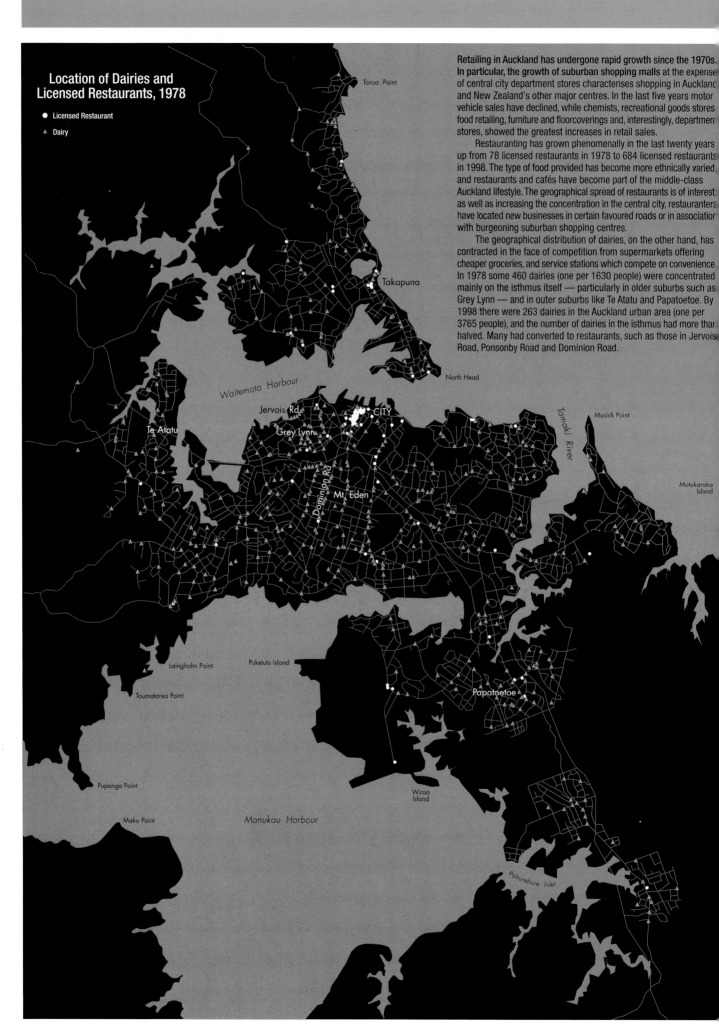

Location of Dairies and Licensed Restaurants, 1978

● Licensed Restaurant

▲ Dairy

Toroa Point

Takapuna

Waitemata Harbour

North Head

Jervois Rd

Grey Lynn

CITY

Te Atatu

Musick Point

Tamaki River

Motukaraka Island

Dominion Rd

Mt Eden

Laingholm Point

Puketutu Island

Papatoetoe

Taumatarea Point

Puponga Point

Wiroa Island

Mako Point

Manukau Harbour

Pahurehure Inlet

Retailing in Auckland has undergone rapid growth since the 1970s. In particular, the growth of suburban shopping malls at the expense of central city department stores characterises shopping in Auckland and New Zealand's other major centres. In the last five years motor vehicle sales have declined, while chemists, recreational goods stores, food retailing, furniture and floorcoverings and, interestingly, department stores, showed the greatest increases in retail sales.

Restauranting has grown phenomenally in the last twenty years, up from 78 licensed restaurants in 1978 to 684 licensed restaurants in 1998. The type of food provided has become more ethnically varied, and restaurants and cafés have become part of the middle-class Auckland lifestyle. The geographical spread of restaurants is of interest: as well as increasing the concentration in the central city, restauranters have located new businesses in certain favoured roads or in association with burgeoning suburban shopping centres.

The geographical distribution of dairies, on the other hand, has contracted in the face of competition from supermarkets offering cheaper groceries, and service stations which compete on convenience. In 1978 some 460 dairies (one per 1630 people) were concentrated mainly on the isthmus itself — particularly in older suburbs such as Grey Lynn — and in outer suburbs like Te Atatu and Papatoetoe. By 1998 there were 263 dairies in the Auckland urban area (one per 3765 people), and the number of dairies in the isthmus had more than halved. Many had converted to restaurants, such as those in Jervois Road, Ponsonby Road and Dominion Road.

Bateman Contemporary Atlas New Zealand

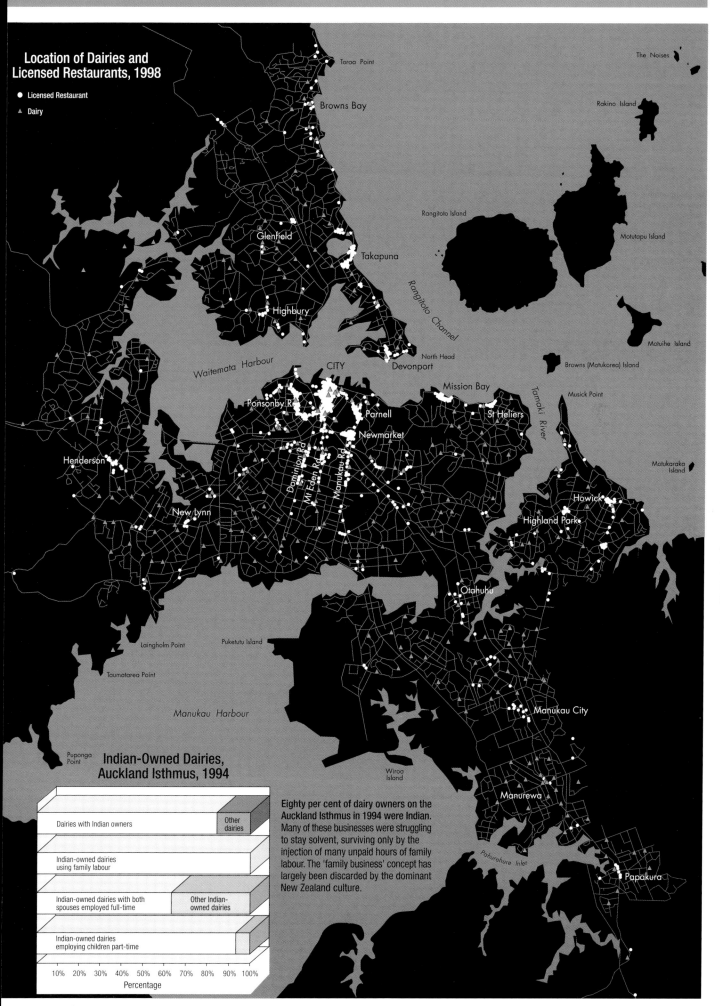

Location of Dairies and Licensed Restaurants, 1998

● Licensed Restaurant

▲ Dairy

The Noises

Rakino Island

Toroa Point

Browns Bay

Motutapu Island

Rangitoto Island

Glenfield

Takapuna

Motuihe Island

Highbury

Rangitoto Channel

Waitemata Harbour

North Head

Browns (Motukorea) Island

CITY

Devonport

Musick Point

Mission Bay

Ponsonby Rd

Parnell

St Heliers

Tamaki River

Newmarket

Dominion Rd

Mt Eden Rd

Manukau Rd

Motukaraka Island

Henderson

Howick

New Lynn

Highland Park

Otahuhu

Laingholm Point

Puketutu Island

Manukau City

Taumatarea Point

Manukau Harbour

Puponga Point

Wiroa Island

Indian-Owned Dairies, Auckland Isthmus, 1994

Manurewa

Pahurehure Inlet

Papakura

Dairies with Indian owners	Other dairies
Indian-owned dairies using family labour	
Indian-owned dairies with both spouses employed full-time	Other Indian-owned dairies
Indian-owned dairies employing children part-time	

10% 20% 30% 40% 50% 60% 70% 80% 90% 100%
Percentage

Eighty per cent of dairy owners on the Auckland Isthmus in 1994 were Indian. Many of these businesses were struggling to stay solvent, surviving only by the injection of many unpaid hours of family labour. The 'family business' concept has largely been discarded by the dominant New Zealand culture.

For more information...

The State of New Zealand's Environment. Ministry for the Environment.
On the Net: http://7am.com/nzwires/crisis1.htm
http://www.moc.govt.nz/inquiry/

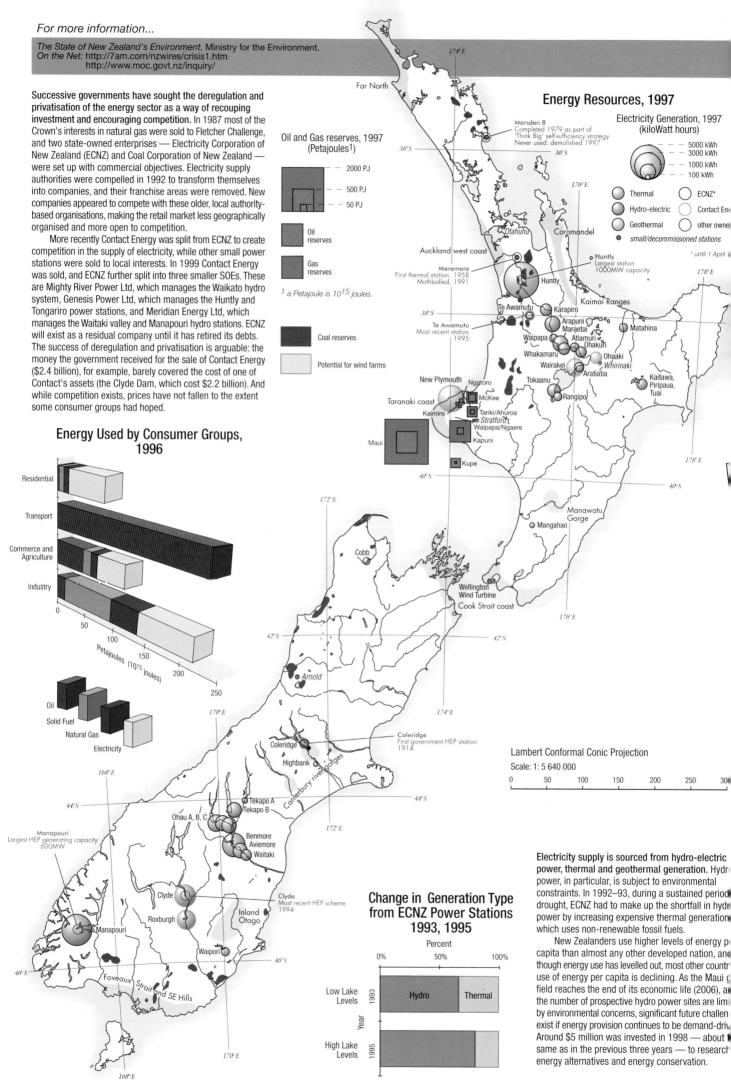

Successive governments have sought the deregulation and privatisation of the energy sector as a way of recouping investment and encouraging competition. In 1987 most of the Crown's interests in natural gas were sold to Fletcher Challenge, and two state-owned enterprises — Electricity Corporation of New Zealand (ECNZ) and Coal Corporation of New Zealand — were set up with commercial objectives. Electricity supply authorities were compelled in 1992 to transform themselves into companies, and their franchise areas were removed. New companies appeared to compete with these older, local authority-based organisations, making the retail market less geographically organised and more open to competition.

More recently Contact Energy was split from ECNZ to create competition in the supply of electricity, while other small power stations were sold to local interests. In 1999 Contact Energy was sold, and ECNZ further split into three smaller SOEs. These are Mighty River Power Ltd, which manages the Waikato hydro system, Genesis Power Ltd, which manages the Huntly and Tongariro power stations, and Meridian Energy Ltd, which manages the Waitaki valley and Manapouri hydro stations. ECNZ will exist as a residual company until it has retired its debts. The success of deregulation and privatisation is arguable: the money the government received for the sale of Contact Energy ($2.4 billion), for example, barely covered the cost of one of Contact's assets (the Clyde Dam, which cost $2.2 billion). And while competition exists, prices have not fallen to the extent some consumer groups had hoped.

Energy Resources, 1997

Electricity Generation, 1997 (kiloWatt hours)

5000 kWh
3000 kWh
1000 kWh
100 kWh

Thermal / ECNZ*
Hydro-electric / Contact En
Geothermal / other owne
small/decommissioned stations

* until 1 April

Marsden B
Completed 1979 as part of 'Think Big' self-sufficiency strategy
Never used: demolished 1997

Huntly
Largest station
1000MW capacity

Meremere
First thermal station, 1958
Mothballed, 1991

Te Awamutu
Most recent station
1995

Oil and Gas reserves, 1997 (Petajoules[1])

2000 PJ
500 PJ
50 PJ

Oil reserves

Gas reserves

[1] a Petajoule is 10^{15} joules.

Coal reserves

Potential for wind farms

Energy Used by Consumer Groups, 1996

Residential
Transport
Commerce and Agriculture
Industry

0   50   100   150   200   250

Petajoules (10^{15} joules)

Oil
Solid Fuel
Natural Gas
Electricity

Lambert Conformal Conic Projection

Scale: 1: 5 640 000

0   50   100   150   200   250   300

Change in Generation Type from ECNZ Power Stations 1993, 1995

Percent

0%   50%   100%

Low Lake Levels — 1993 — Hydro / Thermal

High Lake Levels — 1995

Year

Electricity supply is sourced from hydro-electric power, thermal and geothermal generation. Hydr power, in particular, is subject to environmental constraints. In 1992–93, during a sustained period drought, ECNZ had to make up the shortfall in hydr power by increasing expensive thermal generation which uses non-renewable fossil fuels.

New Zealanders use higher levels of energy p capita than almost any other developed nation, an though energy use has levelled out, most other countr use of energy per capita is declining. As the Maui g field reaches the end of its economic life (2006), a the number of prospective hydro power sites are lim by environmental concerns, significant future challen exist if energy provision continues to be demand-driv Around $5 million was invested in 1998 — about same as in the previous three years — to research energy alternatives and energy conservation.

Bateman Contemporary Atlas New Zealand

Primary Energy Supply, 1974–1996

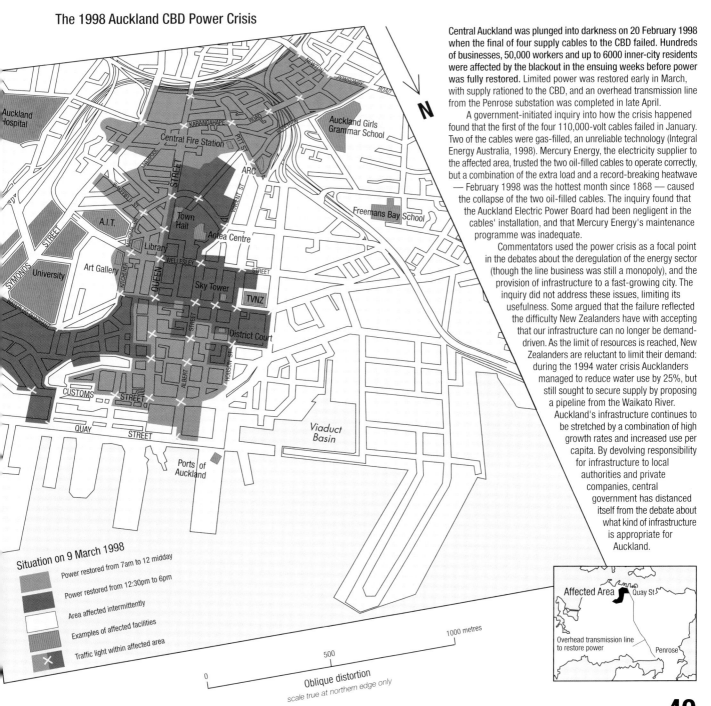

Meremere coal-fired power station, 1980. photograph by Russell Kirkpatrick

Gas

Imported Oil

Hydro
Geothermal

Coal
Indigenous Oil
Wood

Petajoules[1]

Year

[1] a Petajoule is 10^{15} joules.

le New Zealand meets a large proportion of its energy
uirements using its own resources, the shortfall must
made up by expensive imports. Before the 'oil shocks'
e 1970s the largest source of primary energy was imported
However, with dramatically increased prices and an
cure supply, the State, at that time responsible for the
vision of energy in New Zealand, turned to indigenous
ces. This led to an increase in the utilisation of oil and
fields in what became known as 'Think Big' projects.
nately many of these projects proved expensive, but at
time the supply of oil from overseas seemed under threat,
the utilisation of indigenous energy sources seemed
ent. In 1996 New Zealand was self-sufficient in all energy
ns apart from oil.

The trend in consumer energy use (primary energy minus
gy lost in transmission and transformation) is away from
il fuels and towards 'renewable' resources. However,
rent groups have different energy requirements: the
sport industry, for example, utilises a different energy
' than do household consumers, with a much heavier
hasis on non-renewable oil.

The 1998 Auckland CBD Power Crisis

Central Auckland was plunged into darkness on 20 February 1998 when the final of four supply cables to the CBD failed. Hundreds of businesses, 50,000 workers and up to 6000 inner-city residents were affected by the blackout in the ensuing weeks before power was fully restored. Limited power was restored early in March, with supply rationed to the CBD, and an overhead transmission line from the Penrose substation was completed in late April.

A government-initiated inquiry into how the crisis happened found that the first of the four 110,000-volt cables failed in January. Two of the cables were gas-filled, an unreliable technology (Integral Energy Australia, 1998). Mercury Energy, the electricity supplier to the affected area, trusted the two oil-filled cables to operate correctly, but a combination of the extra load and a record-breaking heatwave — February 1998 was the hottest month since 1868 — caused the collapse of the two oil-filled cables. The inquiry found that the Auckland Electric Power Board had been negligent in the cables' installation, and that Mercury Energy's maintenance programme was inadequate.

Commentators used the power crisis as a focal point in the debates about the deregulation of the energy sector (though the line business was still a monopoly), and the provision of infrastructure to a fast-growing city. The inquiry did not address these issues, limiting its usefulness. Some argued that the failure reflected the difficulty New Zealanders have with accepting that our infrastructure can no longer be demand-driven. As the limit of resources is reached, New Zealanders are reluctant to limit their demand: during the 1994 water crisis Aucklanders managed to reduce water use by 25%, but still sought to secure supply by proposing a pipeline from the Waikato River.

Auckland's infrastructure continues to be stretched by a combination of high growth rates and increased use per capita. By devolving responsibility for infrastructure to local authorities and private companies, central government has distanced itself from the debate about what kind of infrastructure is appropriate for Auckland.

Auckland Hospital

Central Fire Station

Auckland Girls Grammar School

ARC

A.I.T.

Town Hall

Aotea Centre

Library

Art Gallery

University

Freemans Bay School

Sky Tower

TVNZ

District Court

CUSTOMS STREET

QUAY STREET

Viaduct Basin

Ports of Auckland

Situation on 9 March 1998

- Power restored from 7am to 12 midday
- Power restored from 12:30pm to 6pm
- Area affected intermittently
- Examples of affected facilities
- Traffic light within affected area

1000 metres

500

0

Oblique distortion
scale true at northern edge only

Affected Area — Quay St

Overhead transmission line to restore power — Penrose

For more information...

New Zealand Official Yearbook. Statistics New Zealand.
Clifford Bay Ferry Terminal. Tranz Rail.
On the Net: http://www.tranzrail.co.nz/interislander

Proposed New Ferry Terminals for the Inter-Island Ferry Service

Tranz Rail operates by far the largest inter-island ferry service. In 1998 this vital link between the economies of the North and South Islands carried 1.071 million passengers, 219,000 cars and 1.328 million lane metres of railway wagons.

Since the late 1970s the company (under its pre-1992 State-owned guise) has been considering relocating the ferry terminals. In the case of Wellington, this would entail a shift of a few hundred metres and a cost of $15 million. However, the proposed relocation of the southern terminal (currently in Picton) is a much larger venture, costing perhaps $100 million.

The Picton facilities leave little room for expansion. Tranz Rail have investigated alternative sites, including Lyttelton, Rarangi, and two sites in Clifford Bay. Marfells Beach, Tranz Rail's preferred site, offers protection from the southerly swells, and its use would cut the Wellington-Christchurch travel time by two hours for a car and three hours for a railway wagon. Moreover, the steepest gradients on the Main Trunk line (at Elevation, just south of Picton, and on the Dashwood Pass) would be avoided, meaning that locomotives could carry up to twice as much as at present.

The proposed terminal would, however, require the construction of a 2.5 km breakwater and associated buildings and railyards. An environmental assessment report has been prepared, as required by the Resource Management Act, and a confitional resource consent has been granted. What is much more difficult to assess, however, is the impact on Picton from the direct loss of jobs, compounded by the loss of revenue from those travelling through the town.

Sites Considered for Ferry Terminals

☐ Urban area

● Alternative Site for Ferry Terminal

── Rail

── State Highway 1

── Inter-Island ferry route

The Quickest Air Route to Wellington, 1998

Time-Distance Projection
2mm: 5 minutes

● Airport with service to Wellington

Data compiled from Air New Zealand and Ansett New Zealand timetables

N.B. Time distances are true only if [...] is used as origin or destination

Bearings are preserved

The map to the far right shows the interconnectedness of New Zealand cities serviced by commercial air services. However, this tells only part of the story. The map to the right takes one city — Wellington — and stretches ordinary distance to show how far away, in total time travelled, each commercial destination is from Wellington. Some destinations are closer than their geographical distance might suggest, because they are reached from Wellington by larger aircraft on a direct route. Others are far further than their geographical distance, either because slower aircraft fly the route, or they require a landing and/or plane change at an intermediate destination. For people in the most distant towns the problem of getting to the nation's capital is a significant one.

Bateman Contemporary Atlas New Zealand

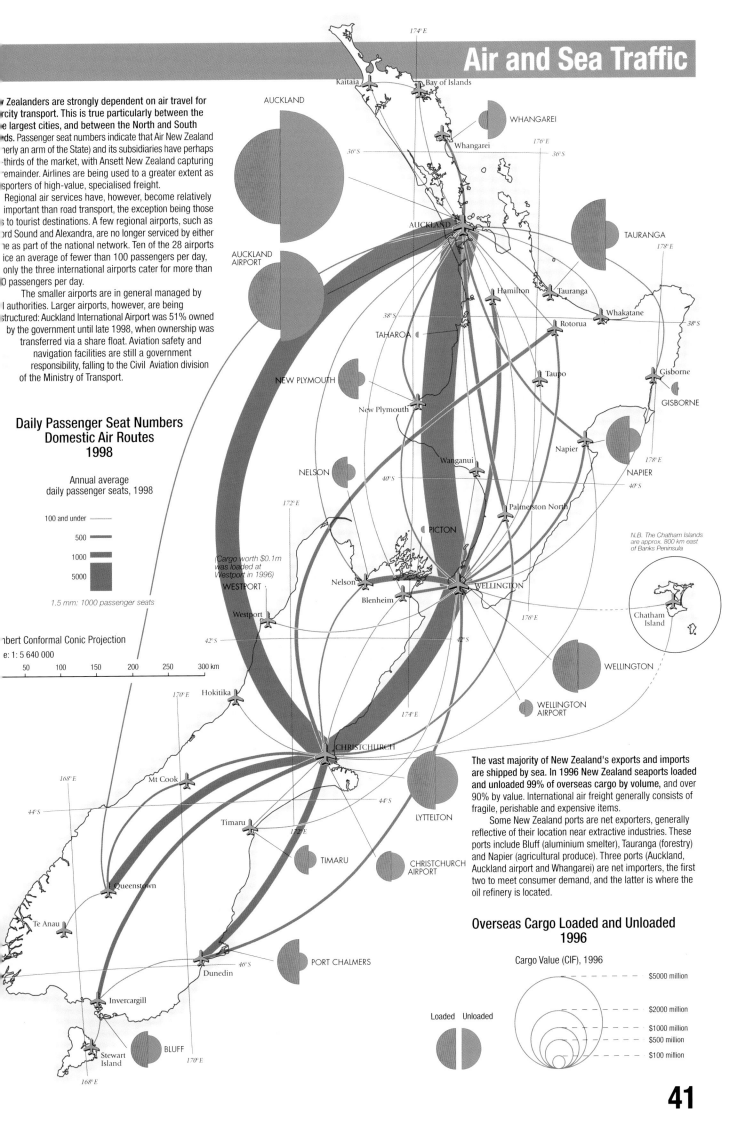

Zealanders are strongly dependent on air travel for
city transport. This is true particularly between the
e largest cities, and between the North and South
ds. Passenger seat numbers indicate that Air New Zealand
nerly an arm of the State) and its subsidiaries have perhaps
-thirds of the market, with Ansett New Zealand capturing
remainder. Airlines are being used to a greater extent as
sporters of high-value, specialised freight.

Regional air services have, however, become relatively
important than road transport, the exception being those
s to tourist destinations. A few regional airports, such as
rd Sound and Alexandra, are no longer serviced by either
ie as part of the national network. Ten of the 28 airports
ice an average of fewer than 100 passengers per day,
only the three international airports cater for more than
0 passengers per day.

The smaller airports are in general managed by
l authorities. Larger airports, however, are being
structured: Auckland International Airport was 51% owned
by the government until late 1998, when ownership was
transferred via a share float. Aviation safety and
navigation facilities are still a government
responsibility, falling to the Civil Aviation division
of the Ministry of Transport.

Daily Passenger Seat Numbers
Domestic Air Routes
1998

Annual average
daily passenger seats, 1998

100 and under
500
1000
5000

1.5 mm: 1000 passenger seats

nbert Conformal Conic Projection
e: 1: 5 640 000

| 50 | 100 | 150 | 200 | 250 | 300 km |

(Cargo worth $0.1m
was loaded at
Westport in 1996)

N.B. The Chatham Islands
are approx. 800 km east
of Banks Peninsula

The vast majority of New Zealand's exports and imports
are shipped by sea. In 1996 New Zealand seaports loaded
and unloaded 99% of overseas cargo by volume, and over
90% by value. International air freight generally consists of
fragile, perishable and expensive items.

Some New Zealand ports are net exporters, generally
reflective of their location near extractive industries. These
ports include Bluff (aluminium smelter), Tauranga (forestry)
and Napier (agricultural produce). Three ports (Auckland,
Auckland airport and Whangarei) are net importers, the first
two to meet consumer demand, and the latter is where the
oil refinery is located.

Overseas Cargo Loaded and Unloaded
1996

Cargo Value (CIF), 1996

Loaded   Unloaded

$5000 million
$2000 million
$1000 million
$500 million
$100 million

41

Traffic Volume State Highway Network 1996

Annual Average Daily Traffic volume (A.A.D.T.)

100 — *actual traffic count*
870 — *actual traffic count*
500
1000
5000
10,000
20,000

1mm: 3000 A.A.D.T. volume

Former State highway redesignated since 1975
New State highway designated since 1993

Change in A.A.D.T. volume since 1993

increase   decline

Tonnage Flows Railways, 1997–98

Agreed Density by Track Section Million Net Tonnes per annum

below 0.1 million tonnes
0.1 - 0.5 million tonnes
0.5 - 1 million tonnes
1 - 2 million tonnes
above 2 million tonnes

Data are for the year ending 30 June 1998

Distribution of Heavy Motor Vehicle (HMV) Types

The Five Monitored Sites:
- Auckland Harbour Bridge
- Auckland Southern Motorway
- Ohakea (near Bulls)
- Pukerua Bay (south of Paekakariki)
- Waipara

% HMVs → increasing size of HMV

0%   20%   40%   60%

For more information...
Long Term Tourism Roading Requirements. Transit New Zealand.
On the Net: http://www.transit.govt.nz
http://www.tranzrail.co.nz

SH 1 Otaika Rd South of Tarewa Rd 19,550
SH 18 23,150
SH 16 Auckland Western Motorway Waterview to Patiki 81,130
SH 1 Auckland Southern Motorway Khyber Pass to Gillies Ave 195,190
SH 22 5750
SH 20 Mangere Bridge 66,715
SH 3 North of Collins Rd 24,260
SH 2 West of Judea Bridge 31,500
SH 2 Papamoa 11,700
SH 30 Te Ngae East of Puarenga Bridge 30,675
SH 1 North end of Control Gates 18,900
SH 3 East of Egmont Rd 18,740
SH 3 North Taranaki Bight 10,900
SH 50 Taradale Rd between Austin & Maadi Rds 12,670
SH 3 Cobham Bridge 7590

Bateman Contemporary Atlas New Zealand

N.B. The Auckland Islands are approx. 400 km south of South Cape

Auckland Islands
Carnley Harbour
Adams I.

see Plate 43

Legend

short truck/bus	o-o
long truck/bus	o--o
3 axle artic	o-o--o
3 axle truck/bus	o--oo
Truck and trailer	o-o-o--o
4 axle artic	o-o--oo
4 axle truck	oo--oo
Truck and trailer	o--oo-o--o
5 axle artic	o-oo--oo
Truck and trailer	o--oo-o--oo
6 axle artic	o-oo--ooo
7 axle B-train	o-oo--oo--oo
Truck and trailer	o--oo-oo--oo
Truck and trailer	oo--oo-o--oo
8 axle B-train	o-oo--ooo--oo
Truck and trailer	oo--oo-oo--oo
Other HMVs (under 3.5 tonnes gross)	

increasing size of HMV

100%

Lambert Conformal Conic Projection
Scale 1: 3 000 000

20 30 40 50 60 70 80 90 100 km

N.B. The Chatham Islands are approx. 800 km east of Banks Peninsula

Chatham Island

Transport and communications are central issues to the economy of any country, none more so than New Zealand. The narrow shape and topographic ruggedness of the country make the provision of road and rail links an expensive proposition, especially relative to the low national population and therefore tax and rating base.

Transit New Zealand, which receives the bulk of its funding from the State, is responsible for the provision and upkeep of State highways. Local roads and streets are currently (1999) funded by territorial local authorities from rates, though proposals for privatisation of the roading system are currently being debated. Local authorities prudently attempt to get their most heavily used roads granted State highway status, so as to attract central government funding. The criteria used to assess a road for inclusion in the national network include length, usage and scenic value. In general the usage of the Transit New Zealand network is increasing, as measured by Annual Average Daily Traffic volumes (A.A.D.T.).

In 1993 the national rail system (New Zealand Rail) was privatised, the resulting company called Tranz Rail Ltd. (originally a consortium of Wisconsin Rail, Berkshire Partners and Fay Richwhite). Operating costs, which traditionally have led to large annual deficits, have been lowered dramatically since the 1970s by shedding 75% of the staff and closing uneconomic branch lines.

Debate continues as to whether the increasing dominance of road over rail as a carrier of long-distance freight is economically and environmentally sound. Higher fuel and road maintenance costs mitigate against road use, but road carriers offer greater convenience.

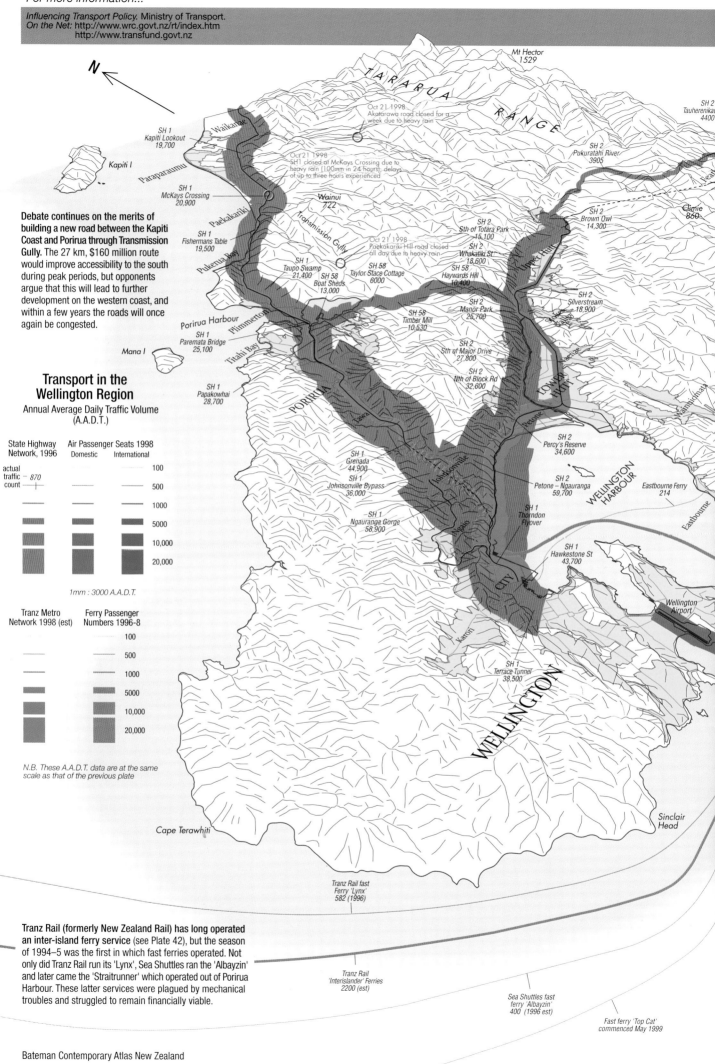

For more information...

Influencing Transport Policy. Ministry of Transport.
On the Net: http://www.wrc.govt.nz/rt/index.htm
http://www.transfund.govt.nz

N

Mt Hector
1529

TARARUA

Kapiti I

SH 1
Kapiti Lookout
19,700

Waikanae

RANGE

SH 2
Tauherenikau
4400

Oct 21 1998
Akatarawa road closed for a
week due to heavy rain

SH 2
Pukuratahi River
3905

Paraparaumu

Oct 21 1998
SH1 closed at McKays Crossing due to
heavy rain (100mm in 24 hours); delays
of up to three hours experienced

Climie
860

SH 1
McKays Crossing
20,900

SH 2
Brown Owl
14,300

Paekakariki

Wainui
722

SH 2
Sth of Totara Park
15,100

SH 1
Fishermans Table
19,500

Transmission Gully

Oct 21 1998
Paekakariki Hill road closed
all day due to heavy rain

SH 2
Whakatiki St
18,600

Debate continues on the merits of
building a new road between the Kapiti
Coast and Porirua through Transmission
Gully. The 27 km, $160 million route
would improve accessibility to the south
during peak periods, but opponents
argue that this will lead to further
development on the western coast, and
within a few years the roads will once
again be congested.

SH 1
Taupo Swamp
21,400

SH 58
Boat Sheds
13,000

SH 58
Taylor Stace Cottage
6000

SH 58
Haywards Hill
10,400

SH 2
Silverstream
18,900

Pukerua Bay

SH 58
Timber Mill
10,530

SH 2
Manor Park
25,700

Upper Hutt

Porirua Harbour

Plimmerton

SH 1
Paremata Bridge
25,100

SH 2
Sth of Major Drive
27,800

Mana I

Titahi Bay

SH 2
Nth of Block Rd
32,600

Lower Hutt

Transport in the
Wellington Region
Annual Average Daily Traffic Volume
(A.A.D.T.)

SH 1
Papakowhai
28,700

PORIRUA

Petone

SH 2
Percy's Reserve
34,600

State Highway
Network, 1996

Air Passenger Seats 1998
Domestic   International

WELLINGTON
HARBOUR

actual
traffic — 870
count

100

SH 1
Grenada
44,900

SH 2
Petone – Ngauranga
59,700

Eastbourne Ferry
214

500

SH 1
Johnsonville Bypass
36,000

Eastbourne

1000

Johnsonville

5000

SH 1
Ngauranga Gorge
58,900

SH 1
Thorndon
Flyover

10,000

Ngaio

20,000

Karori

SH 1
Hawkestone St
43,700

1mm : 3000 A.A.D.T.

CITY

Wellington
Airport

Tranz Metro
Network 1998 (est)

Ferry Passenger
Numbers 1996-8

100

500

1000

SH 1
Terrace Tunnel
38,500

5000

WELLINGTON

10,000

20,000

N.B. These A.A.D.T. data are at the same
scale as that of the previous plate

Cape Terawhiti

Sinclair
Head

Tranz Rail fast
Ferry 'Lynx'
582 (1996)

Tranz Rail (formerly New Zealand Rail) has long operated
an inter-island ferry service (see Plate 42), but the season
of 1994–5 was the first in which fast ferries operated. Not
only did Tranz Rail run its 'Lynx', Sea Shuttles ran the 'Albayzin'
and later came the 'Straitrunner' which operated out of Porirua
Harbour. These latter services were plagued by mechanical
troubles and struggled to remain financially viable.

Tranz Rail
'Interislander' Ferries
2200 (est)

Sea Shuttles fast
ferry 'Albayzin'
400 (1996 est)

Fast ferry 'Top Cat'
commenced May 1999

...e all of New Zealand's cities face issues as increasing ...sure is placed on infrastructure (see Plate 40 for an ...mple), the rugged topography of the Wellington region ...es the transporting of people and goods particularly ...cult. Roads and railways must be constructed along ...ow valleys connecting the widespread dormitory suburbs ...e Wellington urban area. A consequence of this is that,

for example, Wainuiomata's 20,000 people have only one road link. Other corridors experiencing pressure are SH 1 from Paraparaumu to Wellington and SH 2 from Lower Hutt to Wellington. The route from the airport to the city is subject to delays at peak times.

The Wellington Regional Council is responsible for administering the regional transport network. The Council must balance issues of accessibility, regional development, safety, environmental impacts and social equity in their decisions. This is done by paying for maintenance on the existing network, minimising travel by containing development, restraining the growth of commuter road traffic and subsidising

public transport operators (currently $20 million per annum, with another $10 million coming from Transfund).

The suburban railway (Tranz Metro) and the bus services carry a sizeable proportion of the daily commuter flow into Wellington: in 1998 Tranz Metro's suburban rail carried a daily average of 25,549 passengers, while the region's bus services carried 33,284 people. However, vehicle use continues to rise faster than the rate of population growth.

Wellington's transport system is vulnerable to natural hazards, such as happened during heavy rains on October 21, 1998. For a few hours during the morning all commuter access to Wellington from Kapiti and Wairarapa was cut; some links were not restored for days. The network is also exposed to earthquake risk: a severe quake could cut all links between Wellington City and the rest of the region.

A.M. Peak Transport by Mode, 1988 and 2011 (projected)

Data gathered by Transit New Zealand reflects traffic congestion in the weekday morning 'rush-hour'. The site graphed below is on State Highway 1 at the bottom of the Ngauranga Gorge. Vehicles in all four lanes averaged below 30 km/h for the eighty minutes before 9 a.m. This road carries around 60,000 vehicles per day. The highest vehicle speeds are achieved in light traffic, while the densest traffic causes greatly reduced speeds. The maximum capacity for each of the four lanes is achieved at a speed of about 75–80 km/h.

The chosen mode of transport into Wellington during the morning 'rush-hour' is shown for 1988 (above) and 2011 (projected). Planners are expecting a further reduction in the use of public transport, which may turn out to be a self-fulfilling prophecy.

Average Vehicle Speed, SH 1 and SH 2, Ngauranga South Bend Wellington Urban Motorway

...raffic to and from Wellington is low for an international ...ort, especially one serving a nation's capital city. This ...rtly due to Wellington's size — small for a capital, smaller ... Auckland — but also by the lack of available land area. ...airport is in the middle (1999) of a major expansion, but ...ations remain. The single runway is vulnerable to ...swinds, a major problem in Wellington's windy climate; ...es larger than a 737 struggle to land, and in some ...itions the airport is forced to close. The most used ...way', that between Wellington and Auckland, carries ...r travellers per day than State Highway 58, the road ...een the Hutt Valley and Porirua.

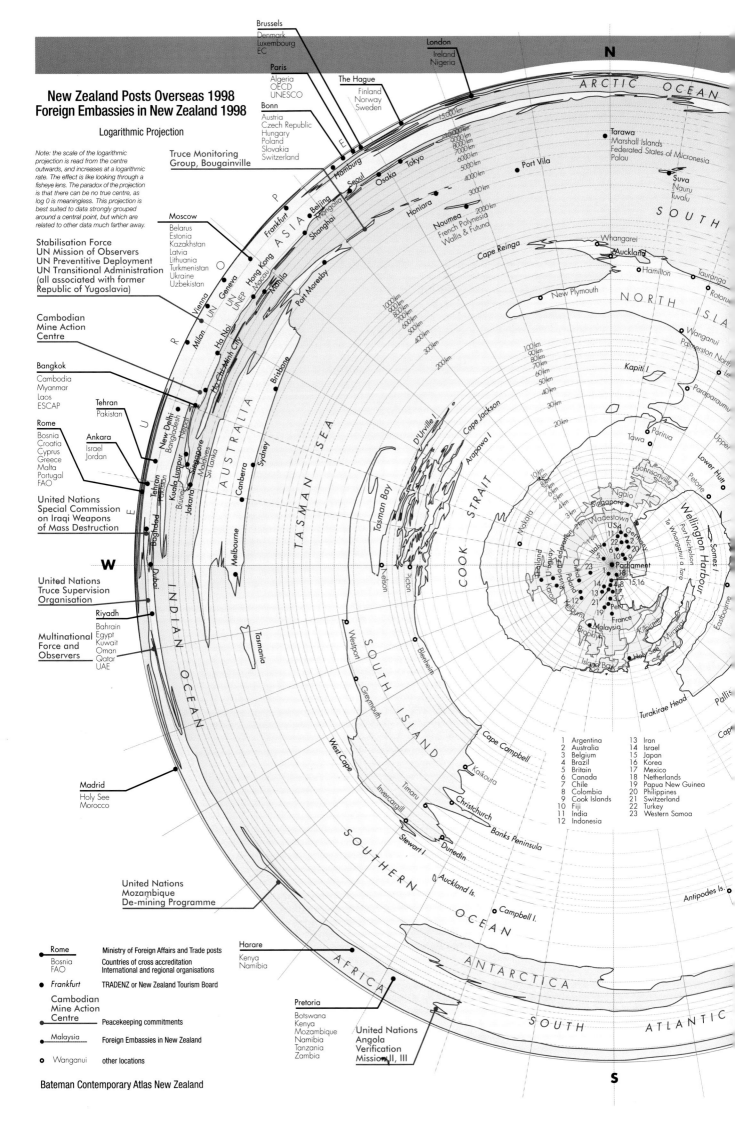

New Zealand Posts Overseas 1998
Foreign Embassies in New Zealand 1998

Logarithmic Projection

Note: the scale of the logarithmic projection is read from the centre outwards, and increases at a logarithmic rate. The effect is like looking through a fisheye lens. The paradox of the projection is that there can be no true centre, as log 0 is meaningless. This projection is best suited to data strongly grouped around a central point, but which are related to other data much farther away.

Stabilisation Force
UN Mission of Observers
UN Preventitive Deployment
UN Transitional Administration
(all associated with former Republic of Yugoslavia)

Cambodian Mine Action Centre

Bangkok
Cambodia
Myanmar
Laos
ESCAP

Rome
Bosnia
Croatia
Cyprus
Greece
Malta
Portugal
FAO

Tehran
Pakistan

Ankara
Israel
Jordan

United Nations Special Commission on Iraqi Weapons of Mass Destruction

United Nations Truce Supervision Organisation

Riyadh
Bahrain
Egypt
Kuwait
Oman
Qatar
UAE

Multinational Force and Observers

Madrid
Holy See
Morocco

United Nations Mozambique De-mining Programme

Moscow
Belarus
Estonia
Kazakhstan
Latvia
Lithuania
Turkmenistan
Ukraine
Uzbekistan

Truce Monitoring Group, Bougainville

Brussels
Denmark
Luxembourg
EC

Paris
Algeria
OECD
UNESCO

Bonn
Austria
Czech Republic
Hungary
Poland
Slovakia
Switzerland

The Hague
Finland
Norway
Sweden

London
Ireland
Nigeria

Legend

- ● **Rome** — Ministry of Foreign Affairs and Trade posts
  - Bosnia / FAO — Countries of cross accreditation / International and regional organisations
- ● *Frankfurt* — TRADENZ or New Zealand Tourism Board
- **Cambodian Mine Action Centre** — Peacekeeping commitments
- ● *Malaysia* — Foreign Embassies in New Zealand
- ○ *Wanganui* — other locations

Bateman Contemporary Atlas New Zealand

Harare
Kenya
Namibia

Pretoria
Botswana
Kenya
Mozambique
Namibia
Tanzania
Zambia

United Nations Angola Verification Mission II, III

Embassy numbered list

1 Argentina	13 Iran
2 Australia	14 Israel
3 Belgium	15 Japan
4 Brazil	16 Korea
5 Britain	17 Mexico
6 Canada	18 Netherlands
7 Chile	19 Papua New Guinea
8 Colombia	20 Philippines
9 Cook Islands	21 Switzerland
10 Fiji	22 Turkey
11 India	23 Western Samoa
12 Indonesia	

Map labels

ARCTIC OCEAN
N
S
SOUTH
NORTH ISLA
COOK STRAIT
SOUTH ISLAND
TASMAN SEA
AUSTRALIA
ASIA
INDIAN OCEAN
SOUTHERN OCEAN
ANTARCTICA
SOUTH ATLANTIC
AFRICA

Tarawa, Marshall Islands, Federated States of Micronesia, Palau
Port Vila
Suva, Nauru, Tuvalu
Noumea, French Polynesia, Wallis & Futuna
Honiara
Port Moresby
Brisbane
Sydney
Canberra
Melbourne
Tasmania
Cape Reinga
Whangarei
Auckland
Hamilton
Tauranga
Rotoru
New Plymouth
Wanganui
Palmerston North
Kapiti I
Paraparaumu
D'Urville I
Cape Jackson
Arapawa I
Tasman Bay
Nelson
Picton
Blenheim
Westport
Greymouth
West Cape
Invercargill
Stewart I
Dunedin
Christchurch
Banks Peninsula
Timaru
Kaikoura
Cape Campbell
Auckland Is.
Campbell I.
Antipodes Is.
Turakirae Head
Wellington Harbour
Holy See

Frankfurt
Hamburg
Seoul
Osaka
Tokyo
Beijing
Shanghai
Mongolia
Hong Kong
Macau
Manila
Geneva
Vienna
Milan
Ha Noi
Ho Chi Minh City
Bangkok
New Delhi
Nepal
Bangladesh
Kuala Lumpur
Singapore
Maldives
Sri Lanka
Brunei
Jakarta
Baghdad
Dubai
Tehran

Distance scale (km)
15,000 km, 10,000 km, 9000 km, 8000 km, 7000 km, 6000 km, 5000 km, 4000 km, 3000 km, 2000 km, 1000 km, 900 km, 800 km, 700 km, 600 km, 500 km, 400 km, 300 km, 200 km, 100 km, 90 km, 80 km, 70 km, 60 km, 50 km, 40 km, 30 km, 20 km, 10 km, 9 km, 8 km, 7 km, 6 km, 5 km, 4 km, 3 km, 2 km

Wellington inset
Parliament
USA, Germany
Wadestown
Singapore
Ngaio
Johnsonville
Lower Hutt
Petone
Somes I
Port Nicholson
Te Whanganui a Tara
Miramar
Island Bay
Brooklyn
Holy See
Malaysia
Kelburn
Karori
China
Poland
Peru
France
Te Whanganui a Tara

more information...

ial Report. Ministry of Foreign Affairs and Trade.
Zealand Official Yearbook. Statistics New Zealand.
he Net: http://www.mft.govt.nz

New Zealand's international relations are shaped by the nation's size, relative isolation and a heavy reliance on overseas trade for prosperity.

The Ministry of Foreign Affairs and Trade — a name which reflects the close relationship between diplomacy and economics — is charged with protecting national interests overseas. This requires membership of global and regional organisations such as the United Nations (UN), the Commonwealth, OECD and ASEAN, the provision of overseas aid, being signatory to environmental and disarmament treaties, accepting refugees, contributing to UN peacekeeping operations and advocating human rights.

National interests include the protection of New Zealand citizens overseas, advocating free trade, the maintenance of international peace and security, regional stability, and sustainable development in harmony with the environment.

New Zealand has 49 diplomatic and consular posts located in 41 countries and territories, their location being both a legacy of colonial links and a reflection of diversifying export markets. Major regions of diplomatic focus are Australia, the South Pacific, South-East Asia, North Asia (including Japan), the United States of America and the European Union. New Zealand is presently attempting to forge closer diplomatic links with China, the Middle East, Central and South America, Eastern Europe (including Russia and the former Soviet republics), and Africa.

Conversely, there are 36 foreign embassies and 84 consulates located in New Zealand, representing 66 countries. Overseas interests seek representation in New Zealand to further their own trading interests, and also to support foreign nationals in New Zealand.

Overseas aid is New Zealand's attempt to be a good international citizen, as well as supporting our security and trade goals. However, New Zealand is ranked near the bottom of the OECD developed countries in supplying aid as a proportion of GNP (0.25% of GNP compared with the UN target of 0.7% GNP), ahead only of the United States. Much of this aid goes to the South Pacific, where New Zealand has historical obligations. Bilateral aid is given directly to the recipient country, while multilateral aid is channelled through agencies such as the UN and the World Bank.

New Zealand's expenditure on defence can be thought of in similar terms: as with aid, defence spending can be seen as a requirement of a good international citizen. Successive governments have had to tackle the difficult issue of defence expenditure in the face of political opposition.

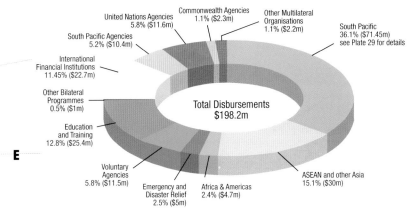

New Zealand Official Development Assistance (NZODA) Programme Allocation 1997-98

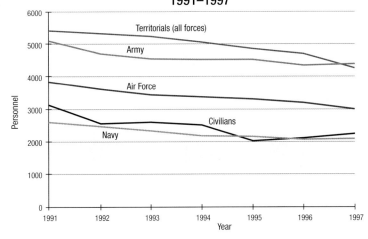

Number of Defence Personnel 1991–1997

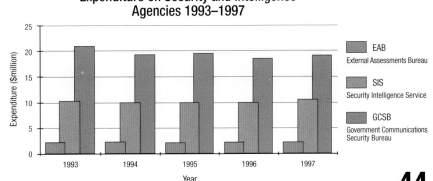

Expenditure on Security and Intelligence Agencies 1993–1997

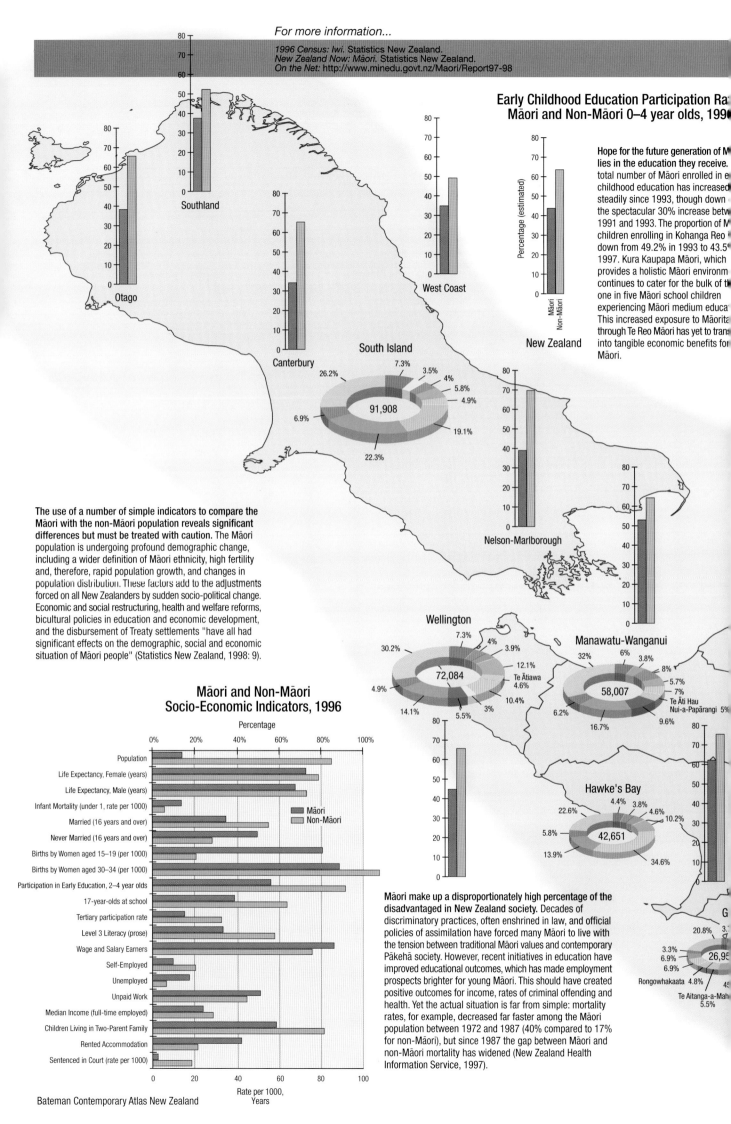

Southland

Otago

West Coast

Early Childhood Education Participation Ra[te]
Māori and Non-Māori 0–4 year olds, 199[6]

Percentage (estimated)

Māori
Non-Māori

New Zealand

Hope for the future generation of M[āori]
lies in the education they receive. [The]
total number of Māori enrolled in e[arly]
childhood education has increased
steadily since 1993, though down [on]
the spectacular 30% increase betw[een]
1991 and 1993. The proportion of M[āori]
children enrolling in Kohanga Reo [is]
down from 49.2% in 1993 to 43.5[% in]
1997. Kura Kaupapa Māori, which
provides a holistic Māori environm[ent,]
continues to cater for the bulk of t[he]
one in five Māori school children
experiencing Māori medium educa[tion.]
This increased exposure to Māorita[nga]
through Te Reo Māori has yet to tran[slate]
into tangible economic benefits for
Māori.

Canterbury

South Island

91,908

7.3%
3.5%
4%
5.8%
4.9%
26.2%
6.9%
22.3%
19.1%

The use of a number of simple indicators to compare the
Māori with the non-Māori population reveals significant
differences but must be treated with caution. The Māori
population is undergoing profound demographic change,
including a wider definition of Māori ethnicity, high fertility
and, therefore, rapid population growth, and changes in
population distribution. These factors add to the adjustments
forced on all New Zealanders by sudden socio-political change.
Economic and social restructuring, health and welfare reforms,
bicultural policies in education and economic development,
and the disbursement of Treaty settlements "have all had
significant effects on the demographic, social and economic
situation of Māori people" (Statistics New Zealand, 1998: 9).

Nelson-Marlborough

Wellington

72,084

7.3%
4%
3.9%
30.2%
12.1%
Te Ātiawa
4.6%
4.9%
10.4%
3%
14.1%
5.5%

Manawatu-Wanganui

58,007

32%
6%
3.8%
8%
5.7%
7%
Te Āti Hau
Nui-a-Papārangi 5%
6.2%
9.6%
16.7%

Māori and Non-Māori
Socio-Economic Indicators, 1996

Percentage

0%   20%   40%   60%   80%   100%

Population
Life Expectancy, Female (years)
Life Expectancy, Male (years)
Infant Mortality (under 1, rate per 1000)
Married (16 years and over)
Never Married (16 years and over)
Births by Women aged 15–19 (per 1000)
Births by Women aged 30–34 (per 1000)
Participation in Early Education, 2–4 year olds
17-year-olds at school
Tertiary participation rate
Level 3 Literacy (prose)
Wage and Salary Earners
Self-Employed
Unemployed
Unpaid Work
Median Income (full-time employed)
Children Living in Two-Parent Family
Rented Accommodation
Sentenced in Court (rate per 1000)

Māori
Non-Māori

0   20   40   60   80   100

Rate per 1000,
Years

Hawke's Bay

42,651

4.4%
3.8%
22.6%
4.6%
10.2%
5.8%
13.9%
34.6%

Māori make up a disproportionately high percentage of the
disadvantaged in New Zealand society. Decades of
discriminatory practices, often enshrined in law, and official
policies of assimilation have forced many Māori to live with
the tension between traditional Māori values and contemporary
Pākehā society. However, recent initiatives in education have
improved educational outcomes, which has made employment
prospects brighter for young Māori. This should have created
positive outcomes for income, rates of criminal offending and
health. Yet the actual situation is far from simple: mortality
rates, for example, decreased far faster among the Māori
population between 1972 and 1987 (40% compared to 17%
for non-Māori), but since 1987 the gap between Māori and
non-Māori mortality has widened (New Zealand Health
Information Service, 1997).

G[isborne]

26,95[1]

20.8%
3.[?]
3.3%
6.9%
6.9%
Rongowhakaata 4.8%
Te Aitanga-a-Mah[aki]
5.5%
4[5?]

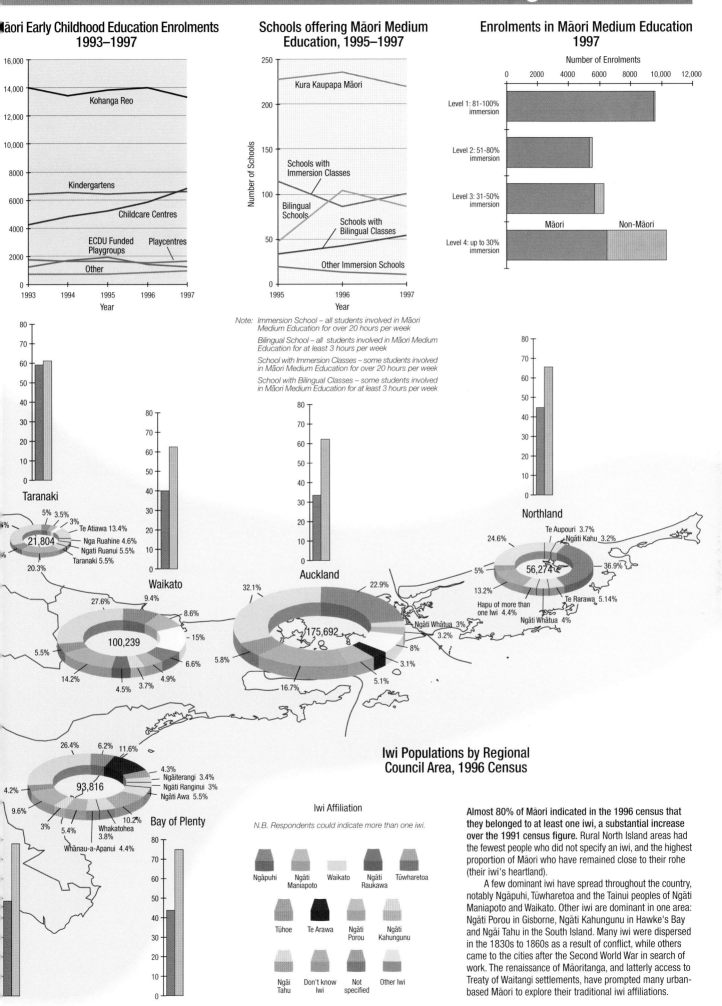

Māori Early Childhood Education Enrolments 1993–1997

Kohanga Reo
Kindergartens
Childcare Centres
ECDU Funded Playgroups
Playcentres
Other

Year

Schools offering Māori Medium Education, 1995–1997

Number of Schools

Kura Kaupapa Māori
Schools with Immersion Classes
Bilingual Schools
Schools with Bilingual Classes
Other Immersion Schools

Year

Note: Immersion School – all students involved in Māori Medium Education for over 20 hours per week

Bilingual School – all students involved in Māori Medium Education for at least 3 hours per week

School with Immersion Classes – some students involved in Māori Medium Education for over 20 hours per week

School with Bilingual Classes – some students involved in Māori Medium Education for at least 3 hours per week

Enrolments in Māori Medium Education 1997

Number of Enrolments

Level 1: 81-100% immersion
Level 2: 51-80% immersion
Level 3: 31-50% immersion
Māori Non-Māori
Level 4: up to 30% immersion

Iwi Populations by Regional Council Area, 1996 Census

Taranaki
21,804
5% 3.5%
3%
Te Atiawa 13.4%
Nga Ruahine 4.6%
Ngati Ruanui 5.5%
Taranaki 5.5%
20.3%

Waikato
100,239
27.6%
9.4%
8.6%
15%
6.6%
4.9%
3.7%
4.5%
14.2%
5.5%

Auckland
175,692
32.1%
22.9%
Ngāti Whātua 3%
3.2%
8%
3.1%
5.1%
16.7%
5.8%

Northland
56,274
Te Aupouri 3.7%
Ngāti Kahu 3.2%
24.6%
36.9%
5%
13.2%
Te Rarawa 5.14%
Hapu of more than one iwi 4.4%
Ngāti Whātua 4%

Bay of Plenty
93,816
26.4% 6.2% 11.6%
4.3%
Ngāiterangi 3.4%
Ngāti Ranginui 3%
Ngāti Awa 5.5%
4.2%
9.6%
3%
5.4%
Whakatohea 3.8%
10.2%
Whānau-a-Apanui 4.4%

Iwi Affiliation

N.B. Respondents could indicate more than one iwi.

Ngāpuhi Ngāti Maniapoto Waikato Ngāti Raukawa Tūwharetoa

Tūhoe Te Arawa Ngāti Porou Ngāti Kahungunu

Ngāi Tahu Don't know Iwi Not specified Other Iwi

Almost 80% of Māori indicated in the 1996 census that they belonged to at least one iwi, a substantial increase over the 1991 census figure. Rural North Island areas had the fewest people who did not specify an iwi, and the highest proportion of Māori who have remained close to their rohe (their iwi's heartland).

A few dominant iwi have spread throughout the country, notably Ngāpuhi, Tūwharetoa and the Tainui peoples of Ngāti Maniapoto and Waikato. Other iwi are dominant in one area: Ngāti Porou in Gisborne, Ngāti Kahungunu in Hawke's Bay and Ngāi Tahu in the South Island. Many iwi were dispersed in the 1830s to 1860s as a result of conflict, while others came to the cities after the Second World War in search of work. The renaissance of Māoritanga, and latterly access to Treaty of Waitangi settlements, have prompted many urban-based Māori to explore their traditional iwi affiliations.

45

For more information...

Changing Places. Le Heron, R. and Pawson, E. (eds).
New Zealand Official Yearbook. Statistics New Zealand.
On the Net: http://www.stats.govt.nz

The economic and structural changes affecting New Zealand since the 1970s are nowhere more apparent than in the working lives of New Zealanders. During the post-war expansionist period of prosperity, the labour force was fully employed, a condition sustained by state intervention (Le Heron and Pawson, 1996). This was abetted by the cultural acceptance of female unpaid household labour. The situation began to change as New Zealand became more exposed to the world economy: as markets became less certain in the 1970s, and with the removal of protectionist barriers in the 1980s, male-dominated jobs in the primary and secondary sectors (agriculture and manufacturing-related) declined in favour of employment in the service sector. A change in social attitudes meant that females could exploit this shift, and most of the new jobs were taken by women. This trend has been described as the 'feminisation' of the labour force.

While the labour force continues to grow (a 5.8% increase between December 1994 and December 1997), full-time employment is growing more slowly than part-time employment (in the last decade, the growth figures are 2% and 40.4% respectively; Statistics New Zealand, 1998). Between 1987 and 1993 the numbers employed full-time actually declined, while part-time employment has grown steadily.

Grouping industries reveals a regional rural-urban pattern: city-based regions employ greater numbers than average in the service sector, while rural-based regions provide opportunities for the primary and secondary sectors. Agriculture, small-scale manufacturing and the construction sector are recovering some ground lost during the 1980s, and the overall migratory trend is from urban to rural areas for the first time in many decades.

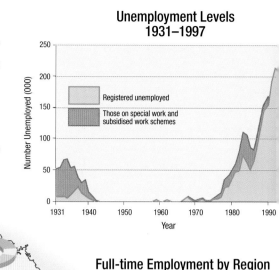

Unemployment Levels 1931–1997

- Registered unemployed
- Those on special work and subsidised work schemes

Number Unemployed (000)

Year

Full-Time Female Employment by Industry, 1996

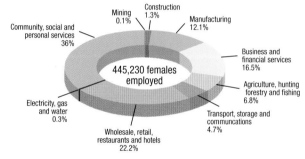

445,230 females employed

- Community, social and personal services 36%
- Mining 0.1%
- Construction 1.3%
- Manufacturing 12.1%
- Business and financial services 16.5%
- Agriculture, hunting forestry and fishing 6.8%
- Transport, storage and communcations 4.7%
- Wholesale, retail, restaurants and hotels 22.2%
- Electricity, gas and water 0.3%

Full-Time Male Employment by Industry, 1996

744,570 males employed

- Community, social and personal services 17.1%
- Mining 0.5%
- Construction 12.9%
- Manufacturing 24.2%
- Electricity, gas and water 0.8%
- Wholesale, retail, restaurants and hotels 19.2%
- Transport, storage and communcations 7.1%
- Agriculture, hunting, forestry and fishing 12.2%
- Business and financial services 11.8%

Full-time Employment by Region 1996 Census

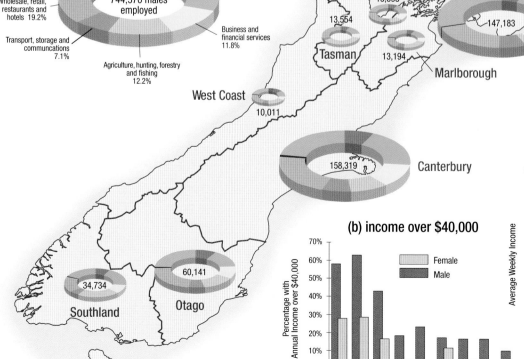

- Northland 36,123
- Auckland 363,831
- Bay of Plenty 64,989
- Waikato 111,132
- Gisborne 12,279
- Taranaki 33,657
- Hawke's Bay 44,541
- Manawatu-Wanganui 70,497
- Nelson 13,398
- Tasman 13,554
- Wellington 147,183
- Marlborough 13,194
- West Coast 10,011
- Canterbury 158,319
- Southland 34,734
- Otago 60,141

Gender Differences in Income (a) weekly income categories

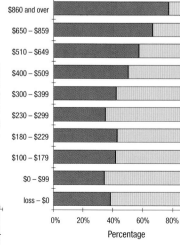

Male / Female

Average Weekly Income

- $860 and over
- $650 – $859
- $510 – $649
- $400 – $509
- $300 – $399
- $230 – $299
- $180 – $229
- $100 – $179
- $0 – $99
- loss – $0

Percentage

(b) income over $40,000

Percentage with Annual Income over $40,000

- Female
- Male

Occupation:
- Legislators, administrators and managers
- Professionals
- Technicians, associate professionals
- Clerks
- Service/Sales
- Agriculture and fishery workers
- Trades
- Plant/Machine operators, assemblers
- Elementary occupations

Bateman Contemporary Atlas New Zealand

Where the Workers Live:
Location of Professionals and Semi/Unskilled Workers, Wellington Urban Area, 1996

rugged topography and the resultant pressure on
nsport links (see Plate 43) make the decision of where to
in relation to work an important issue for Wellingtonians.
As the capital of New Zealand, the site of Parliament and
or financial and corporate headquarters, Wellington attracts
rger than average share of workers classified in the
fessional', 'technicians and associate professional' and
islators, administrators and managers' employment
ssifications. Most residential areas in Wellington City itself
dominated by professionals. These higher-paid groups
afford to live close to their central city employment, in
e expensive city and inner suburban dwellings, while the
thern suburbs of Island Bay and Miramar are home to
her than normal numbers of associate professionals.
Manufacturing is carried out within the urban area,
ably in Porirua and Lower Hutt, and those employed in
sociated semi-skilled and unskilled jobs tend to live close
heir employment. The Wellington Urban Area remains the
st occupationally segregated urban area in New Zealand.

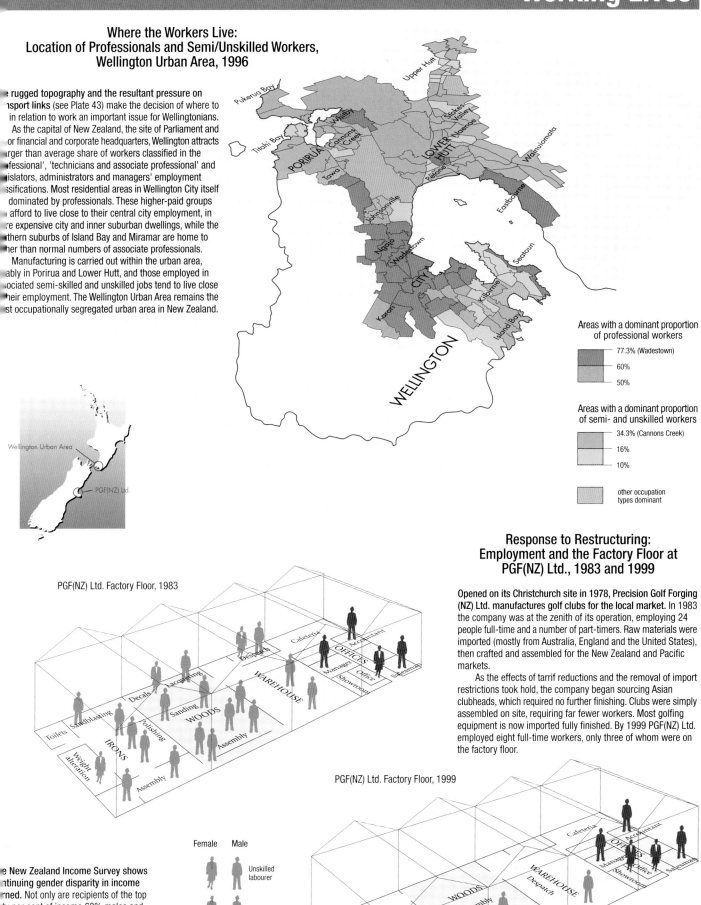

Areas with a dominant proportion
of professional workers

77.3% (Wadestown)

60%

50%

Areas with a dominant proportion
of semi- and unskilled workers

34.3% (Cannons Creek)

16%

10%

other occupation
types dominant

PGF(NZ) Ltd. Factory Floor, 1983

Response to Restructuring:
Employment and the Factory Floor at
PGF(NZ) Ltd., 1983 and 1999

Opened on its Christchurch site in 1978, Precision Golf Forging
(NZ) Ltd. manufactures golf clubs for the local market. In 1983
the company was at the zenith of its operation, employing 24
people full-time and a number of part-timers. Raw materials were
imported (mostly from Australia, England and the United States),
then crafted and assembled for the New Zealand and Pacific
markets.

As the effects of tarrif reductions and the removal of import
restrictions took hold, the company began sourcing Asian
clubheads, which required no further finishing. Clubs were simply
assembled on site, requiring far fewer workers. Most golfing
equipment is now imported fully finished. By 1999 PGF(NZ) Ltd.
employed eight full-time workers, only three of whom were on
the factory floor.

Female   Male

Unskilled
labourer

Foreperson

Clerical,
management

PGF(NZ) Ltd. Factory Floor, 1999

New Zealand Income Survey shows
tinuing gender disparity in income
ned. Not only are recipients of the top
ty per cent of income 63% males and
% females, the proportion of females in
h full-time occupation who earn over
0,000 annual income is substantially lower
n males. This is true even in occupations
h far more females than males employed,
ch as Clerks and Service/Sales.

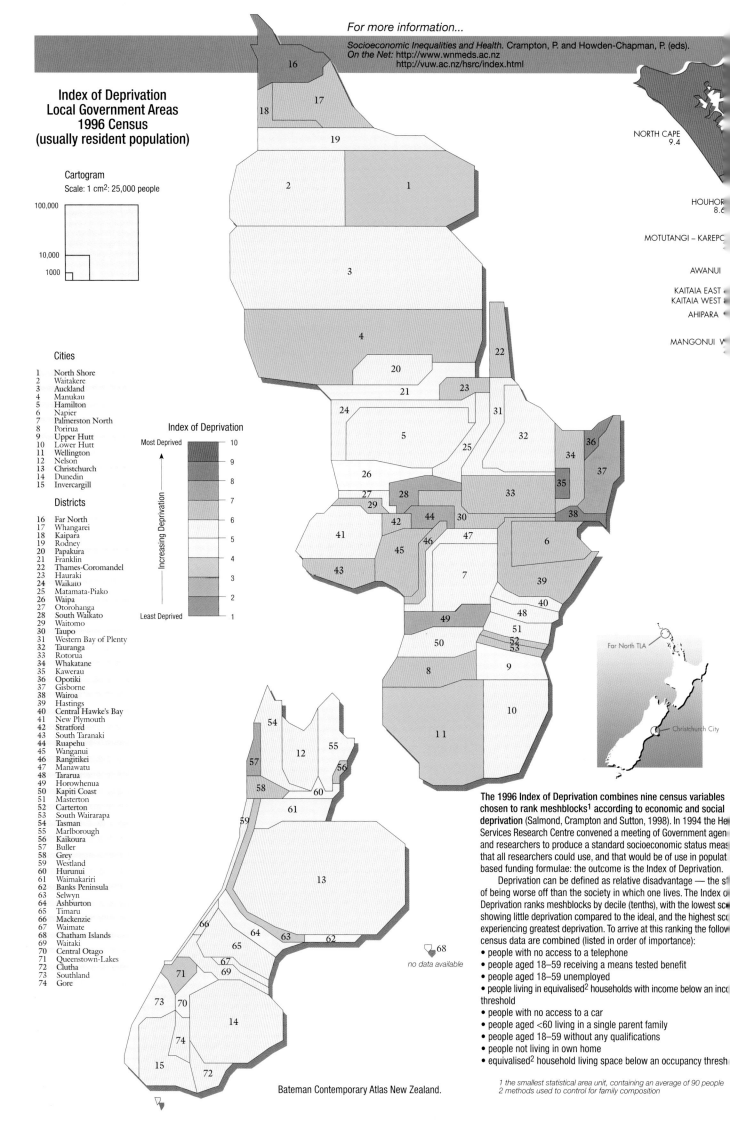

Index of Deprivation
Local Government Areas
1996 Census
(usually resident population)

Cartogram
Scale: 1 cm² : 25,000 people

100,000
10,000
1000

NORTH CAPE
9.4

HOUHOR
8.6

MOTUTANGI – KAREP

AWANUI

KAITAIA EAST
KAITAIA WEST
AHIPARA

MANGONUI

Cities

1	North Shore
2	Waitakere
3	Auckland
4	Manukau
5	Hamilton
6	Napier
7	Palmerston North
8	Porirua
9	Upper Hutt
10	Lower Hutt
11	Wellington
12	Nelson
13	Christchurch
14	Dunedin
15	Invercargill

Districts

16	Far North
17	Whangarei
18	Kaipara
19	Rodney
20	Papakura
21	Franklin
22	Thames-Coromandel
23	Hauraki
24	Waikato
25	Matamata-Piako
26	Waipa
27	Otorohanga
28	South Waikato
29	Waitomo
30	Taupo
31	Western Bay of Plenty
32	Tauranga
33	Rotorua
34	Whakatane
35	Kawerau
36	Opotiki
37	Gisborne
38	Wairoa
39	Hastings
40	Central Hawke's Bay
41	New Plymouth
42	Stratford
43	South Taranaki
44	Ruapehu
45	Wanganui
46	Rangitikei
47	Manawatu
48	Tararua
49	Horowhenua
50	Kapiti Coast
51	Masterton
52	Carterton
53	South Wairarapa
54	Tasman
55	Marlborough
56	Kaikoura
57	Buller
58	Grey
59	Westland
60	Hurunui
61	Waimakariri
62	Banks Peninsula
63	Selwyn
64	Ashburton
65	Timaru
66	Mackenzie
67	Waimate
68	Chatham Islands
69	Waitaki
70	Central Otago
71	Queenstown-Lakes
72	Clutha
73	Southland
74	Gore

Index of Deprivation

Most Deprived — 10
9
8
7
6
5
4
3
2
Least Deprived — 1

Increasing Deprivation

Far North TLA

Christchurch City

68
no data available

The 1996 Index of Deprivation combines nine census variables chosen to rank meshblocks[1] according to economic and social deprivation (Salmond, Crampton and Sutton, 1998). In 1994 the He Services Research Centre convened a meeting of Government agen and researchers to produce a standard socioeconomic status meas that all researchers could use, and that would be of use in populat based funding formulae: the outcome is the Index of Deprivation.

Deprivation can be defined as relative disadvantage — the s of being worse off than the society in which one lives. The Index o Deprivation ranks meshblocks by decile (tenths), with the lowest sc showing little deprivation compared to the ideal, and the highest sc experiencing greatest deprivation. To arrive at this ranking the follow census data are combined (listed in order of importance):

- people with no access to a telephone
- people aged 18–59 receiving a means tested benefit
- people aged 18–59 unemployed
- people living in equivalised[2] households with income below an inc threshold
- people with no access to a car
- people aged <60 living in a single parent family
- people aged 18–59 without any qualifications
- people not living in own home
- equivalised[2] household living space below an occupancy thresh

Bateman Contemporary Atlas New Zealand.

1 the smallest statistical area unit, containing an average of 90 people
2 methods used to control for family composition

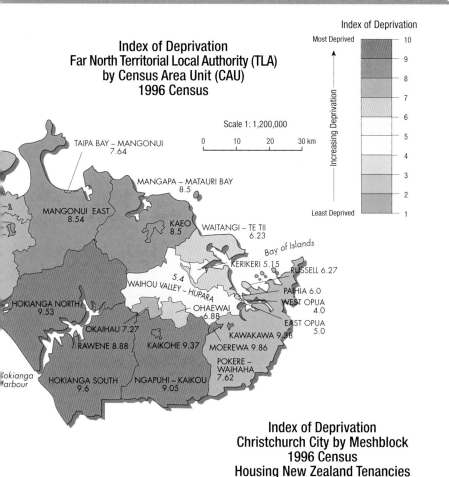

Index of Deprivation Far North Territorial Local Authority (TLA) by Census Area Unit (CAU) 1996 Census

Scale 1: 1,200,000

0   10   20   30 km

Index of Deprivation

Most Deprived   10

9

8

Increasing Deprivation

7

6

5

4

3

2

Least Deprived   1

TAIPA BAY – MANGONUI
7.64

MANGAPA – MATAURI BAY
8.5

MANGONUI EAST
8.54

KAEO
8.5

WAITANGI – TE TII
6.23

Bay of Islands

KERIKERI 5.15

RUSSELL 6.27

5.4
WAIHOU VALLEY – HUPARA

PAIHIA 6.0
WEST OPUA
4.0

OHAEWAI
6.88

HOKIANGA NORTH
9.53

OKAIHAU 7.27

EAST OPUA
5.0

KAWAKAWA 9.38

RAWENE 8.88

KAIKOHE 9.37

MOEREWA 9.86

okianga
arbour

HOKIANGA SOUTH
9.6

NGAPUHI – KAIKOU
9.05

POKERE –
WAIHAHA
7.62

The far north of the country has been the subject of a great deal of publicity regarding poor housing and economic conditions, and this perception is borne out by the Index of Deprivation. All areas of the Far North Territorial Local Authority (TLA) are more deprived than average, with most of the Census Area Units (CAU) ranking in the bottom 20% of the country. The only CAU of the Far North which approach the average level of deprivation are a few areas around the Bay of Islands, predominantly horticultural and tourist areas: the other CAU are rural and poor. The Far North TLA has the second-largest Māori population of any TLA in the country, behind only Manukau City, and it is these people who tend to fare worst. Between 1991 and 1996 conditions worsened slightly in the less deprived areas, and improved slightly in the more deprived areas, but overall the area remains one of the most disadvantaged in the country.

The Christchurch Urban Area demonstrates a clear geographical spread based on the Index of Deprivation. The poorer city suburbs in the east (New Brighton, Aranui, Bromley, Linwood), the older inner-suburban housing immediately to the south of the central city (Waltham, Sydenham, Addington), and the western areas of Upper Riccarton and Hornby show up as a continuous band of above-average deprivation. Much of this can be correlated with the incidence of Housing New Zealand tenancies (former State housing), though private low-rental accommodation accounts for the bulk of housing in inner eastern suburbs. Smaller areas which average above 8 on the Index reflect pockets of state housing amongst wealthier areas. Northern and western Christchurch, and almost all rural lifestyle areas, are well below average on the Index.

Index of Deprivation Christchurch City by Meshblock 1996 Census Housing New Zealand Tenancies by Census Area Unit (CAU), 1999

Scale 1: 120,000

0   1   2   3 km

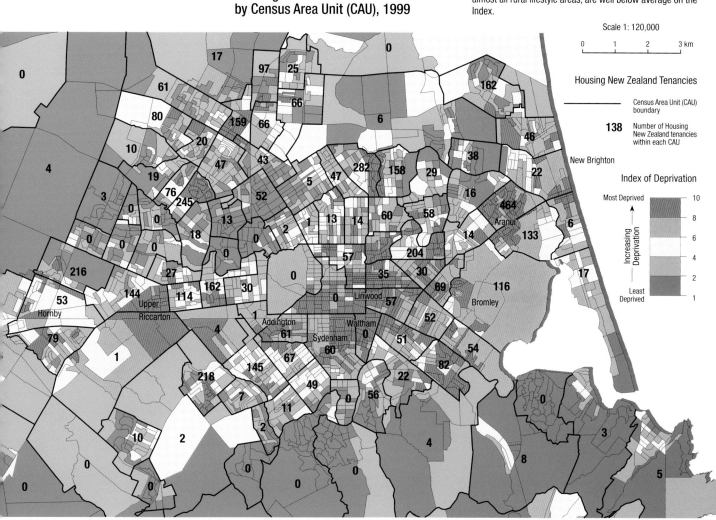

Housing New Zealand Tenancies

Census Area Unit (CAU) boundary

138 Number of Housing New Zealand tenancies within each CAU

New Brighton

Index of Deprivation

Most Deprived   10

8

Increasing Deprivation

6

4

2

Least Deprived   1

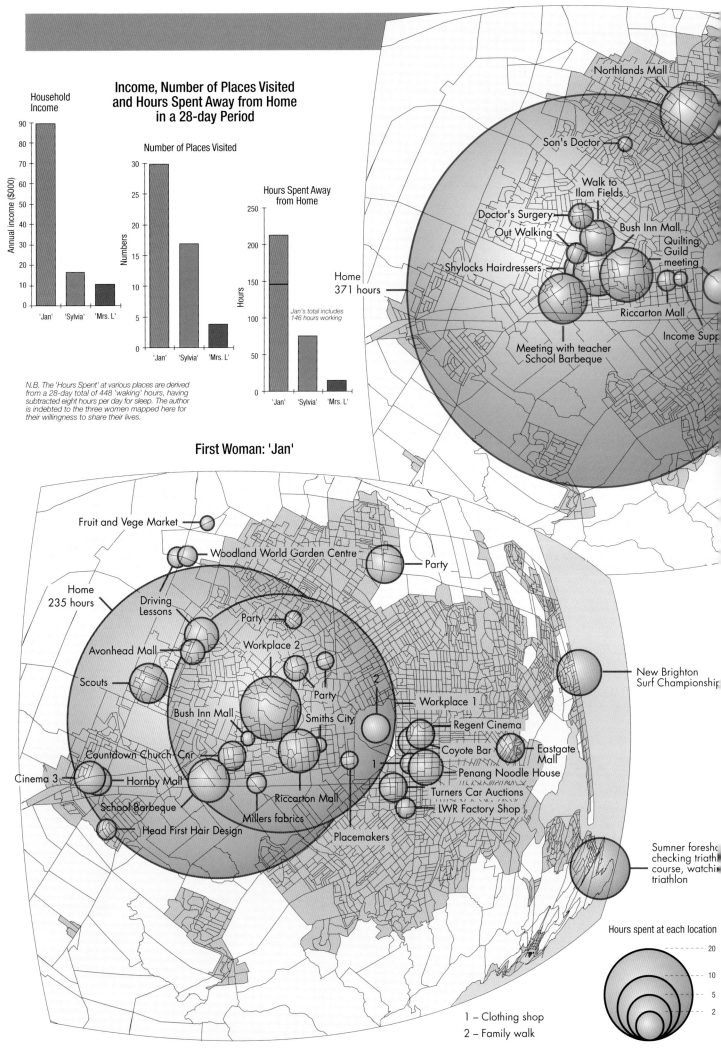

Income, Number of Places Visited and Hours Spent Away from Home in a 28-day Period

Household Income

Annual income ($000)
90, 80, 70, 60, 50, 40, 30, 20, 10, 0

'Jan', 'Sylvia', 'Mrs. L'

Number of Places Visited

Numbers
30, 25, 20, 15, 10, 5, 0

'Jan', 'Sylvia', 'Mrs. L'

Hours Spent Away from Home

Hours
250, 200, 150, 100, 50, 0

'Jan', 'Sylvia', 'Mrs. L'

Jan's total includes 146 hours working

N.B. The 'Hours Spent' at various places are derived from a 28-day total of 448 'waking' hours, having subtracted eight hours per day for sleep. The author is indebted to the three women mapped here for their willingness to share their lives.

First Woman: 'Jan'

Northlands Mall
Son's Doctor
Walk to Ilam Fields
Doctor's Surgery
Out Walking
Bush Inn Mall
Quilting Guild meeting
Shylocks Hairdressers
Home 371 hours
Riccarton Mall
Income Supp
Meeting with teacher School Barbeque

Fruit and Vege Market
Woodland World Garden Centre
Party
Home 235 hours
Driving Lessons
Party
Workplace 2
Avonhead Mall
Scouts
Party
New Brighton Surf Championship
Bush Inn Mall
Smiths City
Workplace 1
2
Regent Cinema
Coyote Bar
Eastgate Mall
Countdown Church Cnr
Penang Noodle House
Cinema 3
Hornby Mall
1
Turners Car Auctions
LWR Factory Shop
School Barbeque
Riccarton Mall
Millers fabrics
Head First Hair Design
Placemakers
Sumner foresho checking triath course, watchi triathlon

Hours spent at each location
20
10
5
2

1 – Clothing shop
2 – Family walk

Bateman Contemporary Atlas New Zealand

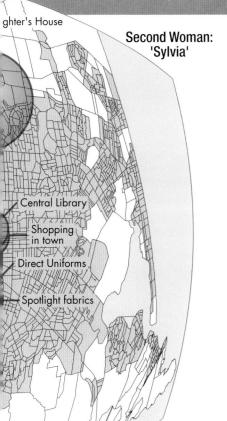

ghter's House

Central Library

Shopping
in town

Direct Uniforms

Spotlight fabrics

Second Woman: 'Sylvia'

The experience of living in the city is quite different for different people, depending on a number of factors — not all of them geographical. A brief exploration of the movements of three Christchurch women over a 28-day period helps uncover the socio-economic constraints which limit the ability of women to make use of the amenities offered in a city.

'Jan', the first woman, is in her mid-thirties, married with two children. She works part-time as a librarian's assistant. An annual household income of around $90,000 allows her relative freedom of movement about the city, as well as providing an adequate disposable income to take advantage of a variety of consumer options. The major constraint on her activity is the needs of her teenage daughter, who does not yet drive (though she is having driving lessons, and looking to purchase a car). 'Jan' spends much of her time driving her daughter to and from activities, such as triathlons and parties. Ready access to transport means that 'Jan' is able, for example, to shop for fresh produce at a specialist store, and she can take advantage of what the different malls offer. Finally, their financial situation allows her and her partner to visit restaurants, bars and the cinema.

The second woman, 'Sylvia', is in her mid-fifties. Twice-married and with four adult children, she now lives without a partner but with her adopted thirteen-year-old son. Because of the dependency of her adopted son (who suffers some

impairment due to injuries sustained in an accident) 'Sylvia' has been unable to work, and receives state assistance amounting to about $17,000 per annum. She cannot afford to own a car, so is forced in the main to use amenities within walking distance of her home, or to take the bus when she wants to go to 'town' or the Central Library. Another daughter lives a few kilometres away, so 'Sylvia' is able to go shopping once a week with her daughter at a mall some distance from her home. The limits of her lifestyle do not allow her much freedom outside school hours.

'Mrs. L' is the third woman. She is a widow of about seventy years of age, and resides with her youngest daughter and son-in-law. She lives a house-bound life, dictated by an immobility linked to heart problems, failing eyesight and a series of small strokes. 'Mrs. L' has never learned to drive a car, and is now not able to make use of public transport. She therefore depends on others (her daughter, Age Concern) to take her on outings. Her income is a superannuation of about $11,000 per annum. 'Mrs. L's typical day consists of sitting in her chair listening to the radio in the mornings and watching television in the evenings, interspersed with a number of household tasks she is still able to perform. She receives regular visits from an out-of-town daughter and a son, and has her hair done at home once a week by a friend.

Third Woman: 'Mrs. L'

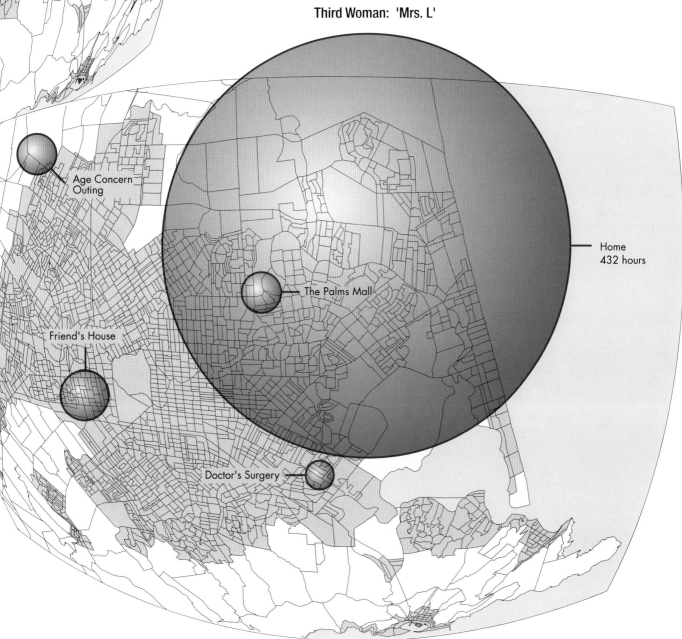

Age Concern
Outing

The Palms Mall

Home
432 hours

Friend's House

Doctor's Surgery

For more information...

Hospital Management Data. New Zealand Health Information Service (annual)
New Zealand Official Yearbook. Statistics New Zealand.
On the Net: http://www.moh.govt.nz

By 1985 Hospital Boards had seen a century of service, and had been fully funded by central government since 1957. In 1985 there were 181 public hospitals providing a total of 25,585 beds, of which 7663 were in 17 psychiatric and psychopaedic hospitals. Private health providers played only a small role in the health system.

By 1999 the health system had been radically reorganised. Twenty-nine Hospital Boards made way for 23 Hospital and Health Services (HHSs), funded by the Health Funding Authority (HFA). These HHSs — formerly Crown Health Enterprises, or CHEs — compete with each other, and with other service providers, for funding. Private hospitals conduct much non-acute surgery, and many public hospitals in both urban and rural areas have been downsized or closed, so much so that by 1997 116 hospitals provided 14,930 beds, 60% of the beds available in 1985. Of these, 2359 were psychiatric or psychopaedic, only 30% of those available in 1985. This is a result of a concerted government effort to reintegrate residential psychiatric patients into the community. Some communities have successfully tendered for State funding, and a number of rural hospitals (such as Ranfurly) are still State-funded, though they are no longer State-owned.

Public Hospitals, 1985 by Number and Type of Beds

Tauranga — Hospital Board

Hospital Size by Number of Beds: 1000, 500, 100, 30, 5

Hospital Type:
- General (surgical; often includes geriatric, maternity and psychiatric)
- Geriatric
- Maternity
- Psychiatric
- Other (psychopaedic or residential)

N.B. The Chatham Islands are approx. 800 km east of Banks Peninsula

Chatham Islands (part of North Canterbury)

*Lyndhurst closed 31.3.85

Bateman Contemporary Atlas New Zealand

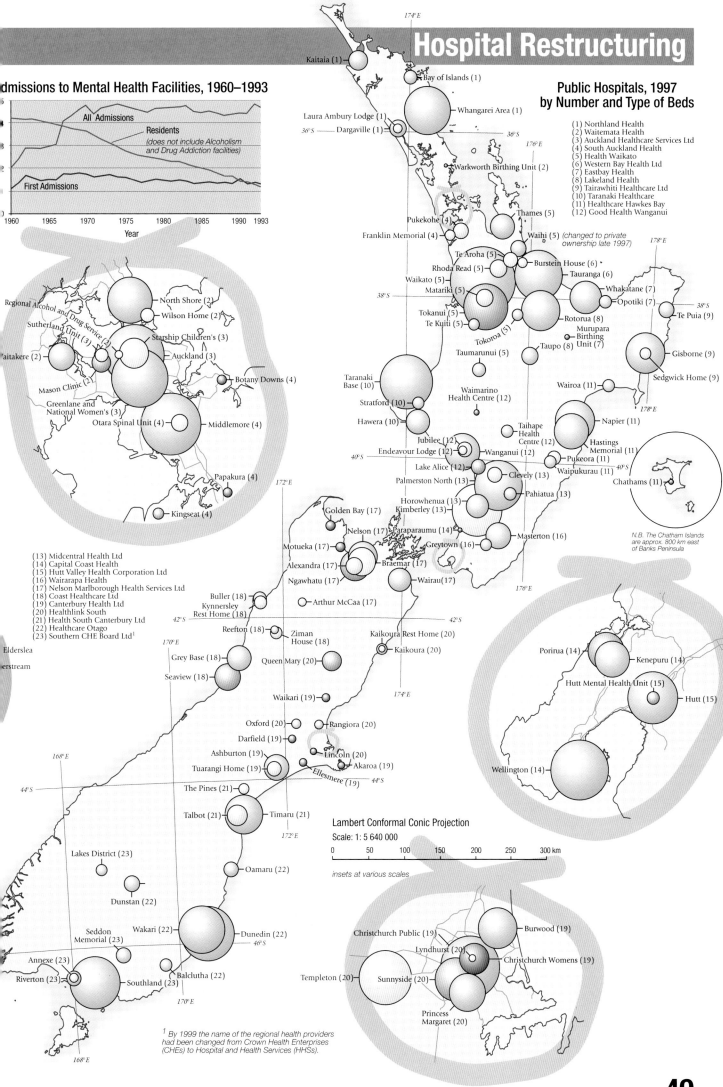

Admissions to Mental Health Facilities, 1960–1993

All Admissions

Residents
(does not include Alcoholism and Drug Addiction facilities)

First Admissions

Year
1960 1965 1970 1975 1980 1985 1990 1993

Public Hospitals, 1997
by Number and Type of Beds

(1) Northland Health
(2) Waitemata Health
(3) Auckland Healthcare Services Ltd
(4) South Auckland Health
(5) Health Waikato
(6) Western Bay Health Ltd
(7) Eastbay Health
(8) Lakeland Health
(9) Tairawhiti Healthcare Ltd
(10) Taranaki Healthcare
(11) Healthcare Hawkes Bay
(12) Good Health Wanganui

(13) Midcentral Health Ltd
(14) Capital Coast Health
(15) Hutt Valley Health Corporation Ltd
(16) Wairarapa Health
(17) Nelson Marlborough Health Services Ltd
(18) Coast Healthcare Ltd
(19) Canterbury Health Ltd
(20) Healthlink South
(21) Health South Canterbury Ltd
(22) Healthcare Otago
(23) Southern CHE Board Ltd[1]

Kaitaia (1)
Bay of Islands (1)
Whangarei Area (1)
Laura Ambury Lodge (1)
Dargaville (1)
Warkworth Birthing Unit (2)
Pukekohe (4)
Franklin Memorial (4)
Thames (5)
Waihi (5) *(changed to private ownership late 1997)*
Te Aroha (5)
Burstein House (6) *
Rhoda Read (5)
Tauranga (6)
Waikato (5)
Matariki (5)
Whakatane (7)
Tokanui (5)
Opotiki (7)
Te Kuiti (5)
Rotorua (8)
Te Puia (9)
Tokoroa (5)
Murupara Birthing Unit (7)
Taumarunui (5)
Taupo (8)
Gisborne (9)
Taranaki Base (10)
Waimarino Health Centre (12)
Sedgwick Home (9)
Stratford (10)
Wairoa (11)
Hawera (10)
Napier (11)
Taihape Health Centre (12)
Jubilee (12)
Hastings Memorial (11)
Endeavour Lodge (12)
Wanganui (12)
Pukeora (11)
Lake Alice (12)
Waipukurau (11)
Clevely (13)
Chathams (11)
Palmerston North (13)
Pahiatua (13)
Horowhenua (13)
Kimberley (13)
Masterton (16)
Golden Bay (17)
Nelson (17)
Paraparaumu (14)
Motueka (17)
Greytown (16)
Alexandra (17)
Braemar (17)
Ngawhatu (17)
Wairau (17)
Arthur McCaa (17)
Buller (18)
Kynnersley Rest Home (18)
Reefton (18)
Ziman House (18)
Kaikoura Rest Home (20)
Porirua (14)
Kenepuru (14)
Grey Base (18)
Queen Mary (20)
Kaikoura (20)
Hutt Mental Health Unit (15)
Seaview (18)
Hutt (15)
Waikari (19)
Oxford (20)
Rangiora (20)
Darfield (19)
Wellington (14)
Ashburton (19)
Lincoln (20)
Tuarangi Home (19)
Akaroa (19)
Ellesmere (19)
The Pines (21)
Talbot (21)
Timaru (21)
Lakes District (23)
Oamaru (22)
Dunstan (22)
Seddon Memorial (23)
Wakari (22)
Dunedin (22)
Annexe (23)
Riverton (23)
Balclutha (22)
Southland (23)

Auckland inset
North Shore (2)
Wilson Home (2)
Regional Alcohol and Drug Service (2)
Starship Children's (3)
Sutherland Unit (3)
Auckland (3)
Waitakere (2)
Botany Downs (4)
Mason Clinic (2)
Greenlane and National Women's (3)
Otara Spinal Unit (4)
Middlemore (4)
Papakura (4)
Kingseat (4)
Elderslea
erstream

Christchurch inset
Christchurch Public (19)
Burwood (19)
Lyndhurst (20)
Christchurch Womens (19)
Templeton (20)
Sunnyside (20)
Princess Margaret (20)

N.B. The Chatham Islands are approx. 800 km east of Banks Peninsula

Lambert Conformal Conic Projection
Scale: 1: 5 640 000
0 50 100 150 200 250 300 km
insets at various scales

[1] By 1999 the name of the regional health providers had been changed from Crown Health Enterprises (CHEs) to Hospital and Health Services (HHSs).

For more information...

Hillary Commission for Sport, Fitness and Leisure.
Ministry of Cultural Affairs.
On the Net: http://www.hillarysport.org.nz

Sport is central to New Zealand's image, both at home and abroad. New Zealanders participate in a wide variety of sporting and recreational activities, and accord successful sportswomen and men high status.

Long after New Zealand's provinces ceased having any geographical meaning (they were abolished in 1876), inter-provincial sports competition has helped keep provincial identity alive. Rugby, cricket and netball all base their premier domestic competitions on provincial identity, a strategy which has attracted corporate sponsors whose products often play on inter-provincial rivalry.

The Hillary Commission for Sport, Fitness and Leisure, funded by the Lottery Grants Board and the government, spends around $11 million each year encouraging high-performance sport by funding elite athletes, $10 million annually in general sports development, $9 million per annum on community fitness and leisure, and $5 million each year in the area of junior sport. As a major funder it influences the way sport is structured, as clubs and sports trusts reorganise to become eligible for funding.

Many cultural activities, such as attendance at marae, art galleries, museums and churches are available free of charge. Even so, household spending on cultural activities (4.8% of total expenditure) is rising much faster than spending in other areas, though the nature of this spending suggests that most people still primarily engage in passive pursuits.

Provincial Rugby Unions
Super 12 Teams 1999
First-Class Grounds

———	Provincial boundary
Buller 1886	Rugby province and date of establishment
———	Super 12 boundary
ury Cru	Super 12 Franchise
○Carisbrook	First-class rugby ground hosting a 1999 fixture

Northland 1920
Lowe Walker Stadium
Auckland Blues

North Harbour 1985 — Albany Stadium
Auckland 1883 — Eden Park
Counties 1955 — Pukekohe
Thames Valley 1922 — Paeroa
WestpacTrust Park
Waikato 1887
The Chiefs
Bay of Plenty 1911
Rotorua International Stadium
Te Kuiti
East Coast 1921 — Ruatoria
Poverty Bay 1890 — Gisborne
New Plymouth
King Country 1922
Hawkes Bay 1884
Taranaki 1885
Wanganui 1888 — McLean Park
Wellington Hurricanes
Wanganui
Central Vikings 1997-8
Manawatu 1886 — Palmerston North
Horowhenua 1893 — Levin Domain
Masterton
Wairarapa Bush 1971
Athletic Park
Wellington 1879

Central Vikings 1997-8
An amalgamation of Hawkes Bay and Manawatu, the Central Vikings were initially hailed as the first fruits of the new professional provincial rugby era. But after two years, and having won the right to promotion to the First Division, they were denied entry on financial grounds and subsequently disbanded into their separate unions.

South Island
Nelson Bays 1969 — Nelson
Buller 1886 — Blenheim
Victoria Park
Marlborough 1888
Greymouth
Canterbury Crusaders
West Coast 1890
Canterbury 1079
Jade Stadium at Lancaster Park
Mid-Canterbury 1904
Ashburton Domain
South Canterbury 1888 — Timaru
North Otago 1904 — Centennial Park
Otago 1881
Otago Highlanders
Southland 1887 — Carisbrook
Homestead Stadium

Average Weekly Household Expenditure on Cultural Activities
Year ended March 1996

Average weekly household expenditure on culture $31.80

- Publications 23% ($7.32)
- Other 40.3% ($12.80)
- Television sets 7.3% ($2.31)
- Recorded music 5.6% ($1.78)
- Stereo systems 5.3% ($1.67)
- Public broadcasting fee 5.2% ($1.66)
- Cinema 3.4% ($1.08)
- Theatre, Ballet, & Concerts 3.3% ($1.04)
- Video hire 2.4% ($0.76)
- Video recorders 2.2% ($0.70)
- Music, singing and dancing lessons 2.1% ($0.67)

Bateman Contemporary Atlas New Zealand

North Island grounds
Cobham Oval
Victoria
Auckland 1883
Cornwall Park — Domain
Eden Park No. 2 (outer oval)
Eden Park
Bledisloe Park
Recrea Grour
WestpacTrust Park (Seddon Park)
Smallbone P
North Distr
Pukekura Park
King Edward Park — Bayly Park — Nelson — Farndon
Cook's Gardens — Victoria
Central Districts 1950
Fitzherbert Park
Levin Domain
Eliz
Trafalgar Park
Victory Square
Petone Recreation Ground
Botanical Gardens
Horton Park
Maidstor Park
Wellington College Ground
Hutt Recre Ground
Basin Reserve
Welling 1875

Canterbury 1877
Burnside Park
Hagley Park (new)
Hagley Park (old)
Dudley Park
Jade Stadium at Lancaster Park
Temuka Oval

Otago 1876
Molyneux Park
Centennial Park
University Oval — Logan Park
Carisbrook
Sunnyvale Oval
Caledonian Ground
South Dunedin Recreation Ground
Rugby Park
Queens Park

Souther Sting
Inverca

Recreational Participation by Gender, 1996

Top ten sports and physical activities for women and men

Female / Male

Percentage participation (0–70)

Activity: Gardening, Short Walks, Long Walks, Swimming, Exercising at Home, Golf, Aerobics, Running/Jogging, Exercise Classes, Cycling, Touch, Netball, Tramping

t-Class Cricket Districts
First-Class Grounds

ber of First-Class games

- --- 300
- 100
- 20
- 4

of first First-Class match

| 1950– | after |
| 1975 | 1975 |

ga Domain (inner)
ga Domain (outer)

Harry Barker Reserve

McLean Park
Recreation Ground
son Cricket Ground

Netball New Zealand
Coca-Cola Cup Franchise Venues

*N.B. Franchise Regions do not
have definite boundaries.*

Sky City Diamonds

Northern Force Glenfield
Mt Albert ○ ○ Auckland
○ Papatoetoe

*CMTV
Comets*

Hamilton ○   ○ Tauranga

○ Rotorua

Waikato–Bay of Plenty Magic

New Plymouth ○

Western Flyers

Wanganui ○

○ Palmerston
North

*Capital
Shakers*

○ Wellington

*Canterbury
Flames*

Christchurch ○

*go
ls*

○ Dunedin

Age Trends in Selected Sports Participation, 1996

Touch football

Golf

Netball

Cricket   Tennis

Basketball

Bowls

Percentage participation

Age Group

18–24   25–34   35–49   50+

Distribution of
Golf Clubs

Date of Establishment
of Golf Club

n.b. not golf course

- ▶ 1980-99
- ▶ 1960-79
- ▷ 1940-59
- ▷ 1920-39
- ▷ before 1920
- ▷ date unavailable

ert Conformal Conic Projection
1 : 8 300 000

50   100   150   200   250   300 km

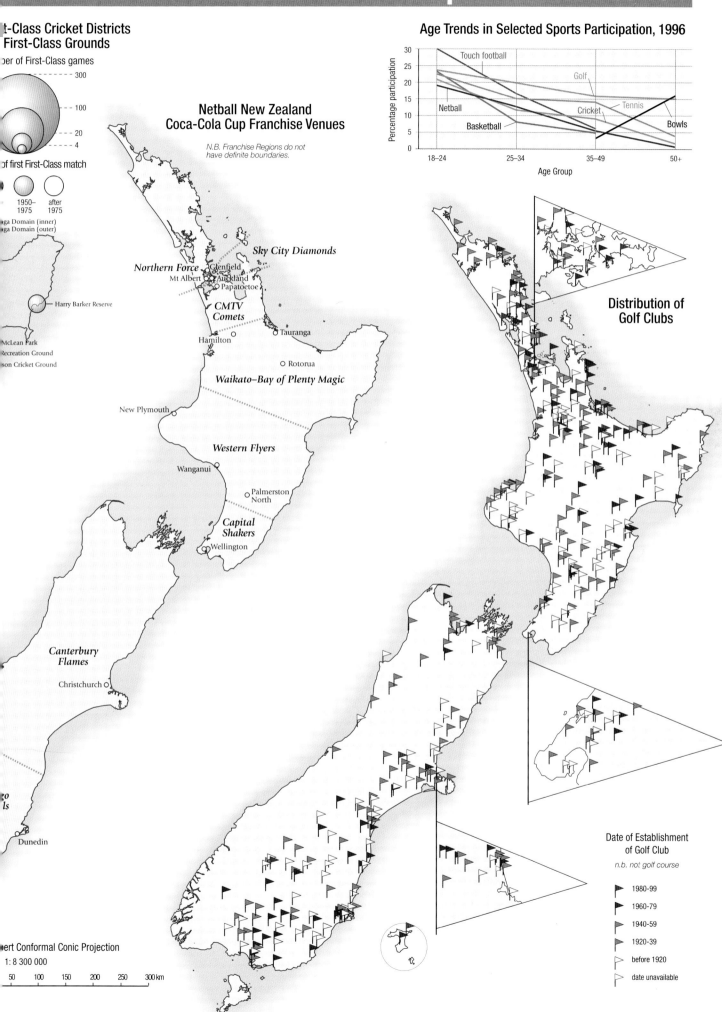

ACKNOWLEDGMENTS

N o endeavour such as this one could have been completed without an enormous amount of assistance. For the most part this help was offered without expectation of financial reward, for which I am most grateful. The advent of computers made this project possible. Past atlases have been painstakingly constructed by teams of cartographers over many years. The need to commit ideas to paper early in these projects, and the difficulty of changing maps once they are drawn, shaped these projects, giving them an innate conservatism. With computer technology this need no longer be the case. Many databases are available on disk or through the Internet, as are commentaries and articles on many aspects of New Zealand's geography. It is even possible to formulate and draw a draft plate from start to finish without leaving one's chair, as I did while constructing Plate 40: Energy. What once took years now takes only months. The analytical and retrieval capabilities of Geographical Information Systems (GIS) are speeding up this process even further.

Nevertheless, certain key people and organisations have assisted me greatly, and I wish to take this opportunity to thank them. The Department of Geography at the University of Canterbury generously granted me access to their resources and, by appointing me as an honorary fellow, enabled me to make use of the University library. I thank Professor Bob Kirk, the then Head of Department, for his support and encouragement. Other members of the academic staff made valuable contributions: Doug Johnston offered a number of useful general comments, Ian Owens assisted with natural hazards material, and Andy Sturman reviewed the climate material. Ross Barnett was of great assistance with regards to health restructuring, and introduced me to the Index of Deprivation. Map Librarian Janet Bray and her assistant Sue Christophers were particularly helpful, in spite of the sour and grumpy face I often presented them with at library opening time. Tim Nolan, the Department's cartographer, provided constant moral support.

The Canterbury Branch of the New Zealand Geographical Society made a number of informal comments on early drafts of the work: I would like to acknowledge the input of Kay Booth and Professor Chris Kissling from Lincoln University, Neville Jones from Mapworld New Zealand, Greg Lauer and Andy Kliskey of the Department of Geography at the University of Canterbury, Tony Clay of Burnside High School, and others who attended discussion groups.

Geography Departments at other universities were most supportive of the project. Professor Richard Bedford facilitated two trips to the Waikato Geography Department: he and his co-workers at the Population Research Centre, Joanne Goodwin and Bridget Spragg, provided much of the data used in the Population Shapes section of the *Atlas*. To do this they worked between Christmas 1998 and New Year's day 1999. Professor Lex Chalmers contributed valuable criticism of aspects of the work in progress, as did Mairi Jay, Lars Brabyn and Robyn Longhurst. The Waikato Branch of the New Zealand Geographical Society helped sharpen much of the latter sections of the *Atlas*. Professor Pip Forer at the Department of Geography, University of Auckland, kindly arranged a trip to Auckland in 1998. Head of Department Professor Richard Le Heron, Peter Fraser, Gael Arnold, Scott Nichol, Laurence Murphy and Gordon Winder of the Tamaki campus generously gave of their time, as did students who attended discussion groups. Brian Marshall of the Map Library made helpful suggestions. Of immense help were Jan Kelly and Jonette Surridge, the two cartographers who were bold enough to offer detailed, informed criticism of the work and, most gratifyingly, advice as to how it might be improved – perhaps unwisely as it turned out, because this encouraged the publisher to ask them to undertake a full cartographic review of the project.

A number of other organisations were of assistance to the project. I would like to thank Alan Hewitt and John Leathwick of Manaaki Whenua Landcare Research, Dennis Jamieson and Lionel Carter of the National Institute of Water and Atmospheric Research, Annemarie Crampton of the Ministry of Commerce and Peter Crampton and Clare Salmond of the Health Services Research Centre. Tony Trewinnard of Blue Skies Weather and Climate Services Ltd provided specific climate data and long-term critical assessment of the project. Staff at Statistics New Zealand, the Institute of Geological and Nuclear Sciences, the Department of Conservation, the Health Information Service, Land Information New Zealand, Transit New Zealand, Tranz Rail, Clement and Associates and the Ministry of Fisheries were unfailingly courteous and helpful.

I reserve my highest praise for the editorial and publishing team. Chris O'Brien was able to inject needed sanity into some of my more outrageous ideas, and proved an ideal copy editor. Jan Kelly and Jonette Surridge performed magnificently as cartographic editors, both true professionals who were able to provide much-needed guidance without discouraging my efforts. Shelley Watson has enhanced the *Atlas* with a delightful book design, capturing the essence of the bright, refreshing cartography I hoped to present within its pages. Malcolm McKinnon, the editor of the *New Zealand Historical Atlas*, reviewed early drafts of the project and provided the sectional framework. Later he made constructive comments on the final shape of the *Atlas*. Paul Bateman, Publishing Director of David Bateman Ltd, provided a great deal of energy which helped turn the dream of a contemporary atlas into a reality, and I am grateful to the publishers for their patience and support. Finally I want to thank Tracey Borgfeldt, Associate Publisher of David Bateman Ltd, whose combination of patience, diligence and professionalism is the substantive reason why this work was finished before the original deadline.

I dedicate this work to my partner Dorinda, and my two boys Iain and Alex. Though I was fortunate to work from home for the duration of the project, my family bore the burden of my long working hours, my obsessiveness and preoccupation, and the absence of holidays, and never wavered in their belief in me.

Russell Kirkpatrick

MAP NOTES AND SOURCES

General References

Franklin, H., 1993. "A Power to Disconcert: geography in the 1990s". Opening Address to the New Zealand Geographical Society Conference 1993, in *Proceedings of the Seventeenth Conference*, New Zealand Geographical Society, pp 1-4.

Le Heron, R. and Pawson, E. (eds), 1996. *Changing Places: New Zealand in the nineties*. Longman Paul, Auckland.

Kelly, J. and Marshall, B., 1996. *Atlas of New Zealand Boundaries*. Auckland University Press, Auckland.

Kirkpatrick, R., Chittenden, C. and Phillips, R. (eds), 1996. *Macmillan New Zealand World Atlas*. Macmillan Publishers New Zealand Ltd, Auckland.

Lewis, N. and Moran, W., 1998. "Restructuring, Democracy and Geography in New Zealand", in *Environment and Planning C: Government and Policy* 16, pp 127-153.

McKinnon, M. (ed) with Bradley, B. and Kirkpatrick, R., 1997. *New Zealand Historical Atlas: Visualising New Zealand*. David Bateman Ltd in association with Historical Branch, Department of Internal Affairs, Auckland.

McLintock, A.H. (ed), 1960. *A Descriptive Atlas of New Zealand*. Government Printer, Wellington.

Ministry for the Environment, 1997. *The State of New Zealand's Environment 1997*. GP Publications, Wellington.

Ministry of Agriculture and Fisheries, 1990. *Impact of the Treaty of Waitangi on Government Agencies*. Ministry of Agriculture and Fisheries, Brooker and Friend, Wellington.

Mosley, M.P. (ed), 1992. *Waters of New Zealand*. New Zealand Hydrological Society Inc, Wellington North.

Roche, M.M., 1993. "Atlases, Ethics and Freezing Works", in *Proceedings of the Seventeenth Conference*, New Zealand Geographical Society, pp 11-15.

Roche, M.M. and Mansvelt, J., 1996. "Ethical Research in a Public Good Funding Environment", in *New Zealand Geographer* 52 (1), pp 41-46.

Statistics New Zealand, 1998. *New Zealand Official Yearbook*. GP Publications and Statistics New Zealand, Wellington.

Sturman, A.P. and Tapper, N.J., 1996. *The Weather and Climate of Australia and New Zealand*. Oxford University Press, Melbourne.

Thorns, D. and Sedgwick, C., 1997. *Understanding Aotearoa/New Zealand: historical statistics*. Dunmore Press Ltd, Palmerston North.

Wards, I. McL. (ed), 1976. *New Zealand Atlas*. Government Printer, Wellington.

Preface References

Balogun, O.Y., 1985. "The Training of Nigerian Surveyors in the Colonial Era", in *Surveying and Mapping* 45 (2), pp 159-167.

Brockie, W.J. and Moran, W., 1977. "Review: New Zealand Atlas", in *New Zealand Geographer*, October 1977, pp 96-97.

Brown, P. and Levinson, S., 1978. "Universals in Language Usage: politeness phenomena", in Goody, E. (ed), *Questions and Politeness: strategies in social interaction*. Cambridge University Press, Cambridge, pp 56-289.

Collins, L. and Lapierre, D., 1982. *Freedom at Midnight*. Collins, London.

Freshfield, D., 1886. "The Place of Geography in Education", in *Proceedings of the Royal Society* 8, pp 698-714.

Goffman, E., 1967. *Interaction Ritual*. Aldine Publishing Company, Chicago.

Haggett, P., 1990. *The Geographer's Art*. Basil Blackwell, Oxford.

Harley, J.B., 1988. "Maps, Knowledge and Power", in Cosgrove, D. and Daniels, S. (eds), *The Iconography of Landscape*. Cambridge University Press, Cambridge, pp 277-311.

Harvey, D., 1984. "On the History and Present Condition of Geography: an historical materialist manifesto", in *The Professional Geographer* 36 (1), pp 1-10.

Keates, J.S., 1982. *Understanding Maps*. Longman, London.

Kirkpatrick, R.I., 1987. "The Social Context of Mapping". Unpublished MA thesis, Department of Geography, University of Canterbury.

Lister, R.G., 1979. "The Need for a National Atlas in New Zealand", in *New Zealand Geographer*, October 1979, pp 284-287.

McKinnon, M. (ed), with Bradley, B. and Kirkpatrick, R., 1997. *New Zealand Historical Atlas: Visualising New Zealand*. David Bateman Ltd in association with Historical Branch, Department of Internal Affairs, Auckland.

McLintock, A.H. (ed), 1960. *A Descriptive Atlas of New Zealand*. Government Printer, Wellington.

Muehrcke, P.C., 1974. "Map Reading and Abuse", in *The Journal of Geography* 1974, pp 11-23.

Overton, J., 1998. "Review: New Zealand Historical Atlas: Visualising New Zealand", in *New Zealand Geographer* 54 (1), pp 56-57.

Smith, Neil, 1979. "Geography, Science and Post-positivist Modes of Explanation", in *Progress in Human Geography* 3 (3), pp 356-383.

Southard, R.B., 1983. "The Development of U.S. National Mapping Policy", in *The American Cartographer* 10 (1), pp 5-15.

The Editors, 1960. "Mirror For New Zealanders: a Descriptive Atlas reviewed", in *New Zealand Geographer* 16, pp 84-89.

Section 1: Physical Shapes

Plate 1: Physical

- **New Zealand Physical 1:3,000,000**
Data for superlatives from: Statistics New Zealand, 1998. *New Zealand Official Yearbook*. GP Publications and Statistics New Zealand, Wellington, p 1-2.

- **Lake Type by Cause of Entrapment**
McKinnon, M. (ed), with Bradley, B. and Kirkpatrick, R., 1997. Unpublished material from the New Zealand Historical Atlas project. Historical Branch, Department of Internal Affairs, Wellington.

- **Largest Lakes**
Graphic based on data from: Statistics New Zealand, 1998. *New Zealand Official Yearbook*. GP Publications and Statistics New Zealand, Wellington, p 2.

Area of Te Whanga Lagoon, Chatham Islands, derived from "Islands of New Zealand", in Wards, I. (ed), 1976. *New Zealand Atlas*. Government Printer, Wellington, p 3-4.

- **Mountain Heights**
Graphic based on data from: Statistics New Zealand, 1998. *New Zealand Official Yearbook*. GP Publications and Statistics New Zealand, Wellington, p 1.

Various maps from NZMS 260 1:50,000 series, produced by Lands and Survey Department (pre-1987), Department of Survey and Land Information (1987-1996), Terralink New Zealand (post 1996).

- **Longest Rivers**
Graphic based on data from: Statistics New Zealand, 1998. *New Zealand Official Yearbook*. GP Publications and Statistics New Zealand, Wellington, p 2.

See also:
Cotton, C.A., 1958. *Geomorphology: an introduction to the study of landforms*, seventh edition. Whitcombe and Tombs, Christchurch.

Homer, L., Spratt, P. and Begg, J., 1990. *Landforms*. Department of Scientific and Industrial Research, Geology and Geophysics Division, Lower Hutt.

Joint Earth Sciences Working Group in Geopreservation, 1990. *New Zealand Landform Inventory, second approximation*. Occasional Paper No. 4, Physical Geography, Victoria University of Wellington, Research School of Earth Sciences.

Soons, J.M., 1992. "Landforms and Environmental Change in a High-energy Environment", in *Sveriges Geologiska Underskoning* Ser. Ca. 81, pp 333-338.

Soons, J.M. and Selby, M.J., 1992. *Landforms of New Zealand*, second edition. Longman Paul, Auckland.

Notes: While the A3 landscape format allows the production of an affordable atlas, it is not the ideal layout for a country the shape of New Zealand. In order to achieve the largest scale for the more detailed maps of New Zealand, a scale of 1:3,000,000 was chosen. This means that the North and South Islands are positioned side by side, rather than in their true relative positions. However, this is partially overcome by overlapping each map, so that something of the other main island can be seen.

The Chatham Islands have never, in any previous atlas of New Zealand, been integrated into the main maps of the country. This lack is particularly regrettable given that they are, after all, inhabited. Throughout this atlas the Chatham Islands are included, as data availability allows. The Auckland Islands, representative of New Zealand's sub-Antarctic islands, are also included on all 1:3,000,000 scale maps.

Plate 2: The Sea Floor

- **The Sea Floor in the Vicinity of New Zealand**
This relief model was created using Macromedia Freehand 5.5, VistaPro 3 and Adobe Photoshop 4. Various New Zealand Oceanic Institute charts were of assistance in data modelling, along with:

Charting Around New Zealand (CANZ) Group, 1996. *Undersea New Zealand. Bathymetric compilation, interpretation and terrain model*, second edition. National Institute of Water and Atmospheric Research, Wellington.

Charting Around New Zealand (CANZ) Group, 1997. *New Zealand Region Bathymetry 1:4,000,000*. NIWA Chart, Miscellaneous Series No. 73. National Institute of Water and Atmospheric Research, Wellington.

The CANZ group comprises L. Carter, J.D. Cook, G.A. Foster, R.D. Garlick, N.J. Litchfield, J.S. Mitchell and J.C. Wright.

While the model approximates what is currently known about the shape of the sea floor, it is important to remember that soundings are sparse in many areas, which remain little more than conjectural.

See also:
Kamp, P.J.J., 1986. "Late Cretaceous-Cenozoic Tectonic Development of the Southwest Pacific Region", in *Tectonophysics* 121, pp 225-251.

Stevens, G.R., 1980. *New Zealand Adrift: the theory of continental drift in a New Zealand setting*. A.H. & A.W. Reed, Wellington.

Stevens, G.R., 1985. *Lands in Collision: discovering New Zealand's past geography*. DSIR Science Information Publishing Centre, Wellington.

• The Louisville Seamount Chain
Watts, A.B., Weissel, J.K., Duncan, R.A. and Larson, R.L., 1988. "Origin of the Louisville Ridge and Its Relationship to the Eltanin Fracture Zone System", in *Journal of Geophysical Research* 93, B4, pp 3051-3077.

Lonsdale, P., 1988. "Geography and History of the Louisville Hotspot Chain in the Southwest Pacific", in *Journal of Geophysical Research* 93, B4, pp 3078-3104.

Thanks to Lionel Carter of the National Institute of Water and Atmospheric Research (NIWA) for his help in interpreting this material.

Plate 3: Geology

• **New Zealand Geology 1:3,000,000**
Based on: Riddolls, P.M., 1987. *New Zealand Geology, Geological Map of New Zealand 1:2,000,000*. Department of Scientific and Industrial Research, Wellington.

Also used:
Lensen, G.J., 1977. *Late Quaternary Tectonic Map of New Zealand 1:2,000,000*, first edition. New Zealand Geological Survey Miscellaneous series map 12.

New Zealand Geological Survey, 1973. *Quaternary Geology, North Island 1:1,000,000*, first edition. New Zealand Geological Survey Miscellaneous series map 5. Department of Scientific and Industrial Research, Wellington.

New Zealand Geological Survey, 1973. *Quaternary Geology, South Island 1:1,000,000*, first edition. New Zealand Geological Survey Miscellaneous series map 6. Department of Scientific and Industrial Research, Wellington.

See also:
Fleming, C.A., 1979. *The Geological History of New Zealand and its Life*. Auckland University Press, Auckland.

Gage, M., 1980. *Legends in the Rocks: an outline of New Zealand geology*. Whitcoulls, Christchurch.

Stevens, G.R., 1974. *Rugged Landscape: the geology of Central New Zealand, including Wellington, Wairarapa and the Marlborough Sounds*. A.H. & A.W. Reed, Wellington.

• **Geological Time Scale**
Based on: Figure 2: Geological Time Scale, from Suggate, R.P. and Riddolls, P.M., 1976; "Geology", in Wards, I. (ed), *New Zealand Atlas*. Government Printer, Wellington, p 91.
Note that the linear time scale used by Suggate and Riddolls has here been replaced by a logarithmic time scale, allowing more detail to be included for the most recent periods.

Plate 4: Mineral Resources

• **New Zealand Minerals 1:3,000,000**
Based on information from: Thompson, B.N., Brathwaite, R.L. and Christie, A.B., 1995. *Mineral Wealth of New Zealand*. Institute of Geological and Nuclear Sciences Information Series 33, Institute of Geological and Nuclear Sciences, Lower Hutt.

See also:
Forsyth, P.J., 1985. *A Beginner's Guide to New Zealand Rocks and Minerals*. New Zealand Government Printer, Wellington.

New Zealand Crown Minerals, 1996. *Mineral Resources of New Zealand*, 1996 edition. Louthean Publishing, in association with Ministry of Commerce.

Railton, G.T. and Watters, W.A., 1990. *Minerals of New Zealand*. Department of Scientific and Industrial Research, Geology and Geophysics, Lower Hutt.

• Minerals by Value 1996
Based on data from: "Mineral Production Summary 1996 Calendar Year", Ministry of Commerce, 1998. *New Zealand Mining* 23, Jan 1998, p 11.

Thank you to Annemarie Crampton, Ministry of Commerce for providing this table.

• Gold Production by Mining Area 1994-1998
Based on data from: Statistics New Zealand, 1996. *New Zealand Official Yearbook*. GP Publications and Statistics New Zealand, Wellington. Gold Production by mining operations, 1994, p 429.

• New Zealand Coals Ranked by Carbon and Energy Content
Based on data kindly provided by the Ministry of Commerce.

Plate 5: The Auckland Volcanic Field

• The Auckland Volcanic Field (Block Diagram)
Based on: Kermode, L.O., 1992. *Geology of the Auckland Urban Area. Geological Map of New Zealand 1:50,000 Sheet R11*. Institute of Geological and Nuclear Sciences, Lower Hutt.

Radiometric Dates: "Only four radiometric dates can be quoted with any confidence", (Kermode, 1992). These are (years before present):
• Rangitoto: 620±70 (Law, 1975; Robertson, 1986; Adams, 1986).
• Mt Wellington: 9160±320 (Grant-Taylor and Rafter, 1963, 1971; Searle, 1965; McDougall and others, 1969).
• Panmure Basin: 26,630±160 (McDougall and others, 1969).
• Crater Hill: 29,100±800 (Searle, 1965). There is a conspicuous terrace on the western flank of Pukekiwiriki volcano, which could have been cut during the marine transgression which peaked about 124,000 years ago (Campbell and Shackelton, 1986).

For more detailed information: Adams, M., 1986. "Thermoluminescence Dating of Plagioclase Feldspar". Unpublished MSc thesis, University of Auckland.

Grant-Taylor, T.C. and Rafter, T.A., 1963. "New Zealand Natural Radiocarbon Measurements I-V", in *Radiocarbon (American Journal of Science)* 5, pp 118-162.

Grant-Taylor, T.C. and Rafter, T.A., 1971. "New Zealand Radiocarbon Age Measurements 6", in *New Zealand Journal of Geology and Geophysics* 14 (2), pp 364-402.

Law, R.G., 1975. "Radiocarbon Dates for Rangitoto and Motutapu, a Consideration of the Dating Accuracy", in *New Zealand Journal of Science* 18, pp 441-451.

McDougall, I., Polach, H.A. and Stipp, J.J., 1969. "Excess Radiogenic Argon in Young Sub-aerial Basalts from the Auckland Volcanic Field, New Zealand", in *Geochemica and Cosmochimica* acta 33, pp 1485-1520.

Robertson, D.J., 1986. "A Paleomagnetic Study of Rangitoto Island, Auckland, New Zealand", in *New Zealand Journal of Geology and Geophysics* 29, pp 405-411.

Searle, E.J., 1961. *Auckland Volcanic District*. Department of Scientific and Industrial Research Information Series 49, pp 90-103.

Searle, E.J., 1964. *City of Volcanoes: a geology of Auckland*. Paul's Book Arcade, Auckland.

- **Relative Ages of Auckland Volcanoes**
Redrawn from: "Figure 2: Relative Time Sequence", in Smith, I.E.M. and Allen, S.R., 1993. *Volcanic Hazards at the Auckland Volcanic Field*. Volcanic Hazards Information Series No. 5, Ministry of Civil Defence, Wellington, p 7.

- **Eruption Sequence, Auckland Volcanoes**
Data taken from text discussion in: Smith, I.E.M. and Allen, S.R., 1993. *Volcanic Hazards at the Auckland Volcanic Field*. Volcanic Hazards Information Series No. 5, Ministry of Civil Defence, Wellington.

- **The Initial Phreatomagmatic Explosion**
Based on: "Figure 11.2a: Phreatomagmatic Explosions, Eruption Scenario", from Smith, I.E.M. and Allen, S.R., 1993. *Volcanic Hazards at the Auckland Volcanic Field*. Volcanic Hazards Information Series No. 5, Ministry of Civil Defence, Wellington, p 21.

Notes: The main block diagram was drawn as a perspective diagram to emphasise elevation. The volcanic cones are small features, so the vertical exaggeration of the block diagram is in the order of 1000% (10x). The cross-section accompanying Kermode's map is here integrated into the diagram, reinforcing the three-dimensional nature of the volcanic field.

Plate 6: The Last Ice Age

- **The Rakaia Piedmont Glacier (Block Diagram)**
Glacial advances and associated surfaces based on: Burrows, C.J. and Russell, J.B., 1975. "Moraines of the Upper Rakaia Valley", in *Journal of the Royal Society of New Zealand* 5 (4), pp 463-477.

New Zealand Geological Survey, 1973. *Quaternary Geology, South Island 1:1,000,000,* first edition. New Zealand Geological Survey Miscellaneous series map 6. Department of Scientific and Industrial Research, Wellington.

Soons, J.M. 1963. "The Glacial Sequence in Part of the Rakaia Valley, Canterbury, New Zealand", in *New Zealand Journal of Geology and Geophysics* 6 (5), pp 735-756.

Soons, J.M. and Gullentops, F.W., 1973. "Glacial Advances in the Rakaia Valley, New Zealand", in *New Zealand Journal of Geology and Geophysics* 16 (3), pp 425-438.

Wilson, D.D., 1989. *Quaternary Geology of Northwestern Canterbury Plains (NZMS 260 sheets L35 and parts sheets L36, M35 and M36) 1:100,000*. New Zealand Geological Survey miscellaneous series map 14. Department of Scientific and Industrial Research, Wellington.

See also:
Burrows, C.J., 1977. "Late Pleistocene and Holocene Glacial Episodes in the South Island, New Zealand, and Some Climatic Implications", in *New Zealand Geographer* 33, pp 34-37.

Fitzsimons, S.J., 1993. "Pleistocene Glaciation of the Southern Alps", in *New Zealand Geographer* 49 (1), pp 38-39.

Gage, M., 1985. "Glaciation in New Zealand – the First Century of Research", in *Quaternary Science Reviews* 4, pp 189-214.

Gage, M. and Suggate, R.P., 1958. "Glacial Chronology of the New Zealand Pleistocene", in *Bulletin of the Geological Society of America* 69, pp 589-598.

Mabin, M.C.G., 1984. "Late Pleistocene Glacial Sequence in the Lake Heron Basin, Mid-Canterbury", in *New Zealand Journal of Geology and Geophysics* 27, pp 191-202.

Suggate, R.P., 1965. "Late Pleistocene Geology of the Northern Part of the South Island, New Zealand", in *New Zealand Geological Survey Bulletin* NS 77. New Zealand Geological Survey, Wellington.

Suggate, R.P., 1990. "Pliocene and Pleistocene Glaciations of New Zealand", in *Quaternary Science Reviews* 9, pp 175-198.

- **Retreat of Permanent Snowline**
Based on: "Retreat of New Zealand Glaciers", in McKinnon, M. (ed), with Bradley, B. and Kirkpatrick, R., 1997. *New Zealand Historical Atlas: Visualising New Zealand*. David Bateman Ltd, in association with Historical Branch, Department of Internal Affairs, Auckland, Plate 7.

- **New Zealand at the Last Glacial Maximum**
Simplified from: "New Zealand at the Last Glacial Maximum", in McKinnon, M. (ed), with Bradley, B. and Kirkpatrick, R., 1997. *New Zealand Historical Atlas: Visualising New Zealand*. David Bateman Ltd, in association with Historical Branch, Department of Internal Affairs, Auckland, Plate 7.

Plate 7: Climate

- **Southern Hemisphere Pressure Field, January and July**
Redrawn from: Sturman, A.P. and Tapper, N.J., 1996. *The Weather and Climate of Australia and New Zealand*. Oxford University Press, Melbourne.

Thanks to Michelle Rogan for permission to use her line work to redraw this graphic.

- **Southern Hemisphere Cyclonic and Anticyclonic Activity, January and July**
Diagrams adapted from: Sturman, A.P. and Tapper, N.J., 1996. *The Weather and Climate of Australia and New Zealand*. Oxford University Press, Melbourne.

- **Climate Districts**
Based on: New Zealand Meteorological Service, 1983. *New Zealand Climatic Regions, 1:2,000,000*. Miscellaneous Publication 175 Part 2, Edition 1, New Zealand Meteorological Service, Wellington.

See also:
Mullan, A.B. and Renwick, J.A., 1996. *Predictability of New Zealand Climate on Monthly and Seasonal Timescales*. NIWA Science and Technology series No. 40, National Institute of Water and Atmospheric Research, Wellington.

Plate 8: Rainfall

- **Annual Rainfall**
Based on: New Zealand Meteorological Service, 1986. *New Zealand Annual Rainfall, Normal 1951-1980, 1:2,000,000*. Miscellaneous Publication 175 Part 6(i), Edition 1, New Zealand Meteorological Service, Wellington.

See also:
Sansom, J. and Tomlinson, A.I., 1994. *Rainfall Normals for New Zealand for the Period 1961 to 1990*. NIWA Science and Technology series No. 3, National Institute of Water and Atmosphere Research, Wellington.

Tomlinson, A.I., 1992. "Precipitation and Atmosphere", in *Waters of New Zealand*, Mosley, M.P. (ed), New Zealand Hydrological Society, Wellington North, pp 63-74.

- **Season of Most Raindays**
Based on: New Zealand Meteorological Service, 1986. *New Zealand Season of Most Raindays, 1:2,000,000*. Miscellaneous Publication 175 Part 7(v), Edition 1, New Zealand Meteorological Service, Wellington.

- **Variability of Average Rainfall**
Based on: New Zealand Meteorological Service, 1976. "The Variability of Average Rainfall", in Wards, I. (ed), 1976. *New Zealand Atlas*. Government Printer, Wellington.

- **Rainfall Cross-section, Bruce Bay to Banks Peninsula**
Derived from: New Zealand Meteorological Service, 1986. *New Zealand Annual Rainfall, Normal 1951-1980, 1:2,000,000*. Miscellaneous Publication 175 Part 6(i), Edition 1, New Zealand Meteorological Service, Wellington.

Note: Explanations on diagram kindly provided by Tony Trewinnard, Blue Skies Weather and Climate Services Ltd, Christchurch.

- **Westerly Rainfall Events and SALPEX**

Text based on: Wratt, D.S., Ridley, R.N., Sinclair, M.R., Larsen, H., Thompson, S.M., Henderson, R., Austin, G.L., Bradley, S.G., Auer, A., Sturman, A.P., Owens, I.F., Fitzharris, B., Ryan, B.F. and Gayet, J-F., 1996. "The New Zealand Southern Alps Experiment", in *Bulletin of the American Meteorological Society*, Spring 1996.

See also:
Chater, A.M. and Sturman, A.P., 1997. "Atmospheric Conditions Influencing the Spillover of Rainfall to Lee of the Southern Alps, New Zealand", in *International Journal of Climatology* 17, pp 1-16.

McGowan, H.A. and Sturman, A.P., 1996. "Short- and Medium-Term Trends in the Hydrometeorology of the Central Southern Alps, New Zealand", in *International Journal of Climatology* 16, pp 1267-1279.

McKendry, I.G., Sturman, A.P. and Owens, I.F., 1986. "A Study of Interacting Multi-Scale Wind Systems, Canterbury Plains, New Zealand", in *Meteorology and Atmospheric Physics* 35, pp 242-252.

Wratt, D.S. and Sinclair, M., 1996. "SALPEX – The Southern Alps Experiment", in *Water and Atmosphere* 4, pp 26-28.

Notes: The New Zealand Meteorological Service 1:2,000,000 map series is based on the 1951-1980 'rainfall normals'. That is, the annual rainfall is averaged over a period of thirty years, the minimum period considered reliable by meteorologists. Though the 1961-1990 rainfall normals were published in 1994, they have not yet been published in map form. This has particular significance in the light of the aberrant climate during the 1980s. Drier Mays were experienced in western New Zealand, while the Gisborne area suffered wetter than average March conditions. The west coast of the South Island endured very much wetter than normal Decembers and Januarys. These variations should be taken into account when using the maps rendered here.

Plate 9: Temperature, Sunshine and Wind

- **Mean Annual Temperature**

Based on: New Zealand Meteorological Service, 1985. *New Zealand Air Temperatures – Annual, 1:2,000,000.* Miscellaneous Publication 175 Part 4(v), Edition 1, New Zealand Meteorological Service, Wellington.

See also:
Salinger, M.J., McGann, R., Coutts, L., Collen, B. and Fouhy, E., 1992. *Temperature Trends in New Zealand and Outlying Islands, 1920-1990.* New Zealand Meteorological Service, Wellington.

Tomlinson, A.I. and Sansom, J., 1994. *Temperature Normals for New Zealand for the Period 1961 to 1990.* NIWA Science and Technology series No. 4. National Institute of Water and Atmospheric Research, Wellington.

- **Extreme Temperature Maximums**

Based on: New Zealand Meteorological Service, 1976. "Average Number of Days Per Year with a Maximum Temperature of 25°C or Greater", in Wards, I. (ed), 1976. *New Zealand Atlas.* Government Printer, Wellington.

See also:
Crawford, J.P., 1977. *High Temperatures in Canterbury, Marlborough and Hawke's Bay 7th February 1973.* Technical Information Circular 159, New Zealand Meteorological Service, Wellington.

- **Wind and Sunshine**

Data obtained from: Blue Skies Weather and Climate Services, Christchurch, and the National Institute of Water and Atmospheric Research digital database.

- **Orographically Reinforced Nor'wester, 1 August 1975**

Based on: Hill, H.W., 1976. *Severe Damage to Forests in Canterbury, New Zealand, Resulting from Orographically Reinforced Winds.* Miscellaneous Publication, New Zealand Meteorological Service, Wellington.

Notes: The New Zealand Meteorological Service 1:2,000,000 map series is based on the 1951-1980 'temperature normals'. That is, the annual temperature is averaged over a period of thirty years, the minimum period considered reliable by meteorologists. Though the 1961-1990 temperature normals were published in 1994, they have not yet been published in map form. This has particular significance in the light of the aberrant climate during the 1980s. Temperatures were generally higher in the 1980s than at any time in New Zealand's recorded history; indeed, the '80s are regarded as the warmest decade ever. This significant variation should be taken into account when using the maps rendered here.

Plate 10: La Niña and El Niño Rainfall

• **Rainfall January 1997, Selected Climate Stations**
Data obtained from: Blue Skies Weather and Climate Services, Christchurch, and the National Institute of Water and Atmospheric Research digital database.

Information for text and superlatives data (highest, greatest, lowest, etc.) for 1997 obtained from: McGavin, T., 1997. "Notable Recent Weather", in *Newsletter* 68, March 1997. Meteorological Society of New Zealand (Inc).

McGavin, T., 1997. "National Climate Summary", in *Newsletter* 68, March 1997. Meteorological Society of New Zealand (Inc).

• **Rainfall January 1998, Selected Climate Stations**
Data obtained from: Blue Skies Weather and Climate Services, Christchurch, and the National Institute of Water and Atmospheric Research digital database.

Information for text and superlatives data (highest, greatest, lowest, etc.) for 1998 obtained from: McGavin, T., 1998. "Notable Recent Weather", in *Newsletter* 72, March 1998. Meteorological Society of New Zealand (Inc).

Salinger, J., 1998. "National Climate Summary", in *Newsletter* 72, March 1998. Meteorological Society of New Zealand (Inc).

See also:
Australian Bureau of Meteorology, 1998. *The 1997 El Niño in the Western Pacific*. Australian Bureau of Meteorology, 31 January 1998 (CD-ROM).

Basher, R.E., 1998. "The 1997/98 El Niño Event: impacts, responses and outlooks for New Zealand". *Ministry of Research, Science and Technology Report* No. 73, Ministry of Research, Science and Technology, Wellington.

• **Southern Oscillation Index 1967-1998**
Data obtained from: http://www.tao.atmos.washington.edu/pacs/additional_ analyses/soi.html

• **Southern Oscillation Index, January 1997-January 1998**
Data obtained from: http://www.tao.atmos.washington.edu/pacs/additional_ analyses/soi.html

See also:
Gordon, N.D., 1985. "The Southern Oscillation: a New Zealand perspective", in *Journal of the Royal Society of New Zealand* 15 (2), pp 137-155.

Gordon, N.D., 1986. "The Southern Oscillation and New Zealand Weather", in *Bulletin of the American Meteorological Society* 114, pp 371-387.

Plate 11: Soils

• **New Zealand Soil Classification 1:3,000,000**
Based on: Hewitt, A.E., Horsfall, H. et al, 1995. *Soil Map of New Zealand: South Island, 1:1,000,000*. Manaaki Whenua Landcare Research, Lincoln.

Hewitt, A.E., Horsfall, H. et al, 1995. *Soil Map of New Zealand: North Island, 1:1,000,000*. Manaaki Whenua Landcare Research, Lincoln.

Leamy, M.L., 1974. "Soils of Stewart Island (Rakiura), New Zealand". *New Zealand Soil Survey Report* No. 22, New Zealand Soil Bureau.

Wright, A.C.S., 1959. "Soils of Chatham Island (Rekohu)". *New Zealand Soil Bureau Bulletin* No. 19, New Zealand Soil Bureau.

See also:

Clayden, B. and Hewitt, A.E., 1994. *Horizon Notation for New Zealand Soils*. Manaaki Whenua Landcare Research, Lincoln.

Hewitt, A.E., 1993. *Methods and Rationale of the New Zealand Soil Classification*. Landcare Research Science Series No. 2, Manaaki Whenua Landcare Research, Lincoln.

Hewitt, A.E., 1998. *New Zealand Soil Classification*, second edition. Landcare Research Science series No. 1, Manaaki Whenua Press, Lincoln.

Kelliher, F.M. and Scotter, D.R., 1992. "Evaporation, Soil, and Water", in *Waters of New Zealand*, Mosley, M.P. (ed), New Zealand Hydrological Society, Wellington North, pp 135-146.

• North Island Soils by Area, South Island Soils by Area

Data from: Hewitt, A.E., Horsfall, H. et al. 1995. *Soil Map of New Zealand: South Island, 1:1,000,000*. Manaaki Whenua Landcare Research, Lincoln.

Hewitt, A.E., Horsfall, H. et al. 1995. *Soil Map of New Zealand: North Island, 1:1,000,000*. Manaaki Whenua Landcare Research, Lincoln.

My grateful thanks to Alan Hewitt, of Manaaki Whenua Landcare Research, Dunedin, for supplying a copy of his soil classification, and for his advice and assistance.

Plate 12: Vegetation

• Contemporary New Zealand Vegetation 1:3,000,000

Based on: Newsome, P.F.J., 1987. *The Vegetative Cover of New Zealand*. New Zealand National Water and Soil Conservation Authority by the Water and Soil Directorate, Ministry of Works and Development, Wellington.

See also:

Dick, R.S., 1953. "A New Classification and Map of New Zealand Vegetation", in *New Zealand Geographer* 9, pp 58-65.

Page, M.J., 1987. "Revised Vegetation Classification – New Zealand Land Resource Inventory, 24 August 1987". Unpublished Report, Water and Soil Division, Ministry of Works and Development, Aokautere.

Wilde, R.H., 1996. "Updating the Vegetation Layer of the New Zealand Land Resource Inventory Database using Satellite Imagery: an initial investigation", in *New Zealand Geographer* 52 (1), April 1996.

• New Zealand Vegetation c.1840

Based on: McGlone, M.S., 1983. "Polynesian Deforestation of New Zealand: a preliminary synthesis", in *Archaeology in Oceania* 18 (1), pp 11-25.

McGlone, M.S., Salinger, M.J. and Moar, N.T., 1994. "Paleovegetation Studies of New Zealand's Climate Since the Last Glacial Maximum", in Wright, H.E. et al (eds), *Global Climate Since the Last Glacial Maximum*. University of Minnesota Press, Minneapolis.

"Extent of Forest c.1840", from McKinnon, M. (ed), with Bradley, B. and Kirkpatrick, R., 1997. *New Zealand Historical Atlas: Visualising New Zealand*. David Bateman Ltd, in association with Historical Branch, Department of Internal Affairs, Auckland, Plate 12.

• New Zealand Wetlands

Based on: Cromarty, P. and Scott, D.A. (compilers), 1996. *A Directory of Wetlands in New Zealand*. Department of Conservation, Wellington.

Ministry for the Environment, 1997. "Significant Wetlands in New Zealand", in *The State of New Zealand's Environment 1997*. GP Publications, Wellington, pp 7.85-7.86.

Plate 13: Pureora Mountain Vegetation

• Distribution of Vegetation, Pureora Mountain
Based on: Leathwick, J.R., 1990. *Vegetation Map of the Pureora Mountain Ecological Area, North Island, New Zealand*. Forest Research Institute Bulletin No. 157, New Zealand Ministry of Forestry.

See also:
Ericksen, N.J. (ed), 1978. *Critique of the BDC Report on the Social and Economic Impacts of Indigenous Forestry in Pureora*. University of Waikato, Environmental Studies Unit.

• Area of Vegetation Type (ha), Pureora Mountain Ecological Area
Based on: Leathwick, J.R., 1990. *Vegetation Map of the Pureora Mountain Ecological Area, North Island, New Zealand*. Forest Research Institute Bulletin No. 157, New Zealand Ministry of Forestry.

• Generalised Distribution of Vegetation Types by Altitude and Topography, Pureora Mountain Ecological Area
Based on: Leathwick, J.R., 1990. *Vegetation Map of the Pureora Mountain Ecological Area, North Island, New Zealand*. Forest Research Institute Bulletin No. 157, New Zealand Ministry of Forestry.

I wish to thank John Leathwick of Manaaki Whenua Landcare Research, Hamilton, for allowing me to use his research, and for his helpful comments on a draft of this plate.

Section 2: Environmental Shapes

Plate 14: Cultural and Environmental

• New Zealand Cultural and Environmental 1:3,000,000
Note: This map takes the place of the standard 'physical and political' maps found in most atlases. It is my view that the standard maps are misleading at best, suggesting a deterministic link between land elevation and 'cultural' data (such as roads, rail and towns). While this may have had some validity a century ago, and patterns can still be discerned in New Zealand even today, I believe that a much more meaningful link can be made between the point and line data of roads, rail and towns (cultural), and the area data of land use (environmental), as both are human artefacts. The material presented here is simplified from various land use maps, including the New Zealand Land Resource Inventory.

One interesting web site on which to view the New Zealand Land Resource Inventory is Manaaki Whenua Landcare Research's GUILD (Geographic User Interface to Landcare Data), found at: http://www.massey.landcare.cri.nz

Settlement Hierarchy based on: Dickson, Phil, 1993. "When is a City not a City? Place Names on Maps", in *Proceedings of the Seventeenth New Zealand Geographical Society Conference*, New Zealand Geographical Society, pp 70-72.

All place names checked against Land Information New Zealand's geographic database, found at: http://www.linz.govt.nz/databases/geographic/geoname.html

• Comparative City Sizes
Built-up areas from: Macquarie Library, 1994. *The Macquarie World Atlas*. The Macquarie Library Pty. Ltd., Sydney.
Note: This graphic is indicative only. It demonstrates the huge variation in population density within cities on the Pacific Rim: Southeast Asian cities are more densely populated (and therefore have a smaller area) than cities in the developed world. However, there is a fundamental difficulty with this crude approach. It is much more difficult to determine the boundaries of cities in the developing world, particularly in densely populated 'satellite' rural areas. This graphic is not intended to be used for detailed comparisons.

• Land Use by Area
Based on: "Land Use", in Statistics New Zealand, 1998. *New Zealand Official Yearbook*. GP Publications and Statistics New Zealand, Wellington, p 349.

Plate 15: Farming and Horticulture

• Agricultural Land Use 1996
Simplified from: New Zealand Land Resource Inventory, as retrieved from GUILD (Geographic User Interface to Landcare Data), found at: http://www.massey.landcare.cri.nz

• Land Use by Farm Type 1996
Based on: "Land Use by Farm Type, as at 30 June 1996", from Statistics New Zealand, 1998. *New Zealand Official Yearbook*. GP Publications and Statistics New Zealand, Wellington. Table 18.2, p 388.
Note: The table as presented in the 1998 *Yearbook* contains a significant amount of what Statistics New Zealand describes as 'estimates of very poor statistical quality'. Some estimates have been suppressed for 'reasons of respondent confidentiality'. Nevertheless, the graph gives a broad picture of land use. Note further that the seeming differences between this graph and the map it accompanies are merely different ways of grouping the data. Depicting this kind of information accurately on a map or in tabular form is difficult, as the different categories are not separated by 'hard' boundaries. Sheep farming merges into and mixes with dairying and cropping, for example. Testament to the difficulties involved is the large amount of ongoing research in New Zealand on land use classification and mapping. Please treat this information as indicative only.

• Relative Farm Expenditure on Sheep Farms During the Period of Restructuring, 1981-1992
Data from: Statistics New Zealand, 1996. *Agriculture Production Survey*. Statistics New Zealand, Wellington.
Note: Data is readily available beyond 1992, but I have chosen here to highlight the period when the agricultural reforms of the mid 1980s had most impact on farm finances. In particular, the huge blowout in the interest component is highlighted in this graph.

• Farmer Assistance 1995
Based on: "Farmer Assistance 1995", from Statistics New Zealand, 1998. *New Zealand Official Yearbook*. GP Publications and Statistics New Zealand, Wellington, p 390.

• Arable and Grain Crops: Area in Production by Regional Council 1996
Data from: Statistics New Zealand, 1998. *Agriculture Statistics 1996*. Statistics New Zealand, Wellington.

• Fruit Trees and Vines: Area in Production by Regional Council 1996
Data from: Statistics New Zealand, 1998. *Agriculture Statistics 1996*. Statistics New Zealand, Wellington.

• Outdoor-Grown Vegetables: Area in Production by Regional Council 1996
Data from: Statistics New Zealand, 1998. *Agriculture Statistics 1996*. Statistics New Zealand, Wellington.

See also:
Akroyd, P., 1993. *Politics, Economics and Pastoral Land Management in New Zealand: tenures for the times*. Information Paper No. 44, Centre for Resource Management, Lincoln University.

Bess, M., 1992. "Rural Women: a case study of dairy farm women", in *Proceedings of the Sixteenth New Zealand Geography Conference* Vol. 1, New Zealand Geographical Society, pp 31-36.

Davison, R.M., 1993. "A Review of Financial Production Trends in the New Zealand Sheep and Beef Sector". Address to the Meat and Wool Boards' Electoral Committee 24 March 1993, New Zealand Meat and Wool Boards' Economic Service, Wellington.

Dominy, M., 1993. "Lives Were Always Here: the inhabited landscape of the New Zealand high country". Reprint from *Anthropological Forum*.

Lees, N., 1993. *Changes in the New Zealand Kiwifruit Industry, 1980-1992*. Ministry of Agriculture and Fisheries Policy Technical Paper 92/20, Ministry of Agriculture and Fisheries, Wellington.

Ministry of Agriculture and Fisheries, 1994. *Aspects of New Zealand's Experience in Agricultural Reform since 1984: detailed historical analysis addressing the issue of the farm sector*. Ministry of Agriculture and Fisheries Policy Technical Paper 94/5, Ministry of Agriculture and Fisheries, Wellington.

Ministry of Agriculture and Fisheries, 1995. *Strategic Directions to the Year 2000: agriculture, horticulture, food*. Ministry of Agriculture and Fisheries, Wellington.

Sandrey, R.A. and Reynolds, R. (eds), 1990. *Farming Without Subsidies – New Zealand's Recent Experience*. Ministry of Agriculture and Fisheries Policy Services, GP Books, Wellington.

Willis, R., 1991. "Farming", in *Pacific Viewpoint* 32 (2), pp 163-170.

Plate 16: Commercial Fisheries

• **The Exclusive Economic Zone (EEZ) and Quota Management Areas (QMAs), 1998**
Based on: Kelly, J. and Marshall, B., 1996. *Atlas of New Zealand Boundaries*. Auckland University Press, Auckland.

With reference to: Clement and Associates Ltd., 1998. *New Zealand Commercial Fisheries: The Atlas of Area Codes and TACCs, 1998/99*. Clement and Associates, Tauranga.

• **1997-98 Fish Catch**
Data courtesy of: Clement and Associates Ltd., 1998. *New Zealand Commercial Fisheries: The Atlas of Area Codes and TACCs, 1998/99*. Clement and Associates, Tauranga.

• **Registered Commercial Fishing Vessels, 1997**
Data from: "Registered Commercial Fishing Vessels", from Statistics New Zealand, 1998. *New Zealand Official Yearbook*. GP Publications and Statistics New Zealand, Wellington. Table 19.14, p 427. Data at 30 September 1997.

• **Percentage of Total Catch by Type of Fleet, 1997**
Simplified from: "Catch by Domestic and Foreign Fishers", data supplied by New Zealand Fishing Industry Board.

• **The Orange Roughy Fishery, 1980-81 to 1996-97 seasons**
Data from: Annala, J.H., 1998. *Report from the Fishery Assessment Plenary, May 1998: stock assessment and yield estimates*. Ministry of Fisheries, Wellington.

See also:
Collier, K., 1990. *Fisheries and Forestry*. Science and Research Internal Report 74. Department of Conservation, Wellington.

Fisheries Task Force, 1992. *Sustainable Fisheries*. Report to the Ministry of Fisheries on the review of the fisheries legislation, April 1992. Ministry of Fisheries, Wellington.

New Zealand National Fisheries Management Advisory Committee, 1983. "Future Policy for the Inshore Fishery", a discussion paper, August 1983. Ministry of Agriculture and Fisheries, Wellington.

Plate 17: Chatham Islands Agriculture and Fisheries

• **Chatham Islands Land Use, Extent of Pastoral Land, Agricultural Processing Factories 1996**
Simplified from: Department of Lands and Survey, 1983. *Existing Land Use and Archaeology, NZMS 290 Chatham Islands, New Zealand Land Inventory, 1:1,000,000*. Department of Lands and Survey, Wellington.

• **Land Use, Chatham Islands and New Zealand Compared**
New Zealand data from: "Land Use by Farm Type, as at 30 June 1996", from Statistics New Zealand, 1998. *New Zealand Official Yearbook*. GP Publications and Statistics New Zealand, Wellington. Table 18.2, p 388.

Chatham Islands data estimated for 1996. Estimates based on: "Farmland Use by Regional Council Area as at 30 June 1994", from Statistics New Zealand, 1996. *New Zealand Official Yearbook*. GP Publications and Statistics New Zealand, Wellington. Table 18.1, p 369-70.

• **The Chatham Islands Crayfish Catch, 1964-68, 1998**
Data sourced from: Clement and Associates Ltd., 1998. *New Zealand Commercial Fisheries: The Atlas of Area Codes and TACCs, 1998/99*. Clement and Associates, Tauranga.

George, W., 1993. *The Chatham Islands – a backgrounder*. Department of Internal Affairs, Wellington.

Ministry of Fisheries (1998 vessels).

See also:

Clay, A.H., 1970. "The Chatham Islands Rock Lobster Industry". Unpublished MA thesis, Department of Geography, University of Canterbury.

• The Chatham Island Fishing Industry Annual Catch
1992-93 graph based on data from: George, W., 1993. *The Chatham Islands – a backgrounder*. Department of Internal Affairs, Wellington.

1997-98 graph based on data supplied courtesy Ministry of Fisheries.

• Significance of Chatham Islands Catch 1997-98
New Zealand data courtesy of: Clement and Associates Ltd., 1998. *New Zealand Commercial Fisheries: The Atlas of Area Codes and TACCs, 1998/99*. Clement and Associates, Tauranga.

Chatham Islands data courtesy of Ministry of Fisheries.

See also:

Department of Conservation, 1996. *Draft Chatham Islands Conservation Management Strategy: context, goals, objectives, implementation and schedules*. Canterbury Conservancy management planning series No. 9, Department of Conservation, Wellington.

Macmillan, D.R., 1980. *Land Development in the Chatham Islands*. Farm Advisory Officer, Ministry of Agriculture and Fisheries, Wellington.

Statistics New Zealand, 1997. *What the Census Told Us... Chatham Islands District*. Statistics New Zealand, Wellington.

Communicado, 1995. *Heartland: Chatham Islands*. TVNZ, Auckland.

Plate 18: Forestry

• Exotic Forests, Major Owners, Mills 1996
Based on: Carter Holt Harvey Forests, 1996. *New Zealand Plantation Forestry: Land Interests of Major Forest Owners, 1:1,000,000*, revised September 1996. Carter Holt Harvey Forests, Auckland.
Note: Ownership of New Zealand's exotic forests is in a constant state of flux. Because small companies own 30% of the resource, it is difficult to keep track of ownership.

• Average Five-Yearly Timber Yield by Region
Data provided courtesy of Ministry of Agriculture and Forestry.
Note: Only the 1991-96 figures are actual; the other five-year periods are estimated data.

• Indigenous and Exotic Timber Production 1921-1997
Based on: "Timber Production, Indigenous and Plantation", from Statistics New Zealand, 1998. *New Zealand Official Yearbook*. GP Publications and Statistics New Zealand, Wellington, p 414.

See also:

Cox, O., Horgan, G. and Maplesden, F., 1993. *The New Zealand Forestry Sector in 1993*. New Zealand Forest Research Institute Bulletin No. 185.

Cumberworth, S., Bacon, P. and Jarvis, P., 1995. *Forestry and Community Part 2: statistical data and commentary by wood supply region*. Ministry of Agriculture and Fisheries Policy Technical Paper 95/2, Ministry of Agriculture and Fisheries, Wellington.

Ministry of Forestry, 1993. *Forestry Sector Issues: a post-election briefing for the Minister of Forestry*. Ministry of Forestry, Wellington.

Plate 19: West Coast Forests

• West Coast Forestry 1987-1998, Timberlands West Coast Interests
Based on: Timberlands West Coast, 1997. *West Coast Forestry: Sustaining Our Forestry Future: a guide to Timberlands West Coast Ltd*. Timberlands West Coast Ltd, Greymouth.

Material from the Timberlands West Coast website: http://www.timberlands.co.nz

Material from the Native Forest Action website: http://converge.org.nz/nfa/

Note: A number of the sawmills operational in 1993 have closed; others have changed owners. Various mills have been embroiled in controversy during that time: Paynter Sawmills Ltd in Whataroa, for example, argued for an extension of time to clear-fell rimu in the Ianthe Forest from the 1992 deadline. The 1993 date is representative of the number and size of mills operational during the period 1987-1998.

• **Land Ownership in New Zealand and on the West Coast, 1998**
Data provided courtesy of Department of Conservation.

• **Management Status of West Coast Beech Forests, 1998**
Material from the Timberlands West Coast website: http://www.timberlands.co.nz

• **Origin of Submissions to the 1987 Public Discussion Document: "Resource Management Strategies in South Westland".**
Based on: Scott, G.A., 1989. "Environmental Politics and Place: a political geography of the South Westland native forests controversy". Unpublished MA thesis, Department of Geography, University of Canterbury.

See also:
Dawson, D.G. and Flux, J.E.C, 1975. *Log Now, Pay Later. An ecological evaluation of the beech forest schemes.* Beech Forest Information Series No. 3, Beech Forest Action Committee.

Department of Conservation, 1996. *West Coast: conservation management strategy 1996-2005 draft,* vols 1-2. West Coast Conservancy conservation management planning series 2, 1996. Department of Conservation, Wellington.

Frontline, 1993. *Green or Grab: clear felling of rainforest in South Westland.* TVNZ, Auckland.

Ministry for the Environment, 1986. *West Coast Forests: integrating conservation and development.* Preliminary report of working party, New Zealand Ministry for the Environment.

Ministry of Forestry, 1994. *Regional Studies: West Coast.* Ministry of Forestry, Wellington.

Native Forests Council, 1977. *The Future of West Coast Forests.* A submission. Native Forests Council.

Parliamentary Commissioner for the Environment, 1995. *Timberlands West Coast Ltd. Draft Beech Management Prescriptions: review panel report.* Parliamentary Commissioner for the Environment.

Pawson, E.J. and Scott, G.A., 1992. "The Regional Consequences of Economic Restructuring: the West Coast, New Zealand (1984-1991)", in *Journal of Rural Studies* 8 (4), pp 373-386.

Scott, G.A., 1995. "Place Struggles: a critical analysis of changing patterns of work, unemployment and local development in New Zealand and the West Coast of the South Island". Unpublished PhD thesis, Department of Geography, University of Canterbury.

Steng, H., 1990. *Area of Freehold Land in the West Coast Region Under Indigenous Forest Cover and Effects of the Indigenous Forest Policy.* West Coast Regional Council, Hokitika.

Plate 20: The Conservation Estate

• **The Conservation Estate, 1997**
Based on: Kelly, J. and Marshall, B., 1996. *Atlas of New Zealand Boundaries.* Auckland University Press, Auckland.

Updated courtesy of the Department of Conservation, and checked against the map "Parks of New Zealand", from Statistics New Zealand, 1998. *New Zealand Official Yearbook.* GP Publications and Statistics New Zealand, Wellington, p 358, and Figure 9.8: "Land Administered by the Department of Conservation in 1996", from Ministry for the Environment, 1997. *The State of New Zealand's Environment 1997.* GP Publications, Wellington.

- **Area of National Parks and Reserves, 1997.**
Based on material from: Ministry for the Environment, 1997. *The State of New Zealand's Environment 1997.* GP Publications, Wellington.

Note: The totals in this graph add up to more than 100%. This is because some special areas, which I have grouped together, are in fact scattered throughout different classes of reserves. Examples of this are the Wilderness, Sanctuary and Ecological Areas. The main purpose of the graph is to demonstrate the many different classifications of reserved land in New Zealand, and to give an indication of the amount of land reserved under each classification.

See also:
Department of Conservation, 1993. *Greenprint Overview: the state of conservation in New Zealand.* Volume One of the brief to the incoming Government. Department of Conservation, Wellington.

Department of Conservation, 1998. *Conservation Action: conservation at work in 1997/1998.* Department of Conservation, Wellington.

Plate 21: Environmental Issues

- **The 'Black Drain': Industrial Discharge into the Tarawera River Catchment 1996**
Information compiled from: Environment B.O.P., 1996. *Proposed Regional Plan for the Tarawera River Catchment.* Bay of Plenty Regional Council.

- **Measurements of River Pollution, Tarawera River 1996**
Based on: Environment B.O.P., 1996. *Proposed Regional Plan for the Tarawera River Catchment.* Bay of Plenty Regional Council.

- **Ozone Depletion, October 16, 1998**
Based on: material downloaded from the United States Environmental Protection Agency's web site at: http://www.epa.gov
The latest ozone hole information, often accompanied by diagrams, is available at a wide variety of web sites.

- **Average October Total Ozone, Halley Bay, Antarctica, 1960-1994**
Based on: Figure 5.20: "Average October Total Ozone, Halley Bay, Antarctica, 1957-94", from Ministry for the Environment, 1997. *The State of New Zealand's Environment 1997.* GP Publications, Wellington, p 5-37.

See also:
Cambridge Research Group, 1996. *Ozone.* Cambridge Research Group Ltd, Cambridge.

Statistics New Zealand, 1998. *Air Quality, Climate Change and the Ozone Layer.* Statistics New Zealand, Wellington.

World Meteorological Organisation, 1995. *Rapid Ozone Decline Over the Antarctic: press release.* World Meteorological Organisation No. 576.

World Meteorological Organisation, 1998. *Update on the State of the Ozone Layer in 1997 until April 1998.* World Meteorological Organisation, Geneva.

- **Potentially Contaminated Sites by Region, 1992-1996.**
Material assembled from: Ministry for the Environment, 1997. *The State of New Zealand's Environment 1997.* GP Publications, Wellington.

Ministry for the Environment, 1997. *The 1995 National Landfill Census.* Ministry for the Environment, Wellington.

Worsley Consultants, 1992. *Potentially Contaminated Sites in New Zealand: a broad scale assessment.* Ministry for the Environment, Wellington.

See also:
Memon, P.A. and Perkins, H.C. (eds), 1993. *Environmental Planning in New Zealand.* Dunmore Press, Palmerston North.

Ministry for the Environment, 1995. *Environment 2010 Strategy. A Statement of the Government Strategy on the Environment.* Ministry for the Environment, Wellington.

Ministry of Foreign Affairs and Trade, 1994. *International Environmental Issues: a New Zealand perspective.* Information Bulletin No. 50, United Nations conference on environment and development, 1992.

Plate 22: Resource Management of the Avon-Heathcote Estuary

• **The Avon-Heathcote Estuary: Conflicting Uses of a Sensitive Ecological Area**
Based on: Owen, S-J. (ed), 1992. *The Estuary: Where Our Rivers Meet The Sea. Christchurch's Avon-Heathcote Estuary and Brooklands Lagoon.* Parks Unit, Christchurch City Council, Christchurch.

See also:
Crossland, A., 1996. *Port Hills Birdlife: inventory, analysis and restoration potential.* Parks Unit, Christchurch City Council, Christchurch.

• **Idealised Sediment Core from the Estuary over the Last 600 Years**
Redrawn from: Owen, S-J. (ed), 1992. *The Estuary: Where Our Rivers Meet The Sea. Christchurch's Avon-Heathcote Estuary and Brooklands Lagoon.* Parks Unit, Christchurch City Council, Christchurch.

See also:
Briggs, L. and Keller, J., 1991. *The Estuary and Environment: issues and opportunities.* Technical Report No. 92/4, School Resource Kit, Environmental Policy and Planning Unit, Christchurch City Council, Christchurch.

Canterbury Regional Council, Christchurch City Council and Department of Conservation, 1992. *Avon and Heathcote Catchment, Rivers and Estuary: issues and options for managing these resources.* Report No. R92/32, Canterbury Regional Council, Christchurch.

Hicks, D.M., 1993. *Sedimentation and Erosion in the Avon-Heathcote Catchment and Estuary.* Miscellaneous Report No. 27, Freshwater Division, National Institute of Water and Atmospheric Research.

Hutchison, A.H., 1972. "Resource management in the estuarine environment: a case study, the Avon-Heathcote Estuary, Christchurch". Unpublished MSc thesis, Department of Geography, University of Canterbury.

McKenna, A.P., 1979. "A recreational geography of the Avon-Heathcote Estuary, Christchurch". Unpublished MA thesis, Department of Geography, University of Canterbury.

Plate 23: Natural Hazards

• **Natural Hazards of Geological Origin**
Material compiled from: Blong, 1996. *Natural Hazards: their potential in the Pacific Southwest.* Australian Geological Survey Organisation.

See also: Dingwall, P.R., Fitzharris, B.B. and Owens, I.F., 1989. "Natural Hazards and Visitor Safety in New Zealand's National Parks", in *New Zealand Geographer* 45, 1989, pp 68-79.

Glade, T. and Crozier, M., 1997. *Rainfall Related Landslides in New Zealand: a bibliography.* Department of Geography, Research School of the Earth Sciences, Victoria University of Wellington.

Ministry of Agriculture and Fisheries, 1993. *Risk Perceptions and Management Responses to Risk in New Zealand Farming and Horticulture.* Ministry of Agriculture and Fisheries Policy Technical paper 93/17, Ministry of Agriculture and Fisheries, Wellington.

Roche, M.M., 1997. "'The Land We Have We Must Hold': soil erosion and soil conservation in late nineteenth- and twentieth-century New Zealand", in *Journal of Historical Geography* 23 (4), pp 447-458.

• **Natural Hazards of Meteorological Origin**
Material compiled from: Blong, 1996. *Natural Hazards: their potential in the Pacific Southwest.* Australian Geological Survey Organisation.

See also:
Finklestein, J., 1971. *The 1969-70 Drought in New Zealand*. Technical note 204, New Zealand Meteorological Service, Wellington.

Harmsworth, G.R. and Page, M.J., 1991. *A Review of Selected Storm Damage Assessments in New Zealand*. Scientific Report No. 9, DSIR Land and Resources, Department of Scientific and Industrial Research.

Ministry of Agriculture and Fisheries, 1991. *The 1988/89 South Island Drought and the Assistance Package Provided by the Government*. Ministry of Agriculture and Fisheries Policy Technical Paper 91/2, Ministry of Agriculture and Fisheries, Wellington.

Mosley, P.M. and Pearson, C.P. (eds), 1997. *Floods and Droughts: the New Zealand experience*. New Zealand Hydrological Society, Wellington.

See also:
Ericksen, N.J., 1986. *Creating Flood Disasters? New Zealand's need for a new approach to urban flood hazard*. Water and Soil Miscellaneous Publication No. 77, Ministry of Works and Development, Wellington.

Ericksen, N.J. and Barbour, R.H., 1985. "Natural Hazards: people and processes", in *Proceedings of the Thirteenth New Zealand Geographical Society Conference 1985*, New Zealand Geographical Society.

Gregory, G., Loveridge, A. and Gough, J., 1997. "Social and Cultural Aspects of Natural Hazards, Perception and Response", in *New Zealand Geographer* 53 (1), April 1997, pp 47-54.

Hull, A.G. and Coory, R. (eds), 1995. *Proceedings of the Natural Hazards Management Workshop '95*, Auckland 28-29 November 1995. IGNS Information Series No. 38, Institute of Geological and Nuclear Sciences, Lower Hutt.

Johnston, D.M. and Kingsbury, P.A. (eds), 1998. *Proceedings of the Natural Hazards Management Workshop*, Christchurch 4-5 November 1998. IGNS Information Series No. 45, Institute of Geological and Nuclear Sciences, Lower Hutt.

Ministry for the Environment, 1997. *The State of New Zealand's Environment 1997*. GP Publications, Wellington.

Ministry of Civil Defence, 1996. *Risk Management and Natural Disasters*. Special Issue of *Tephra* 15 (1), June 1996.

Plate 24: Volcano, Avalanche and Earthquake

• Ruapehu Volcanic Hazard
Simplified from: Department of Scientific and Industrial Research (DSIR), 1987. *Volcanic Hazard Map of Tongariro National Park Region, 1:1,000,000: volcanic risk map of Tongariro National Park and surrounding areas showing zones of risk from forms of volcanic activity*. DSIR, Wellington.

See also:
Montgomery, R.L. and Keys, H.J.R., 1993. *Volcanic Hazard Management in Tongariro National Park*. Department of Conservation Science and Research Series No. 61, Department of Conservation, Wellington.

Williams, K., 1985. *Volcanoes of the South Wind: a field guide to the volcanoes and landscape of Tongariro National Park*. Tongariro Natural History Society, Wellington.

• Ruapehu Ash Cloud, 17 June 1996
Image supplied courtesy of Manaaki Whenua Landcare Research.

• Avalanche Tracks and 1981 Hazard Index, Central Section of Milford Road
Fitzharris, B.B. and Owens, I.F., 1981. *Avalanche Atlas of the Milford Road and an Assessment of the Hazards to Traffic*, New Zealand Mountain Safety Council Avalanche Committee, Report No. 4, Wellington.

See also:
Dingwall, P.R. (ed), 1977. *The Avalanche Hazard in New Zealand*. Department of Lands and Survey Information Series No. 2, Proceedings of a seminar, Christchurch, November 1976.

Glade, T. and Crozier, M., 1996. "Towards a National Landslide Information Base for New Zealand", in *New Zealand Geographer* 52 (1), April 1996, pp 29-40.

Owens, I.F. and Fitzharris, B.B., 1985. "Assessing Avalanche Hazard on the Milford Track", in *Proceedings of the Thirteenth New Zealand Geographical Society Conference 1985*, New Zealand Geographical Society, pp 122-124.

• **Average Daily Traffic Flows, Milford Road, 1981.**
Fitzharris, B.B. and Owens, I.F., 1981. *Avalanche Atlas of the Milford Road and an Assessment of the Hazards to Traffic*, New Zealand Mountain Safety Council Avalanche Committee, Report No. 4, Wellington.

• **Murchison Earthquake, 1929, Changes to the Landscape**
Compiled from: Adams, J., 1981. "Earthquake-dammed Lakes in New Zealand", in *Geology* 9, pp 215-219.

Downes, G.L., 1995. *Atlas of Isoseismal Maps of New Zealand Earthquakes*. Monograph 11, Institute of Geological and Nuclear Sciences, Wellington.

Henderson, J., 1937. "The West Nelson Earthquakes of 1929", in *New Zealand Journal of Science and Technology* 19 (2), pp 65-144.

McKinnon, M. (ed), with Bradley, B. and Kirkpatrick, R., 1997. *New Zealand Historical Atlas: Visualising New Zealand*. David Bateman Ltd in association with Historical Branch, Department of Internal Affairs, Auckland.

See also:
Eiby, G.A., 1980. *Earthquakes*. Heinemann, Auckland.

Wallace, C., 1995. "Earthquakes in the New Zealand Region", in *New Zealand Journal of Geography* 99, April 1995, pp 3-17.

Plate 25: Hail, Cyclone and Flood

• **Approximate Tracks of Hailstorms, October to March, 1980-1983**
Map compiled from: Miller, I.D., 1983. *Preliminary Report on the Canterbury Hail Project*. New Zealand Meteorological Service, Christchurch.

See also:
Neale, A.A., 1977. *A Climatology of Severe Hailstorms in New Zealand*. Technical Note No. 230, New Zealand Meteorological Service, Wellington.

Tomlinson, A.I., 1976. "Frequency of Thunderstorms in New Zealand", in *New Zealand Journal of Science* 19 (3), pp 319-325.

• **Halswell Tornado Storm, 19 January 1983**
Based on data presented in: Miller, I.D., 1983. "Report on Hailstorm and Tornado in the Christchurch Area on 19 January 1983". New Zealand Meteorological Service Unpublished Report.

• **Tracks of Selected Tropical Cyclones, 1968-1997**
Map compiled from: Bell, D.H., 1975. "High Intensity Rainstorms and Geological Hazards: Cyclone Alison March 1975, Kaikoura, New Zealand", in *Engineering Geology Bulletin* 14, pp 189-200.

Hill, H.W., 1970. "The Precipitation in New Zealand Associated with the Cyclone of Early April 1968". Meteorological Office Note No. 67, reprinted from the *New Zealand Journal of Science* 13 (4), pp 641-662.

Kerr, I.S., 1976. *Tropical Storms and Hurricanes in the Southwest Pacific, November 1939 to April 1969*. Miscellaneous Publication No. 148, New Zealand Meteorological Service, Wellington.

McGavin, T., 1997. "Notable Recent Weather: Cyclone Fergus, 29-31 December 1996, Cyclone Drena, 10-12 January 1997", in *Newsletter 68*. Meteorological Society of New Zealand, Wellington, pp 7-12.

Revell, C.G, 1981. *Tropical Cyclones in the Southwest Pacific, November 1969 to April 1979*. Miscellaneous Publication No. 170, New Zealand Meteorological Service, Wellington.

Tomlinson, A.I., 1975. *Cyclone Alison.* Technical Information Circular No. 148, New Zealand Meteorological Service, Wellington.

• **The Impact of Cyclone Bola, East Cape, 1988**
Compiled from: *Appendix to the Journals of the House of Representatives*, I-11A, 1989. Inquiry into Planning for Flood Mitigation: map facing foreword.

Ministry of Civil Defence, 1988. *Cyclone Bola; 7-10 March 1988.* Ministry of Civil Defence, Wellington.

Poverty Bay Catchment Board, 1978. *Red Report.* Poverty Bay Catchment Board, Gisborne.

Sinclair, M.R., 1993. "A Diagnostic Study of the Extratropical Precipitation Resulting from Tropical Cyclone Bola", in *Monthly Weather Review* 121, pp 2690-2707.

Sinclair, M.R., 1997. "Anatomy of a Storm", in *Tephra* 16, June 1997, pp 6-13.

Taylor Report, 1970. *Wise Land Use and Community Development: Report of Technical Committee into Inquiry into the Problems of the Poverty Bay-East Cape District of New Zealand.* Water and Soil Division, Ministry of Works and Development, Wellington.

See also:
Korte, C.J., 1989. *The Effect of Cyclone Bola on Hill-country Farms in the Gisborne-East Coast Region: physical damage, government assistance, cash flows and debt.* Ministry of Agriculture and Fisheries, Flock House, Bulls.

Singleton, P., 1990. "Cyclone Bola 1". *Alpha* 63, DSIR Division of Land and Soil Sciences, New Zealand MAFTech, Department of Scientific and Industrial Research Publishing, Wellington.

Trotter, C., 1990. "Cyclone Bola 2". *Alpha* 64, DSIR Division of Land and Soil Sciences, New Zealand MAFTech, Department of Scientific and Industrial Research Publishing, Wellington.

Webber, D., 1992. *Cyclone Bola: Agricultural assistance scheme: social and economic impact study.* Ministry of Agriculture and Fisheries Policy and Technical Paper 90/1, Ministry of Agriculture and Fisheries, Wellington.

• **Southland Flood, January 1984**
Material derived from: "Figure 12" in Hill, H.W. and Quayle, A.M., 1984. "The Southland Flood of January 1984". Unpublished Report, New Zealand Meteorological Service, Wellington.

Erickson, N.J., 1985. *Creating Flood Disasters?* Miscellaneous Publication No. 77, New Zealand National Water and Soil Conservation Authority, Wellington.

Hessell, J.W.D. and Lopdell, J.H.A., 1979. *The Southland/Otago Floods of October 1978.* Technical Information Circular No. 171, New Zealand Meteorological Service, Wellington.

Hessell, J.W.D. and Renwick, J.A., 1980. *The Otago/Southland Floods of January 1980.* Technical Information Circular No. 178, New Zealand Meteorological Service, Wellington.

• **Flooded Area, Invercargill North, January 1984**
Material derived from: Hill, H.W. and Quayle, A.M., 1984. "The Southland Flood of January 1984". Unpublished Report, New Zealand Meteorological Service, Wellington.

See also:
Auer, A.H. jnr., 1997. "Heavy Rainstorms and Snowstorms: causes and effects", in *Tephra* 16, June 1997, pp 20-23.

Ericksen, N.J. and Barbour, R.H., 1985. "Natural Hazards: people and processes", in *Proceedings of the Thirteenth New Zealand Geographical Society Conference 1985*, New Zealand Geographical Society.

McKerchar, A.I. and Pearson, C.P., 1989. *Flood Frequency in New Zealand.* Publication No. 20, Hydrology Centre, Christchurch.

Reid, S. and Turner, R., 1997. "Wind Storms", in *Tephra* 16, June 1997, pp 24-32.

Section 3: Historical Shapes

Plate 26: Discovery

• The Spread of Polynesian Settlement in the Southern Pacific

Data obtained from: Irwin, G.J., 1992. *The Prehistoric Exploration and Colonisation of the Pacific*. Cambridge University Press, Cambridge.

McKinnon, M. (ed), with Bradley, B. and Kirkpatrick, R., 1997. *New Zealand Historical Atlas: Visualising New Zealand*. David Bateman Ltd in association with Historical Branch, Department of Internal Affairs, Auckland.

Note: The base map projection for the two maps on this plate was generated specifically to show the islands of the South Pacific 'spread out', as they might appear if approached from the north. This is a more natural way of portraying the southern Pacific, echoing the view of the explorers, who came to New Zealand from more northerly islands (Polynesians), or from the Northern Hemisphere (Europeans). It has nothing whatever to do with the concept of the 'upside-down' map.

See also:
Davidson, J., 1987. *The Prehistory of New Zealand*, second edition. Longman Paul, Auckland.

Irwin, G.J., 1989. "Against, Across and Down the Wind: a case for systematic exploration of the remote Pacific Islands", in *Journal of the Polynesian Society* 98 (2), pp 167-206.

Lewis, D., 1994. *We, The Navigators: the ancient art of landfinding in the Pacific*, second edition. University of Hawaii Press, Honolulu.

• European Exploration of the Southern Pacific

Voyage paths from:
Historical Atlas Collection, c1950. *Pacific Explorers from Magellan to Cook*. Historical Atlas Collection 1/1/2, Alexander Turnbull Library, Wellington.
Historical Atlas Collection, c1950. *Routes of Tasman and Cook 1769-70*. Historical Atlas Collection 1/1/2, Alexander Turnbull Library, Wellington.

McKinnon, M. (ed), with Bradley, B. and Kirkpatrick, R., 1997. *New Zealand Historical Atlas: Visualising New Zealand*. David Bateman Ltd in association with Historical Branch, Department of Internal Affairs, Auckland.

See also:
MacKay, D.M., 1985. *In the Wake of Cook: exploration, science and empire, 1780-1801*. Victoria University Press, Wellington.

Maling, P.B., 1996. *Historic Charts & Maps of New Zealand, 1642-1875*. Reed, Auckland.

Plate 27: Māori Settlement

• Iwi at the time of European Contact

Iwi information from: McKinnon, M. (ed), with Bradley, B. and Kirkpatrick, R., 1997. *New Zealand Historical Atlas: Visualising New Zealand*. David Bateman Ltd in association with Historical Branch, Department of Internal Affairs, Auckland. Refer specifically to Plates 17-26 (the ten 'Papatuanuku' plates).

Note: Unlike the 'Papatuanuku' plates of the *New Zealand Historical Atlas*, which I designed as regional oblique views (emphasising the elevation of the land) – 'stages' upon which the 'actors' lived their lives – this view of the New Zealand islands emphasises vegetation cover. I have made this selection based on extensive reading which convinces me that the floral environment was more relevant to the lives of the first Māori than mere height above sea level. The oblique view serves three purposes: (1) it emphasises the more densely populated North Island; (2) the viewpoint is from the north-east, the direction from which the first colonisers likely came; and (3) unlike a standard map view, it invites the reader to begin from a defined starting point (the north-east) and explore the New Zealand islands in a manner perhaps similar to the first settlers.

• Nga Unga Waka: the Landing Places of the Canoes

Canoe landing places from: McKinnon, M. (ed), with Bradley, B. and Kirkpatrick, R., 1997. *New Zealand Historical Atlas: Visualising New Zealand*. David Bateman Ltd in association with Historical Branch, Department of Internal Affairs, Auckland.

- **Population Growth During the Pre-European Period**

Graph redrawn from: "Conceptual Models for Early Population Growth", in McKinnon, M. (ed), with Bradley, B. and Kirkpatrick, R., 1997. *New Zealand Historical Atlas: Visualising New Zealand*. David Bateman Ltd in association with Historical Branch, Department of Internal Affairs, Auckland, Plate 11: Settlement.

- **Forest Burning: Radiocarbon Dates for Charcoal**

Graph redrawn from: "Charcoal Radiocarbon Date Frequencies", in McKinnon, M. (ed), with Bradley, B. and Kirkpatrick, R., 1997. *New Zealand Historical Atlas: Visualising New Zealand*. David Bateman Ltd in association with Historical Branch, Department of Internal Affairs, Auckland, Plate 12: A Forceful Impact.

Plate 28: Colonial New Zealand

- **Mission Stations and Te Tiriti o Waitangi**

Number of Signatories based on a map in: Orange, C., *The Treaty of Waitangi*. Allen and Unwin/Port Nicholson Press, pp 62-63.

Mission Stations 1845 based on: "Mission Stations to 1845" in McKinnon, M. (ed), with Bradley, B. and Kirkpatrick, R., 1997. *New Zealand Historical Atlas: Visualising New Zealand*. David Bateman Ltd in association with Historical Branch, Department of Internal Affairs, Auckland, Plate 36: Te Whenua Rangatira.

- **Resource Exploitation 1800-1910**

Note: This map is a compendium of many individual maps in the *New Zealand Historical Atlas*. It must be borne in mind when studying this map that some activities had ceased before others began. The main purpose of the map is not comparison of the spatial location of the data, but to emphasise the more general point that wealth in nineteenth-century New Zealand depended on an ability to identify and exploit natural resources.

Whaling Stations, Late 1830s, based on: "Māori Population, late 1830s and early 1840s", Plate 32: Māori and the Colonial Town.

Gold Rush Sites and Areas Opened Up by Prospectors, 1852-1880, based on: "Gold Mining in New Zealand, Locations and Ghost Towns", Plate 44: Gold Rushes and Goldfields.

Wheat-growing Area, 1886, boundary simplified from: "Distribution of Wheat Farming, 1886", Plate 46: The Wheat Boom.

Property With at Least 5000 sheep, 1879, based on: "Pastoral Properties and Wool Exports, 1879", Plate 43: On the Sheep's Back.

Kauri Gumfields, 1880-1910, based on: "Production From Forests and Gumfields", Plate 48: The Kauri Harvest.

Bush area 1880, 1910, based on: "The Shrinking of the Bush", Plate 47: From Forest to Pasture.

General reference: McKinnon, M. (ed), with Bradley, B. and Kirkpatrick, R., 1997. *New Zealand Historical Atlas: Visualising New Zealand*. David Bateman Ltd in association with Historical Branch, Department of Internal Affairs, Auckland.

- **Māori Land Transactions up to 1884**

Note: This map is derived from a number of maps in the *New Zealand Historical Atlas*. Because the *Historical Atlas* was organised chronologically, maps of the alienation of Māori land are spread through the bulk of the atlas. Here the salient material is gathered into one place, so the rapidity of loss of Māori land, the difference between the islands and the relationship of land loss to conflict in the North Island can readily be seen.

Land Purchased by 1846 based on: "The New Colony 1840-1847", Plate 31: Land and Sovereignty.

Land Purchased 1847-1860 based on: "Māori Land Transactions up to 1860", Plate 31: Land and Sovereignty.

Land Purchased/Confiscated 1861-1884 based on: "Alienation of Māori Land, North Island and Chatham Islands, 1860s-1880s", Plate 41: Native Policy.

- **The Colony in the 1870s: Administration and Communications**
Note: This map is an amalgamation of information spread over a number of maps in the *New Zealand Historical Atlas*.

Urban Population, 1874: The 25 Largest Towns, based on: "Town and Country 1874", Plate 53: The Colony in 1874.

Provincial Boundary 1874 based on: "The Provinces: Separation and Abolition", Plate 51: Colonial Government.

Communications 1880 based on: "Rail, Telegraph and Cable", Plate 52: Space Transformed.

Plate 29: New Zealand and the Pacific

- **New Zealand Territories, South-West Pacific**
Historical information based on: Ross, A., 1964. *New Zealand Aspirations in the Pacific*. Cambridge University Press, Cambridge.

Ross, A. (ed), 1969. *New Zealand's Record in the Pacific Islands in the Twentieth Century*. Longman Paul for New Zealand Institute of International Affairs, Auckland.

- **New Zealand Official Development Assistance South Pacific Allocation 1997-98**
Data obtained from: "Official Development Assistance Programme 1997-98", from Statistics New Zealand, 1998. *New Zealand Official Yearbook*. GP Publications and Statistics New Zealand, Wellington. Table 4.1, p 69.

- **Nauru, 1961**
Map based on: Department of National Development, 1961. *Territory of Nauru, 1:15,840*. Department of Territories, Division of National Mapping, Australia.

See also:
Ellis, A., 1948. "New Zealand Farms and the 'Phosphate Islands'", in *New Zealand Geographer* 4, pp 55-68.

Television New Zealand, 1995. *A Drop in the Ocean – Land Rights for Nauru*. Television New Zealand.

Ross, A. (ed), 1969. *New Zealand's Record in the Pacific Islands in the Twentieth Century*. Longman Paul for New Zealand Institute of International Affairs, Auckland.

Section 4: Population Shapes

Plate 30: Population

- **Population Density, 1996**
Distribution updated from: Kirkpatrick, R., Chittenden, C. and Phillips, R. (eds), 1996. *Macmillan New Zealand World Atlas*. Macmillan Publishers New Zealand Ltd, Auckland.

Various tables from: Statistics New Zealand, 1997, 1998. *Census of Population and Dwellings*. Statistics New Zealand, Wellington.

- **New Zealand Population 1891-2031**
Material derived from: "Population, 1885-1995", from Statistics New Zealand, 1996. *New Zealand Official Yearbook*. GP Publications and Statistics New Zealand, Wellington. Table 5.2, p 82, and "Population Projections 1994-2031", from Statistics New Zealand, 1996. *New Zealand Official Yearbook*. GP Publications and Statistics New Zealand, Wellington. Table 5.16, p 100.

- **Age-Sex Structure 1996 Census**
Based on: Statistics New Zealand, 1997. *Population and Dwelling Statistics*. Statistics New Zealand, Wellington.

- **Population of New Zealand, North Island and South Island 1874-1996**
Based on: "Population of North and South Islands, 1858-1996 Censuses", from Statistics New Zealand, 1998. *New Zealand Official Yearbook*. GP Publications and Statistics New Zealand, Wellington. Table 5, p 87.

- **Population of Territorial Local Authorities (TLAs) and Urban Areas, 1996 Census**

Population data from: "Resident Population of Territorial Authority Areas", from Statistics New Zealand, 1998. *New Zealand Official Yearbook*. GP Publications and Statistics New Zealand, Wellington. Table 5.7, p 90.

Note: I have used these figures rather than the census night figures from the Census of Population and Dwellings, as these figures have been adjusted for the estimated undercount and the estimated number of New Zealand residents temporarily overseas. The combined total of these two adjustments (about 85,000 people) is significant.

Cartogram updated from: Kelly, J., 1985. *A Contiguous-Area Cartogram of New Zealand, 1981 Census*. Department of Geography, University of Auckland.

Note: Though there are a number of algorithms that can generate cartograms more or less automatically, I have produced this cartogram manually, using Jan Kelly's beautiful 1985 cartogram as a reference point. This has been done for two reasons: (1) it allows comparisons with the earlier cartogram (to be found, for example, on Plate 93 of the *New Zealand Historical Atlas*), and (2) I have found algorithms to be less than satisfactory at rendering the shapes of well-known areas in a recognisable fashion.

    The introduction of a cartogram on this plate allows readers to directly compare a population map based on a physical shape (Population Density 1996) and one based on a population shape. The two maps carry complementary but slightly different messages: the Population Density map shows large, sparsely populated rural local authorities and small, densely settled urban areas. The data are mapped by approximate location; that is, it is possible to see the particular parts of local authorities which are densely or sparsely settled. The cartogram, on the other hand, does not supply the same degree of accuracy. What it does do well is give a clear overall impression of where the people live: northern New Zealand looms large when compared to the South Island, and urban areas dominate. This picture is important to bear in mind when studying the rest of this *Atlas*.

    The relative benefits are made clear if two Territorial Local Authority areas are compared. Ruapehu (44 on both maps) is a large area on the Population Density map, but is small on the cartogram. By contrast, Auckland City (3) is extremely small on the Population Density map, but is huge on the cartogram.

- **Post-War Urban-Rural Population 1945-1996**

Data from: "Urban-Rural Population, 1881-1996 Censuses", from Statistics New Zealand, 1998. *New Zealand Official Yearbook*. GP Publications and Statistics New Zealand, Wellington. Table 5.5, p 89.

See also:

Dickson, J., Ball, D., Edmeades, J., Hanson, S. and Pool, I., 1997. *Recent Trends in Reproduction and Family Structures*. Briefing paper prepared for the participants at the Population Conference, Wellington, 12-14 November 1997. Population Studies Centre, University of Waikato.

Pool, I. and Bedford, R., 1996. *New Zealanders: a nation of 'boat people'*. Discussion Papers No. 15, Population Studies Centre, University of Waikato.

Pool, I. and Bedford, R., 1996. *Macro Social Change in New Zealand: historical and international contexts*. Discussion Papers No. 18, Population Studies Centre, University of Waikato.

Statistics New Zealand, 1995. *New Zealand Now: Baby Boomers*. Statistics New Zealand, Wellington.

Statistics New Zealand, 1997. *Ageing and Retirement in New Zealand*. Statistics New Zealand, Wellington.

Statistics New Zealand, 1998. *New Zealand Now: 65 Plus*. Statistics New Zealand, Wellington.

Statistics New Zealand, 1999. *Demographic Trends 1998*. Statistics New Zealand, Wellington.

Plate 31: Population Change

- **Urban Population, 1886, 1936 and 1996 Censuses**

Data from: "Population of 20 Largest Urban Areas at Selected Censuses", from Statistics New Zealand, 1998. *New Zealand Official Yearbook*. GP Publications and Statistics New Zealand, Wellington. Table 5.6, p 89.

- **Average Age of New Mothers, Total Fertility Rate, 1945-1995**

Material derived from: "Fertility Trends and Patterns", from Statistics New Zealand, 1998. *New Zealand Official Yearbook*. GP Publications and Statistics New Zealand, Wellington. Table 5.9, p 93, "Median Age of

Childbearing", from Statistics New Zealand, 1998. *New Zealand Official Yearbook*. GP Publications and Statistics New Zealand, Wellington, p 94, and "Average Age of New Mothers", from Statistics New Zealand, 1996. *New Zealand Official Yearbook*. GP Publications and Statistics New Zealand, Wellington, p 89.

- **Birth and Death Rates 1960-1995**
Material derived from: "Birth and Death Rates", from Statistics New Zealand, 1998. *New Zealand Official Yearbook*. GP Publications and Statistics New Zealand, Wellington, p 95.

- **Average Age at Death 1945-1995**
Material derived from: "Longer Lives", from Statistics New Zealand, 1996. *New Zealand Official Yearbook*. GP Publications and Statistics New Zealand, Wellington, p 92, and "Longer Lives", from Statistics New Zealand, 1998. *New Zealand Official Yearbook*. GP Publications and Statistics New Zealand, Wellington, p 96.

- **Components of Population Growth: Natural Increase and Net Migration, 1945-1995**
Material derived from: "Components of Population Growth", from Statistics New Zealand, 1996. *New Zealand Official Yearbook*. GP Publications and Statistics New Zealand, Wellington, p 94.

- **Population Change, Territorial Local Authorities (TLAs), 1986-1996 Censuses**
Percentage population growth figures from: "Usually Resident Population of Territorial Authority Areas and Ranking Order 1986, 1991, 1996", in *Statistics New Zealand 1997 Population and Dwelling Statistics, Census 96: 1996 Census of Population and Dwellings*. Statistics New Zealand, Wellington, Table 7.
Note: The use of the population-based cartogram as the base shape prevents readers making a common map-reading error. On traditional population change maps, which use the physical shape of area units to show change, it is possible to over-read the importance of large population changes. Between 1986 and 1996, for example, the Queenstown Territorial Local Authority (71) grew much faster than the national average. This TLA covers a large area but has only a small population. On a traditional map this large area would be coloured in (say) bright red, which would give the impression that there has been a large population increase in absolute terms. On the cartogram, however, the area is still brightly coloured but is relatively small, of less significance in purely statistical terms, for example, than the growth of the Tauranga TLA (32). This would not show up on a traditional map. It is for this reason I advocate that, as a general rule, cartograms be used to show population when choropleth mapping (choropleth mapping is when colour is used to represent data in bounded areas).

See also:
Pool, I. and Bedford, R., 1997. *Population Change: from dynamics and structures to policies*. Background paper prepared for a plenary session at the Population Conference, Wellington, 12-14 November. Population Studies Centre, University of Waikato.

Statistics New Zealand, 1995. *New Zealand Now: Baby Boomers*. Statistics New Zealand, Wellington.

Plate 32: Migration

- **Inter-Regional Migration 1991-1996, Major Net Flows**
Data from: Goodwin, J. and Bedford, R., 1997. *Inter-Regional Migration in New Zealand, 1986-1996: A Preliminary Analysis*. Briefing paper prepared for the participants at the Population Conference, 12-14 November, 1997. Population Studies Centre, University of Waikato.

- **Migration into Palmerston North, 1991-1996**
Data from: "Usual Residents, Age Group and Sex by Usual Residents 5 Years Ago (1991) for the Population Usually Resident in Urban and Rural Areas in 1996", in Statistics New Zealand, 1998. *Population Structure and Internal Migration, Census 1996: Census of Population of Dwellings*. Statistics New Zealand, Wellington, Table 22.
Note: This map is based on a logarithmic projection. The scale of the logarithmic projection is read from the centre outwards, and changes at a logarithmic rate. The effect is like looking through a fish-eye lens. The paradox of the projection is that there can be no true centre, as log 0 is meaningless, so the practical cartographic solution is to render the innermost 1 km circle in a more standard fashion.
    The logarithmic projection is best suited to data strongly grouped around a central point, but which are related to other data much farther away. In this case it allows towns and cities close to Palmerston North to be shown without crowding, and the intellectual centre of the map (Massey University Campus) can be placed in the physical centre of the map.

- **Where Palmerston North People Lived on Census Night 1991**
Data from: "Usual Residents, Age Group and Sex by Usual Residents 5 Years Ago (1991) for the Population Usually Resident in Urban and Rural Areas in 1996", in Statistics New Zealand, 1998. *Population Structure and Internal Migration, Census 96: 1996 Census of Population and Dwellings*. Statistics New Zealand, Wellington, Table 22.

- **Age/Sex Structure, Migrants to Palmerston North from within New Zealand, 1996 Census**
Data from: Statistics New Zealand, 1997. *Census 1996 with Supermap 3*. Statistics New Zealand, Wellington.

- **New Zealand Arrivals with an Asian Passport, 1991-1996**
Data compiled from: International Migration Data Set, Permanent Long-Term Arrivals, provided courtesy of the Population Studies Centre, University of Waikato. Thanks to Richard Bedford and Joanne Goodwin for assistance with these data.

- **New Zealanders Living in Asia on Census Night 1991, by Region**
Data from: "Usual Residents, Age Group and Sex by Usual Residents 5 Years Ago (1991) for the Population Usually Resident in Urban and Rural Areas in 1996", in Statistics New Zealand, 1998. *Population Structure and Internal Migration, Census 96: 1996 Census of Population and Dwellings*. Statistics New Zealand, Wellington, Table 22.

- **Net Internal Migration, Four Main Urban Areas, 1991-1996**
Data from: Total Population, Net Migration - Urban (corrected data), provided courtesy of the Population Studies Centre, University of Waikato. Thanks to Richard Bedford and Joanne Goodwin for assistance with these data.

Note: I wish to acknowledge assistance received from members of the Migration Research Group in the Department of Geography and Population Studies Centre, University of Waikato, in the preparation of this plate. In particular I am grateful for access to their corrected data sets, which have been produced by Statistics New Zealand for the Population Studies Centre, and for assistance with the content of the plate.

See also:
Bedford, R. and Goodwin, J., 1997. *Migration and Urban Population Change: a preliminary analysis of the 1996 Census data*. Briefing paper prepared for the participants at the Population Conference, 12-14 November, 1997. Population Studies Centre, University of Waikato.

Bedford, R. and Lidgard, J., 1996. *International Migration in the Asia-Pacific Region in the 1980s and 1990s: two New Zealand perspectives*. Discussion Papers No. 19, Population Studies Centre, University of Waikato.

Lidgard, J., Bedford, R. and Goodwin, J., 1998. *Transformations in New Zealand's International Migration System: 1981-1996*. Discussion Papers No. 25, Population Studies Centre, University of Waikato.

Plate 33: Māori Population and Unemployment

- **Māori Population of Territorial Local Authorities (TLAs), Percentage Māori Ethnicity, Total Population, 1996 Census**
Data from: "Distribution of Māori by Territorial Authority and Age Group 1986-1996, for People of Māori Ethnicity Resident in New Zealand, 1996" in Statistics New Zealand, 1997. *Māori Census 96: 1996 Census of Population and Dwellings*, Table 9.

- **Percentage Change in Māori Unemployment, 1986-1991 Censuses; Māori Population 1991 Census**
Data from: Statistics New Zealand, 1997. *Census 1996 with Supermap 3*. Statistics New Zealand, Wellington.

- **Percentage Change in Māori Unemployment, 1991-1996 Censuses**
Data from: Statistics New Zealand, 1997. *Census 1996 with Supermap 3*. Statistics New Zealand, Wellington.

- **Unemployment Rates, Māori/Non-Māori Men and Women 1996**
Based on: "Unemployment Rates for Māori and Non-Māori, by Age and Sex, 1996", in Statistics New Zealand, 1998. *New Zealand Now: Māori*. Statistics New Zealand, Wellington, Figure 5.10.

"Unemployment Rates for Māori, by Sex, 1986-1996", in Statistics New Zealand, 1998. *New Zealand Now: Māori*. Statistics New Zealand, Wellington, Figure 5.9.

See also:

Jackson, N., Pool, I. and Cheung, M.C., 1994. *Māori and Non-Māori Fertility: convergence, divergence or parallel trends?* Discussion Papers No. 3, Population Studies Centre, University of Waikato.

Johnstone, K. and Smith, S., 1995. *An Overview of New Zealand Population Trends: some implications for the labour force*. Discussion Papers No. 8, Population Studies Centre, University of Waikato.

Plate 34: Ethnic Diversity in South Auckland

• **Percentage Māori Ethnicity, South Auckland Urban Area, 1996 Census**
Data from: Statistics New Zealand, 1997. *Census 96 with Supermap 3*. Statistics New Zealand, Wellington.

Map generated by: Bridget Spragg, Population Studies Centre, University of Waikato, using ArcInfo software.

• **Māori Age-Sex Structure, 1996 Census**
Data from: Statistics New Zealand, 1997. *Census 96 with Supermap 3*. Statistics New Zealand, Wellington.

• **Percentage Asian Ethnicity, South Auckland Urban Area, 1996 Census**
Data from: Statistics New Zealand, 1997. *Census 96 with Supermap 3*. Statistics New Zealand, Wellington.

Map generated by: Bridget Spragg, Population Studies Centre, University of Waikato, using ArcInfo software.

• **Asian Age-Sex Structure, 1996 Census**
Data from: Statistics New Zealand, 1997. *Census 96 with Supermap 3*. Statistics New Zealand, Wellington.

• **Percentage Pacific Island Ethnicity, South Auckland Urban Area, 1996 Census**
Data from: Statistics New Zealand, 1997. *Census 96 with Supermap 3*. Statistics New Zealand, Wellington.

Map generated by: Bridget Spragg, Population Studies Centre, University of Waikato, using ArcInfo software.

• **Pacific Islander Age-Sex Structure, 1996 Census**
Data from: Statistics New Zealand, 1997. *Census 96 with Supermap 3*. Statistics New Zealand, Wellington.

• **Ethnicity, 1996 Census**
Data from: Statistics New Zealand, 1997. *Ethnicity, Census 96: 1996 Census of Population and Dwellings*. Statistics New Zealand, Wellington.

See also:

Curson, P.H., 1970. "Polynesians and Residence in Auckland", in *New Zealand Geographer* 26, pp 162-173.

Population Association of New Zealand and Ministry of Māori Development, 1993. *Ethnicity and Gender: population trends and policy challenges in the 1990s*. Proceedings of the Wellington Conference, 1993.

Statistics New Zealand, 1994. *New Zealand Now: Asian New Zealanders*. Statistics New Zealand, Wellington.

Section 5: Economic Shapes

Plate 35: Administrative Divisions

• **Electorates, 1999 MMP Election**
Boundaries supplied courtesy of: Land Information New Zealand. Thanks to Jill Webster for the JPEG files.

• **Māori Electorates, 1999 MMP Election**
Boundaries supplied courtesy of: Land Information New Zealand. Thanks to Jill Webster for the JPEG files.

• **Local Government Boundaries with Effect from 1 July 1992**
Boundaries from: Kelly, J. and Marshall, B., 1996. *Atlas of New Zealand Boundaries*. Auckland University Press, Auckland.

- **Local Authority Income, Non-Trading Activities, 1996**
Data from: "Local Authority Statistics - Non-Trading Activities", from Statistics New Zealand, 1998. *New Zealand Official Yearbook*. GP Publications and Statistics New Zealand, Wellington. Table 28.15, p 586.

Plate 36: Business Activity

- **Selected Fletcher Challenge Overseas Assets, 1997-1998**
Material from: Fletcher Building, 1998. *Annual Report*. Fletcher Challenge Ltd.
Fletcher Energy, 1998. *Annual Report*. Fletcher Challenge Ltd.
Fletcher Forests, 1998. *Annual Report*. Fletcher Challenge Ltd.
Fletcher Paper, 1998. *Annual Report*. Fletcher Challenge Ltd.

- **The Top 200 Companies, 1987 and 1997**
Map format from: Le Heron, R. and Pawson, E. (eds), 1996. *Changing Places: New Zealand in the nineties*. Longman Paul, Auckland. Original cartographer, Jonette Surridge.

Data from: *Management*, November 1987, November 1997.

- **Business Size, 1997 ANZSIC, Return on Assets, 1995-6 ANZSIC**
Data from: Statistics New Zealand, 1998. *Business Activity Statistics 1997*. Statistics New Zealand, Wellington.

- **Total Retail Sales by Month, 1994-1997**
Data from: Statistics New Zealand, 1998. *Business Activity Statistics 1997*. Statistics New Zealand, Wellington.

- **Annual Retail Sales by Region, 1991-1997**
Data compiled from: "Annual Sales by Geographical Region", in Statistics New Zealand, 1996. *New Zealand Official Yearbook*. GP Publications and Statistics New Zealand, Wellington. Table 24.11, p 487, and "Annual Sales by Geographical Region", in Statistics New Zealand, 1998. *New Zealand Official Yearbook*. GP Publications and Statistics New Zealand, Wellington. Table 24.11, p 504.

- **Retail Sales by Store Type, October 1997**
Data from: Statistics New Zealand, 1998. *Business Activity Statistics 1997*. Statistics New Zealand, Wellington.

- **From Tellers to Sellers: the changing micro-geography of local bank branches**
Material based on: Flux, A., 1994. *From Tellers to Sellers: the impact of restructuring on employment in the New Zealand banking industry*, Monograph. Victoria University of Wellington.

Willis, R. and Flux, A., 1995. "From Tellers to Sellers: restructuring in the banking industry, 1989-92", in Le Heron, R. and Pawson, E. (eds), 1996. *Changing Places: New Zealand in the nineties*. Longman Paul, Auckland, Case Study 6.3, pp 183-185.

Plate 37: Overseas Trade

- **New Zealand's Trade with the World 1995**
Data from: Statistics New Zealand, 1996. *Overseas Trade Statistics 1995*. Statistics New Zealand, Wellington.

For updated aggregated trade figures to 1997, see: "Trade by Geographical Region and Country", from Statistics New Zealand, 1998. *New Zealand Official Yearbook*. GP Publications and Statistics New Zealand, Wellington. Table 25.20, pp 520–526. These figures do not break each country down by commodity.

Cartogram originally developed for: Kirkpatrick, R., Chittenden, C. and Phillips, R. (eds), 1996. *Macmillan New Zealand World Atlas*. Macmillan Publishers New Zealand Ltd, Auckland.

Note: Use of the world cartogram points out the large areas of the world which New Zealand has very little to do with economically. The implication of this is that while both New Zealand and these other countries are part of the global economy, their links are indirect. Some argue that the New Zealand economy shares certain characteristics with these other countries, which are primarily 'developing' nations — in particular the fact that they are mostly primary producers and are price takers in the international markets. Though New Zealand exporters continue working on adding value to their products, New Zealand remains mostly an exporter of raw produce and an importer of finished goods.

- **Total New Zealand Exports 1995**
Data from: Statistics New Zealand, 1996. *Overseas Trade Statistics 1995*. Statistics New Zealand, Wellington.

- **Trade with EU**
Based on: "Trade with EU Countries", from Statistics New Zealand, 1998. *New Zealand Official Yearbook*. GP Publications and Statistics New Zealand, Wellington, p 534. These figures are 1987-1997.

- **Trade with Asia**
Based on: "Trade with Asia", from Statistics New Zealand, 1998. *New Zealand Official Yearbook*. GP Publications and Statistics New Zealand, Wellington, p 536. These figures are 1987-1997.

- **Trade with Japan**
Data from: "Trade with Japan", from Statistics New Zealand, 1998. *New Zealand Official Yearbook*. GP Publications and Statistics New Zealand, Wellington. Table 25.26, p 529. These figures are 1987-1997.

- **Trade with USA**
Based on: "Trade with USA", from Statistics New Zealand, 1998. *New Zealand Official Yearbook*. GP Publications and Statistics New Zealand, Wellington, p 529. These figures are 1987-1997.

- **Trade with Australia**
Based on: "Trade with Australia", from Statistics New Zealand, 1998. *New Zealand Official Yearbook*. GP Publications and Statistics New Zealand, Wellington. Table 25.24, p 528. These figures are 1987-1997.

- **Destination of Exports 1920–1997**
Based on: "Trading Partners: proportion of total exports going to different markets", from Statistics New Zealand, 1998. *New Zealand Official Yearbook*. GP Publications and Statistics New Zealand, Wellington, p 523.

See also:
Le Heron, R., 1996. "Growth and Globalisation in the 1990s", in Le Heron, R. and Pawson, E. (eds), 1996. *Changing Places: New Zealand in the nineties*. Longman Paul, Auckland, pp 23–27.

Le Heron, R., 1996. "Evolving Links and Interactions", in Le Heron, R. and Pawson, E. (eds), 1996. *Changing Places: New Zealand in the nineties*. Longman Paul, Auckland, pp 27–43.

Plate 38: Tourism

Note: The material on this plate, with the exception of 'International Tourists' Choice of Accommodation 1996', is wholly the product of research and data presentation carried out by the Spatial Analysis Facility, Department of Geography, University of Auckland. The assistance of the Spatial Analysis Facility and Lincoln University in the preparation of this plate is gratefully acknowledged.
　　　　In particular I recognise the cartographic work of Igor Drecki, currently working with Environment B.O.P. These graphics are largely unaltered from his original work. Thanks also to Professor Pip Forer for his input.

Note: The cartogram constructed as part of the Tourist Accommodation 1996-97 graphic is quite different in character to the cartogram on Plate 30. Certain recognisable parts of the country have their shapes carefully preserved (for example, 16-Far North, 22-Thames-Coromandel, 54-Tasman, etc.), as do the major cities (3-Auckland, 13-Christchurch and 11-Wellington), while other, less recognisable areas are stretched well out of shape to fill in the gaps (such as 24-Waikato and 63-Selwyn). Every contiguous-area cartogram is a compromise between preserving the overall shape of the islands and preserving the shapes of the individual polygons.

- **International Tourists' Choice of Accommodation, 1996**
Data from: "Tourist accommodation", a textual discussion from Statistics New Zealand, 1998. *New Zealand Official Yearbook*. GP Publications and Statistics New Zealand, Wellington, p 297.

Plate 39: Auckland Dairies and Restaurants

- **Location of Dairies and Licensed Restaurants, 1978**
Data from: 1978. *The Auckland Yellow Pages*, pp 276-278, 761-768.

Telecom New Zealand, 1998. *The Auckland Yellow Pages A–K*, pp 621-623.

Telecom New Zealand, 1998. *The Auckland Yellow Pages L–Z*, pp 1823-1841.

Note: This research was carried out by the author, and is limited by the accuracy of the *Yellow Pages* and the possible omissions of businesses (particularly in 1998) which are not listed in the *Yellow Pages*.

• **Indian-owned Dairies, Auckland Isthmus, 1994**
Data from: Nandan, R.A., 1994. "Open All Hours: Indian dairy entrepreneurship in central urban Auckland." Unpublished MA thesis, Department of Geography, University of Auckland.

See also:
Hewitson, M., 1998. "A Classic Dairy Tale", in *New Zealand Herald*, 8 August 1998: H3.

Plate 40: Energy

• **Energy Resources, 1997**
Oil and Gas Reserves, 1997 data from: "Oil and Condensate Reserves and Production", from Statistics New Zealand, 1998. *New Zealand Official Yearbook*. GP Publications and Statistics New Zealand, Wellington. Table 20.8, p 436.

"Gas Reserves", from Statistics New Zealand, 1998. *New Zealand Official Yearbook*. GP Publications and Statistics New Zealand, Wellington. Table 20.9, p 436.

Electricity Generation, 1997 data from: "ECNZ Electricity Generation", from Statistics New Zealand, 1998. *New Zealand Official Yearbook*. GP Publications and Statistics New Zealand, Wellington. Table 20.5, p 435.

"Contact Electricity Generation", from Statistics New Zealand, 1998. *New Zealand Official Yearbook*. GP Publications and Statistics New Zealand, Wellington, p 435.

Ministry for the Environment, 1997. *The State of New Zealand's Environment 1997*. GP Publications, Wellington, Chapter 3, Production and Consumption Patterns.

Coal reserves from: Thompson, B.N., Brathwaite, R.L. and Christie, A.B., 1995. *Mineral Wealth of New Zealand*. Institute of Geological and Nuclear Sciences Information Series 33, Institute of Geological and Nuclear Sciences, Lower Hutt.

Potential for wind farms, based on: "Areas with the Potential for Wind Farms", in Ministry for the Environment, 1997. *The State of New Zealand's Environment 1997*. GP Publications, Wellington, p 3.28.

• **Energy Used by Consumer Groups, 1996**
Data extracted from: "Energy Supply and Demand Balance, 1996", from Statistics New Zealand, 1998. *New Zealand Official Yearbook*. GP Publications and Statistics New Zealand, Wellington. Table 20.3, p 433.

See also: "Energy consumption by sector in New Zealand", in Ministry for the Environment, 1997. *The State of New Zealand's Environment 1997*. GP Publications, Wellington, p 3.21.

• **Change in Generation Type from ECNZ Power Stations 1993, 1995**
Data from: "Electricity Corporation Power Stations", from Statistics New Zealand, 1996. *New Zealand Official Yearbook*. GP Publications and Statistics New Zealand, Wellington. Table 20.6, p 418.

• **Primary Energy Supply, 1974–1996**
Data from: "Total Primary Energy Supply", from Statistics New Zealand, 1998. *New Zealand Official Yearbook*. GP Publications and Statistics New Zealand, Wellington. Table 20.1, p 432.

Photograph of Meremere coal-fired power station (mothballed in 1991) taken by Russell Kirkpatrick from a moving vehicle on State Highway 1 on a foggy morning, 1980.

• **The 1998 Auckland CBD Power Crisis**
Map based on: Mercury Energy's map of 9 March 1998, published at:
http://www.geocities.com/PicketFence/4390/crisismp.htm

See also: http://www.moc.govt.nz/inquiry/ from which the inquiry report by Integral Energy Australia was downloaded: Kent, H. and Bucea, G., 1998. *Inquiry into the Auckland Power Supply Failure Technical Report*

— *Cable Failures*. Report by Integral Energy Australia, 1998. The site has other technical reports which can be read or downloaded as .pdf files.

http://7am.com/nzwires/crisis1.htm Various bulletins from the 7am news service, 21 February to 2 March, 1998. This site provided the most detailed media coverage of the crisis, enabling me to pinpoint major facilities either within or just outside the most heavily affected area, which suffered significant inconvenience during late February and early March, 1998.

http://www.newsroom.co.nz/stories/HL9802/S00076.htm Another news reporting site which provided ongoing coverage of the power crisis.

Auckland Plunged into Darkness http://www.earthlight.co.nz/business/egl/whatsnew.htm This site delivers a succinct summary of the crisis, and engages in speculation and discussion about Auckland's infrastructure.

The Great Auckland Blackout http://www.kiwiclub.org/kiwiklips/news/news5c.html Another summary site, seemingly run for the benefit of expatriate New Zealanders. This site carries a considerable amount of factual detail.

Plate 41: Air and Sea Traffic

• Daily Passenger Seat Numbers, Domestic Air Routes, 1998
Routes and numbers from: Air New Zealand, 1998. Domestic Timetable, Air New Zealand National and Link.

Ansett New Zealand, 1998. Domestic Timetable, Ansett New Zealand.

Note: Though this is the 'information age' it is sometimes no longer possible to obtain information that was once freely available. As a result of government-run services having been sold to private interests, data collection is often minimal, or data is not released or published due to commercial sensitivity. This is true in this case: it is not possible to obtain actual passenger numbers for our domestic air routes. The nearest surrogate for any route, daily passenger seat numbers, is obtained by multiplying the number of flights per day by the capacity of the aircraft servicing the route. This is almost certainly an over-estimate of the numbers actually carried, but it should be remembered that airlines work hard to maximise passenger numbers per flight.

The issue of commercial sensitivity occurs in a number of other places in the *Atlas*: Hospital bed numbers are used instead of patient numbers on Plate 49, for example, and the difficulty of mapping electricity supply company distribution was compounded by varying degrees of protectiveness, meaning that this topic was not addressed on Plate 40. This protectiveness is not surprising, as in many cases companies seek to preserve their market share, but it increases the difficulty researchers encounter when seeking to understand the important changes taking place in our economy and society at present.

• Overseas Cargo Loaded and Unloaded 1996
Data from: "1996 Overseas Cargo — Loaded", from Statistics New Zealand, 1997. *New Zealand Official Yearbook*. GP Publications and Statistics New Zealand, Wellington.

"1996 Overseas Cargo — Unloaded", from Statistics New Zealand, 1997. *New Zealand Official Yearbook*. GP Publications and Statistics New Zealand, Wellington.

• The Quickest Air Route to Wellington, 1998
Time-distance information generated from: Air New Zealand, 1998. Domestic Timetable, Air New Zealand National and Link.

Ansett New Zealand, 1998. Domestic Timetable, Ansett New Zealand.

Note: The time-distance information strictly influences only the airport locations themselves. The coastline is reproduced only as a guide to understanding how, in practical terms, New Zealand is shaped for an airline traveller to Wellington.

• Proposed New Ferry Terminals for the Inter-Island Ferry Service
Material compiled from: Tranz Rail Ltd, 1996. *Clifford Bay Ferry Terminal: assessment of environmental effects*, Volume 1. Tranz Rail Ltd, Wellington.

See also:
Rails, 1995. "New Ferries, New terminals: possible futures for NZ Rail's Interisland Line", in *Rails* 25 (1), August 1995, pp 4-9.

Rails, 1996. "New South Island Ferry Terminal Moves Closer", in *Rails*, May 1996, pp 212-216.

Rails, 1996. "Transport Implications of Moving South Island Ferry Terminal", in *Rails*, May 1996, pp 216-217.

Plate 42: Road and Rail Networks

• Traffic Volume, State Highway Network 1996
Data kindly provided courtesy of Transit New Zealand: Transit New Zealand (1996) State Highway Traffic Volumes & Related Information.

Change in A.A.D.T. volume since 1993: 1993 figures kindly provided courtesy of Transit New Zealand: Transit New Zealand (1996) State Highway Traffic Volumes & Related Information.

The assistance of the Christchurch office of Transit New Zealand is gratefully acknowledged.

• Tonnage Flows, Railways, 1997-98
Agreed Density by Track Section data kindly provided courtesy of Tranz Rail Ltd. Data are for the period 1 July 1997 to 30 June 1998.

The assistance of Murray King, Executive Manager Corporate Services, is gratefully acknowledged.

• Distribution of Heavy Motor Vehicle (HMV) Types
Data kindly provided courtesy of Transit New Zealand. Transit New Zealand (1996) State Highway Traffic Volumes & Related Information.

Note: Detailed data of this type is collected at five 'Weigh Bridges' around New Zealand: Auckland Harbour Bridge, Auckland Southern Motorway, Ohakea, Pukerua Bay and Waipara.

See also:
Ministry of Transport, 1993. *Influencing Transport Policy: seminar proceedings,* 11–12 October 1993. Ministry of Transport, Wellington.

Ministry of Transport, 1996. *Land Transport Pricing Study: environmental externalities discussion paper.* Ministry of Transport, Wellington.

Transit New Zealand, 1994. *Long Term Tourism Roading Requirements.* Task Force Report, Transit New Zealand and Ministry of Commerce, Wellington.

Plate 43: Transport in the Wellington Region

• Transport in the Wellington Region
State Highway Network, 1996, data supplied by: Average Annual Daily Traffic (A.A.D.T.) volume data kindly provided courtesy of Transit New Zealand. Transit New Zealand (1996) State Highway Traffic Volumes & Related Information.

Air Passenger Seats 1998, Domestic Routes data from a combination of: Air New Zealand, 1998. Domestic Timetable, Air New Zealand National and Link, and Ansett New Zealand, 1998. Domestic Timetable, Ansett New Zealand.

Tranz Metro Network, 1996. These figures are estimates only, based on an extrapolation of the 1992 proportions on each Tranz Metro service (1992 was the last published date for Wellington suburban railway data), and guided by an average of 25,549 passengers per day on the Tranz Metro Network in 1998. Thanks to Fraser Atkins, Database Administrator, Public Transport, Wellington Regional Council for the aggregated average annual daily traffic figures for rail and bus services.

Ferry Passenger Numbers, 1996–98. Ferry numbers gathered from various media releases.

See also:

Rails, 1995. "Lessons Learned from NZ Rail's First Fast Ferry Season", in *Rails*, May 1995, pp 215-217.

Rails, 1995. "Lynx Record", in *Rails*, July 1995, p 270.

October 21, 1998 flooding information from: *Dominion*, 1998. "Big mop-up continues: Kapiti Coast residents hardest hit", in *Dominion*, front page.

The Press, 1998. "Storm lashes lower NI towns", in *The Press*, page 9.

• A.M. Peak Transport by Mode, 1988 and 2011 (projected)
Based on: Wellington Regional Council, 1992. *Beyond 2000 Proposed Transport Policy*. Transport Planning and Policy Department, Wellington Regional Council, Wellington.

See also:
Wellington Regional Council, 1992. *Proposed Regional Land Transport Strategy*. Transport Planning and Policy Department, Wellington Regional Council, Wellington.

• Average Vehicle Speed, SH 1 and SH 2, Ngauranga South Bend, Wellington Urban Motorway
Data kindly provided by Transit New Zealand.

See also:
Rails, 1995. "How New Rules Could Affect Highway Development Plans", in *Rails*, June 1995, pp 238-240.

Plate 44: International Relations

• New Zealand Posts Overseas 1998
Locations from: "Overseas Representation", from Statistics New Zealand, 1998. *New Zealand Official Yearbook*. GP Publications and Statistics New Zealand, Wellington, p 66.

Ministry of Foreign Affairs and Trade, 1998. *Overseas Posts. A List of New Zealand Representatives Abroad*. Ministry of Foreign Affairs and Trade, Wellington.

"Peacekeeping Commitments", from Statistics New Zealand, 1998. *New Zealand Official Yearbook*. GP Publications and Statistics New Zealand, Wellington, p 71.

• Foreign Embassies in New Zealand, 1998
Locations from: Ministry of Foreign Affairs and Trade, 1998. *Diplomatic and Consular List*. Ministry of Foreign Affairs and Trade, Wellington.

Note: The scale of the logarithmic projection used on this plate is read from the centre outwards, and changes at a logarithmic rate. The effect is like looking through a fish-eye lens. The paradox of the projection is that there can be no true centre, as log 0 is meaningless, so the practical cartographic solution is to render the innermost 1 km circle in a more standard fashion.

The logarithmic projection is best suited to data strongly grouped around a central point, but which are related to other data much farther away. In this case it allows the foreign embassies and consulates located in Wellington to be shown clearly on the same map as New Zealand posts overseas.

• New Zealand Official Development Assistance (NZODA) Programme Allocation 1997-98
Data obtained from: "Official Development Assistance Programme 1997-98", from Statistics New Zealand, 1998. *New Zealand Official Yearbook*. GP Publications and Statistics New Zealand, Wellington. Table 4.1, p 69.

• Number of Defence Personnel, 1991-1997
Data obtained from: "Number of Defence Personnel", from Statistics New Zealand, 1996. *New Zealand Official Yearbook*. GP Publications and Statistics New Zealand, Wellington. Table 4.3, p 76.

"Number of Defence Personnel", from Statistics New Zealand, 1998. *New Zealand Official Yearbook*. GP Publications and Statistics New Zealand, Wellington. Table 4.3, p 80.

• Expenditure on Security and Intelligence Agencies 1993-1997
Data from: "Expenditure on Intelligence and Security Agencies", from Statistics New Zealand, 1998. *New Zealand Official Yearbook*. GP Publications and Statistics New Zealand, Wellington. Table 4.10, p 83.

See also:

Institute of International Affairs, 1998. *New Zealand International Review*. Institute of International Affairs, Wellington. (Issues every two months.)

McKinnon, M.A., 1993. *Independence and Foreign Policy: New Zealand in the world since 1935*. Auckland University Press, Auckland.

Section 6: Social and Cultural Shapes

Plate 45: Tangata Whenua

• Iwi Populations by Regional Council Area, 1996 Census
Data from: "Iwi Affiliation, 1991 and 1996, for the New Zealand Māori Descent Population Resident in New Zealand", Statistics New Zealand, 1997. *Iwi, Volume 1, Census 96: 1996 Census of Population and Dwellings*. Statistics New Zealand, Wellington, Table 1.

Note: An iwi is shown separately if its population in that region is above a 3 per cent threshold. Iwi falling below this threshold are grouped together under the heading 'Other Iwi'. Note also that the total Māori population adds up to far more than the actual number who called themselves Māori in the 1996 Census. This is because respondents to the Iwi Affiliation question in the Census could indicate that they belonged to more than one iwi.

• Māori and Non-Māori Socio-Economic Indicators, 1996
Data and analysis from: Statistics New Zealand, 1998. *New Zealand Now: Māori*. Statistics New Zealand, Wellington.

Statistics New Zealand, 1998. *New Zealand Official Yearbook*. GP Publications and Statistics New Zealand, Wellington, Chapters 5, 6, 7, 9, 10, 14.

New Zealand Health Information Service, 1997. *Mortality and Demographic Data 1994*. Ministry of Health, Wellington.

• Early Childhood Participation Rates, Māori and Non-Māori 0-4 year olds, 1996
Material from Ministry of Education website at: http://www.minedu.govt.nz

• Māori Early Childhood Education Enrolments 1993-1997

• Schools Offering Māori Medium Education, 1995-1997

• Enrolments in Māori Medium Education, 1997

Material for all three graphs from: Ministry of Education, 1998: *Ngā Haeata Mātauranga: Annual Report on Māori Education 1997/98, including a Statistical Profile of Māori Participation and Achievement in Education, and Direction for 1999*. Ministry of Education, Wellington.
        This report is available on the Ministry of Education website at: http://www.minedu.govt.nz/Māori/Report97-98 The Ministry of Education's comprehensive website contains a wide range of educational statistics and analysis, and is an excellent starting place for those interested in educational matters.

Note: There are three levels of Māori language learning:
• Taha Māori: learn greetings, songs, simple words
• Te Reo Māori: separate subject to learn the language
• Māori Medium: curriculum subjects at differing degrees of Māori immersion (*New Zealand Now: Māori*, p 55).

The degrees of immersion involved in Māori Medium education are (from highest to lowest):
• Immersion school: all students involved in Māori Medium education for over 20 hours per week
• Bilingual school: all students involved in Māori Medium education for at least 3 hours per week
• School with immersion classes: some students involved in Māori Medium Education for over 20 hours per week
• School with bilingual classes: some students involved in Māori Medium education for at least 3 hours per week (Ministry of Education website).

See also:

Statistics New Zealand, 1997. *Education, Census 1996: Census of Population of Dwellings*. Statistics New Zealand, Wellington.

Statistics New Zealand, 1997. *Māori, Census 1996: Census of Population of Dwellings*. Statistics New Zealand, Wellington.

Plate 46: Working Lives

• Full-time Employment by Region 1996
Data from: "Regional Council by Sex and Industry (ANZSIC96 Major Division) for the Usually Resident Population 1996 Aged 15 Years and Over", Statistics New Zealand, 1998. *Employment and Unemployment, Census 96: 1996 Census of Population and Dwellings*. Statistics New Zealand, Wellington, Table 14.

• Full-Time Female Employment by Industry, 1996
Data from: "Full-Time Female Employment by Industry", from Statistics New Zealand, 1998. *New Zealand Official Yearbook*. GP Publications and Statistics New Zealand, Wellington, p 308.

Total figure from: "Full-Time Labour Force: 1896-1996", from Statistics New Zealand, 1998. *New Zealand Official Yearbook*. GP Publications and Statistics New Zealand, Wellington, p 306. The total was achieved by subtracting Unemployed and Other from the Total Female figure in this table.

• Full-Time Male Employment by Industry, 1996
Data from: "Full-Time Male Employment by Industry", from Statistics New Zealand, 1998. *New Zealand Official Yearbook*. GP Publications and Statistics New Zealand, Wellington, p 308.

Total figure from: "Full-Time Labour Force: 1896-1996", from Statistics New Zealand, 1998. *New Zealand Official Yearbook*. GP Publications and Statistics New Zealand, Wellington, p 306. The total was achieved by subtracting Unemployed and Other from the Total Male figure in this table.

• Unemployment Levels 1931-1997
Data courtesy of the Department of Labour.

Note: Unemployment figures are one of the areas upon which a government's performance is assessed by electors, and as such is vulnerable to political manipulation. This takes the form of altering the definition of what constitutes an unemployed person, and changing how such statistics are collected. At present in New Zealand there are three sources of unemployment data:
• the Household Labour Force Survey
• the five-yearly Census of Population and Dwellings
• Work and Income New Zealand's job seeker register.
Statistics New Zealand offers a discussion of the problems associated with each of these data sets on page 310 of the *1998 New Zealand Official Yearbook*. Interpreting the change in unemployment over time must therefore be done with caution. Nevertheless, broad trends are identifiable in all three data sets. Note further that the inclusion of work schemes on this graph ceases in 1990. After that date, those on work schemes are included in the number of registered unemployed.

• Gender Differences in Income: (a) weekly income categories
Data from: Statistics New Zealand, 1997. *New Zealand Income Survey, June 1997*. Statistics New Zealand, Wellington.

• Gender Differences in Income: (b) income over 40,000
Data from: "Proportion of Males and Females by Occupation Group with Income Over 40,000", from Statistics New Zealand, 1998. *New Zealand Official Yearbook*. GP Publications and Statistics New Zealand, Wellington. Table 14.18, p 321.

• Where the Workers Live: Location of Professionals and Semi/Unskilled Workers, Wellington Urban Area, 1996
Map generated from: Statistics New Zealand, 1997. *Census 96 with Supermap 3*. Statistics New Zealand, Wellington.

- **Response to Restructuring: Employment and the Factory Floor at PGF(NZ) Ltd, 1983 and 1999**

Schematic map from the author's recollection. I worked at PGF(NZ) Ltd from 1982 to 1985 in between stints at university (I'm the rightmost one in the Irons assembly area on the 1983 factory floor).

1983 Factory floor, number and placement of workers: From the combined recollection of Grahame Gay, Russell Kirkpatrick and Kenny Smith.

1999 Factory floor, number and placement of workers: Information supplied by Kenny Smith. Three of the eight workers in 1999 remain from 1983.

See also:
Honey, J. and Lindop, J., 1997. *The Changing Structure of New Zealand's Labour Force, 1976-1996*. Briefing paper prepared for the participants at the Population Conference, Wellington, 12-14 November 1997. Population Studies Centre, University of Waikato.

Martin, B., 1997. *Income Trends Among Individuals and Families, 1976 to 1996*. Briefing paper prepared for the participants at the Population Conference, Wellington, 12-14 November 1997. Population Studies Centre, University of Waikato.

Morrison, P.S. (ed), 1993. *Labour, Employment and Work in New Zealand*. Proceedings of the Fifth Conference, 12-13 November 1992, Victoria University of Wellington.

Statistics New Zealand, 1998. *Employment and Unemployment, Census 96: 1996 Census of Population and Dwellings*. Statistics New Zealand, Wellington.

Statistics New Zealand, 1998. *Incomes, Census 96: 1996 Census of Population and Dwellings*. Statistics New Zealand, Wellington.

Statistics New Zealand, 1998. *Unpaid Work, Census 96: 1996 Census of Population and Dwellings*. Statistics New Zealand, Wellington.

Plate 47: Degrees of Deprivation

- **Index of Deprivation, Local Government Areas 1996 Census**

Data from: Salmond, C., Crampton, P. and Sutton, F., 1998. *NZDep96: Index of Deprivation*. Health Services Research Centre, Victoria University of Wellington.

The data were supplied in electronic format. Thanks to Ross Barnett, Department of Geography, University of Canterbury, for introducing me to the data set.

Note: This map was generated by deriving a weighted average for each Territorial Local Authority (TLA). This is achieved by multiplying each meshblock NZDep96 value by the meshblock population, adding together all meshblocks in the TLA, then dividing by the total TLA population. The result of aggregating many hundreds of meshblocks to create regional values averages out the extreme values, but the resultant pattern still highlights the more deprived regions in northern and central rural North Island areas, and in Buller.
    Note also that once the decile values for meshblocks are aggregated and averaged, the resultant values are no longer whole numbers. This means that the key to the map cannot be constructed in deciles, as there are (using whole numbers) nine, rather than ten, categories. That is, for aggregated areas, the Index of Deprivation falls between two whole numbers rather than being a simple decile.

- **Index of Deprivation, Far North Territorial Local Authority (TLA) by Standard Area Unit (SAU), 1996 Census**

Data from: Salmond, C., Crampton, P. and Sutton, F., 1998. *NZDep96: Index of Deprivation*. Health Services Research Centre, Victoria University of Wellington.

Note: This map was generated in a similar fashion to the one above, though in this case the results aggregate fewer meshblocks per unit, so a greater degree of differentiation can occur. This is masked somewhat as the data are grouped at the most deprived end of the scale.

- **Index of Deprivation, Christchurch City by Meshblock, 1996 Census**

Data from: Salmond, C., Crampton, P. and Sutton, F., 1998. *NZDep96: Index of Deprivation*. Health Services Research Centre, Victoria University of Wellington.

- **Housing New Zealand Tenancies by Standard Area Unit (SAU), 1999**

Aggregated number of Housing New Zealand tenancies within each SAU were kindly provided by Bill King, Housing New Zealand.

See also:

Crampton, P., Salmond, C. and Sutton, F., 1997. *NZDep91: Index of Deprivation*. Research Report No. 5, Health Services Research Centre, Victoria University of Wellington.

Gordon, D., 1995. "Census Based Deprivation Indices: their weighting and validation", in *Journal of Epidemiology and Community Health* 49 (supplement 2), pp 39-44.

Morris, R. and Carstairs, V., 1991. "Which Deprivation? A Comparison of Selected Deprivation Indices", in *Journal of Public Health Medicine* 13, pp 318-326.

Salmond, C., Crampton, P. and Sutton, F., 1998. *NZDep96: Index of Deprivation*. Research Report No. 8, Health Services Research Centre, Victoria University of Wellington.

Townsend, P., 1987. "Deprivation", in *Journal of Social Policy* 16, pp 125-146.

Note: The assistance of Greg Lauer and Ross Barnett was invaluable in the production of this plate, as was the stimulating contact with Peter Crampton and Clare Salmond. The colours were devised by the author and Robyn Scarborough, Project Consultant of Critchlow Associates, and we hope to advocate them as a standard colour ramp when cartographically displaying Index of Deprivation data. Thanks also to Chris Skelly of the Ministry of Health and Jochen Albrecht of the Department of Geography, University of Auckland for their comments on the Index of Deprivation.

Plate 48: Three City Women

- **First Woman: 'Jan'**

- **Second Woman: 'Sylvia'**

- **Third Woman: 'Mrs. L'**

- **Income, Number of Places Visited and Hours Spent Away from Home in a 28-day Period**

The data showing the places visited by each woman over a monthly period were generated by personal interviews with each of the women concerned. These interviews were held between November 1998 and March 1999. I appreciate the willingness of each woman to share her life.

Note: This plate is included in the *Atlas* for a number of reasons. Though it does not pretend to be an in-depth analysis of gender and space, transport or income-related issues, it is an indication to readers that our lives and particularly our spatial experiences are intertwined with socially constructed inequalities.

I am an enthusiastic advocate of 'micro-geography', which I define as the study of small-scale change in the lives of individuals or small groups of people, but when contemplating such studies the matter of ethics must be considered. Statistics New Zealand constantly grapples with this issue: how does one protect the identities and privacy of individuals who contribute to a small-scale sample? Their answer is not to publish any data which might lead to the identification of individual respondents, and to round all data to a multiple of three. Since the introduction of the Privacy Act, the researcher and the publisher must be careful not to allow identification of individuals from published work.

This consideration influenced the type of cartography on this plate. The best method of representing volume (in this case hours spent at each location), which also allows the location to be identified, is to use cones (as is done on Plate 37: Overseas Trade). However, due to ethical considerations I was reluctant to allow the location of each woman's house to be identified too closely, so I have chosen to use spheres instead of cones. The danger with this choice is that a circle might be misinterpreted as a spatial spread instead of a representation of time. This is why each circle is shaded to give the illusion of three-dimensionality. Note also that the home and work circles are offset slightly, so their centre is not exactly where the woman lives or works.

See also:

Roche, M.M. and Mansvelt, J., 1996. "Ethical Research in a Public Good Funding Environment", in *New Zealand Geographer* 52 (1), pp 41-46.

Plate 49: Hospital Restructuring

- **Public Hospitals, 1985 by Number and Type of Beds**
Data from: Ministry of Health, 1985. *Hospital Management Data, 1985*. Ministry of Health, Wellington.

- **Public Hospitals, 1997 by Number and Type of Beds**
Data courtesy of: New Zealand Health Information Service, unpublished data supplied on diskette.

Note: This is an unfortunate case of data becoming unavailable. Hospital bed numbers were freely published in the public domain until 1985, then, as a result of reforms, were no longer available. To procure the data now one must request it from the New Zealand Health Information Service and pay for it. Note further that hospital bed numbers are a surrogate for actual patient numbers, which are not available to the public. Some hospitals in 1985 and in 1997 may be operating well below capacity.

- **Admissions to Mental Health Facilities, 1960-1993**
Material kindly supplied by New Zealand Health Information Service. Note that the 1994 data have just been made available (in May 1999), but the manner in which they have been calculated has changed significantly, making them not directly comparable to earlier data. They are therefore not included here.

Note: Thanks to Ross Barnett of the Department of Geography, University of Canterbury, for his comments on this plate. His work on restructuring in the health sector points out that an increasing number of patients are being cared for by the private sector (which is not examined on this plate). Of the hospitals which have exited the system since 1985, a number are still in existence, being run by community trusts, and continue to receive public funding from the Health Funding Authorities. These hospitals do not feature here, though their effect must be taken into consideration when examining the change between 1985 and 1997.

Hospital and health restructuring continues. This plate, therefore, will rapidly become a historical plate rather than a contemporary analysis.

Plate 50: Sport and Recreation

- **Provincial Rugby Unions, Super 12 Teams 1999, First-Class Grounds**
Boundaries from: Kelly, J. and Marshall, B., 1996. *Atlas of New Zealand Boundaries*. Auckland University Press, Auckland.

Note: The degree of difficulty of assembling these boundaries for the 1996 *Atlas of New Zealand Boundaries* is acknowledged and I am grateful to Jan Kelly for her work.

First-Class Grounds, 1999: Information from the New Zealand Rugby Football Union's website at: http://www.nzrugby.com/nzrfu/Pages/NZRU/fixturef.htm

Note: I have relied on this fixtures list to give me the names of grounds at which first-class fixtures will be played in 1999. Note that some grounds may have different local names than those listed by the NZRFU.

- **First-Class Cricket Districts, First-Class Grounds**
Boundaries from: Kelly, J. and Marshall, B., 1996. *Atlas of New Zealand Boundaries*. Auckland University Press, Auckland.

Number of First-Class games on each ground; data from: Payne, F. and Smith, I. (eds), 1998. *The 1998 Shell Cricket Almanac of New Zealand*. Moa Beckett, in association with the Shell Group of Companies in New Zealand.

Note: It is a recent policy of New Zealand Cricket to introduce the first-class game to new grounds, both in the regions and in city centres. As the popularity of first-class cricket (three, four and five-day games) gives way to one-day cricket (which is not defined as first-class) and crowds diminish, grounds which are less expensive to hire and have a more intimate atmosphere are being sought.

- **Netball New Zealand Coca-Cola Cup Franchise Venues**
Stadium locations used in the 1999 season from Netball New Zealand's website at: http://www.netballnz.co.nz Note that the web page with the fixtures for the 1999 Coca-Cola Cup has been removed from this site.

Note: Despite months of trying I was not able to obtain a map of the franchise boundaries from Netball New Zealand, and so conclude that they do not exist. Netball has never been organised in a methodical fashion, and the authors of the 1996 *Atlas of New Zealand Boundaries* experienced similar difficulties when trying to map netball's provincial regions. Of particular interest to me is the affiliation of Napier and Hastings: which Coca-Cola Cup franchise do they identify with? Netball administration appears to be focused on the urban centres, and each local town organisation (e.g., Ashburton) seems to be informally affiliated to a regional headquarters (e.g., Christchurch). I would appreciate hearing from anyone able to correct this impression, or who can contribute to this discussion.

• Distribution of Golf Clubs
Unpublished map generated by the author from the files of: McKinnon, M. (ed), with Bradley, B. and Kirkpatrick, R., 1997. *New Zealand Historical Atlas: Visualising New Zealand*. David Bateman Ltd in association with Historical Branch, Department of Internal Affairs, Auckland.

• Average Weekly Household Expenditure on Cultural Activities, Year Ended March 1996
Data from: Ministry of Cultural Affairs, 1996. *Household Spending on Culture*. Ministry of Cultural Affairs, Wellington.

• Age Trends in Selected Sports Participation, 1996
Data from: "Top Fifteen Sports for New Zealand Adults of Different Ages and Cultures", in Hillary Commission for Sport, Fitness and Leisure, 1999. *Push Play Facts*. Hillary Commission, Wellington, p 16.

• Recreational Participation by Gender, 1996
Data from: "Top Ten Sports and Physical Activities for Men and Women", in Hillary Commission for Sport, Fitness and Leisure, 1999. *Sport Facts Part 2*. Hillary Commission, Wellington. This paper was downloaded as a .pdf file from the Hillary Commission's website at: http://www.hillarysport.org.nz

Note: At the time of final drafts for this *Atlas,* many of the results of the Hillary Commission's 1996 survey were becoming available. Prior to this, the latest information was the results of the 1992 survey.

See also:
Hillary Commission for Sport, Fitness and Leisure, 1993. *The Business of Sport and Leisure*. Hillary Commission, Wellington.

INDEX

Ministry of Foreign Affairs and
Trade, and international
relations 44
Ministry of Transport, Civil Aviation
division 41
mission stations, in 1845 28
MMP (Mixed-Member Proportional)
representation, election 35
moa, habitat during Ice Age 6;
hunting of 27
Mokohinau Island, wind gust at 9
Montreal Protocol, and CFCs 21
mortality rates, Māori 45
motor vehicles, heavy 42
Motunau, coastal erosion 23
mountain-building 1
mountains, formation 1, 2; highest 1;
3, tourism and recreation 14
Mt Aspiring National Park, area 20;
date established 20
Mt Cook National Park, area 20;
date established 20
Mt Eden, formation of 5
Mt Hikurangi, highest non-volcanic
mountain in North Island 1
Mt Ruapehu, 1995/6 eruptions from
24; ash cloud from 24; formation
of 2; hazards from 24; highest
volcano 1; large volcanic cone 1
Mt Tarawera, 1886 eruption 23;
large volcanic cone 1
Mt Tongariro, formation of 2; large
volcanic cone 1
Mt Wellington, formation of 5
mudstone, formation of 3
Murchison, earthquake 23, 24
Murupara, single-purpose town 33

N

Napier, earthquake 23, 24; high
sunshine hours 10; inflow of
young adults to 32
National Parks Act 1980 20
national parks, extent of 20; first 20
natural hazards 23, 24, 25;
distribution 23
natural population increase,
components of 31; rate of 30, 31
Nauru 29; and phosphate mining 29
Nelson Lakes National Park, area
20; date established 20
Nelson Pine Industries mill 18
Nelson, flood 23; gaining migrants
32; gasworks and contaminated
site 21; north-west, rock type 3,
4; sunshine hours 10
netball, Coca-Cola Cup franchises
50

Nettlebed Cave, deepest cave 1
New Caledonia, part of Rangitoto
landmass 2
New Zealand, climate districts 7;
colonial landscape 28;
colonisation 26; discovery 26;
physical landscape 1; sea floor
2; territories in South-West
Pacific 29
New Zealand Forest Products mills
18
New Zealand Geosyncline,
formation 3
New Zealand Income Survey,
gender disparity in 46
New Zealand Overseas
Development Agency 44; South
Pacific allocation 29
New Zealand Soil Classification
(NZSC) 11
New Zealand Tourism Board,
planning 38
New Zealand Veneers mill 18
new mothers, average age 31
Ngāi Tahu, dominant in South
Island 45; journeys of 27; land
sales by 28; and resource
management 22
Ngā Puhi, spread of 45
Ngāti Awa, and Tarawera pollution
21
Ngāti Kahungunu 27, dominant in
Hawke's Bay 45
Ngāti Māmoe, early Māori settlers
22
Ngāti Maniapoto, spread of 45
Ngāti Porou, dominant in East Cape
45
Ngāti Rangitihi, and Tarawera
pollution 21
Ngāti Toa, land sales by 28
Ngauranga Gorge, vehicle speed 43
Niue, NZ territory 29
nor'wester, damage from 10
North Island, topography 1
Northland, deprivation in 47;
gaining immigrants from
Auckland 32; housing conditions
in 47; losing migrants 32; marae-
based tourism in 38; rainfall of 8;
tectonic volcanoes of 3, 4
NZ Rail, selling of 41, 42

O

oceanic crust, location 2
OECD (Organisation for Economic
Co-operation and Development),
membership of 44

Official Development Assistance,
programme allocation 44; South
Pacific allocation 29
Ohau, Lake, area 1
Ohiwa, coastal erosion 23
oil imports 40; reserves 4, 40;
shocks and import costs 37;
oilfields, and energy generation 40;
formation of 4
Okataina/Rotorua Caldera, lake-
filled 1
oldest rocks, formation of 3
Omaha, coastal erosion 23
One Tree Hill, formation of 5
orange roughy, annual catch 16;
fishery 16
Oreti River, length 1
orographic damage caused by 10;
effect 7; mechanics of 8
Osbourn seamount, size 2
Otago, gaining migrants 32; unusual
rainfall 9
Otara, and ethnicity 34
overseas aid 29, 44
overseas posts 44
overseas trade 37; cargo by volume
41; major exports 37; major
trading partners 37; with the
world 37
ozone depletion 21

P

Pacific, aid to 29; colonisation 26;
New Zealand relationship with
29
Pacific Island New Zealanders,
age/sex structure 34; in South
Auckland 34
Pacific Islands, immigration from
32; territories of 29
Pacific tectonic plate 2, 3
Paeroa, flooding 23
Pakuranga, and Asian immigration
34
Palmerston North, immigration to 32
Pan Pacific Forest Industries mill 18
Pangaea, supercontinent 2
Paparoa National Park, area 20;
date established 20
Papatoetoe, and dairies 39
Paraparaumu, link to Wellington 43
pastoral properties, distribution of
28
peacekeeping commitments 44
peneplain, formation of 3
Permanent Long Term (PLT)
immigrants 32
PGF (NZ) Ltd, factory floor 46

phosphate, imports 29
phreatomagmatic eruption, mechanics of 5; and Ruapehu eruption 24
Picton, ferry terminal 41
Pitt Island 17
Planning Tribunal, and boundary dispute 22
plutonic rocks 3
podocarp forest 13, 19
pollution, from contaminated sites 21; from forestry mills 21; industrial 22; Tarawera River 21
Polynesians, Pacific exploration by 26
population, cartogram 30, change 31; components of 31; demography of 30, density 30; fertility 31; growth 31; Māori 33; migration 31; projection 30; urban-rural split 30
Porters Pass 6
Pouawa Bay, tsunami 23
Poverty Bay, flood 23
power crisis, Auckland 40
provinces, boundaries 28; government 28
public transport, in Wellington region 43
Pukaki, Lake, area 1
Pureora Mountain Ecological Area 13, vegetation 13
Puysegur, fishery 16
pyroclastic surge, mechanics of 5; on Ruapehu 24

Q

Quaternary period, glaciation during 3
Quota Management System (QMS) 16

R

racial conflict, between Māori and early explorers 26; over land sales 28; over resources 22
rail network 14, 42; in 1870s 28; inter-island ferries 41; North Island Main Trunk and volcanic hazard 24; tonnage flows 42; Tranz Rail 41
rainfall 7, 8; extreme events 8; isolates, Wellington Oct 21, 1998 43; La Niña and El Niño 9, natural hazard from 23; regional differences 8; seasonal

differences 8; variability of 8; westerly events 8
Rakaia Peidmont Glacier 6
Rakaia River, glaciation of 6
Rangatira, highest sandhill 1
Rangiora, floods 23; high temperature at 9, 10
Rangitata Orogeny 3
Rangitikei River, length 1
Rangitoto Island, formation of 5
Rangitoto landmass, formation of 2
reafforestation 21
recreation, on Avon-Heathcote estuary 22; and mountain areas 14; participation by gender 50; and volcanic hazard 24
refugees, accepting into NZ 44
Rekohu see Chatham Islands
renewable energy, research into 40; use of 40
Representation Commission 35
Reserves Act 1977 20; area of 20
Resource Management Act 1991 21, 22; and local government 35; and natural hazards 23, and new ferry terminal 41
resources, exploitation, nineteenth century 28; energy 40; mineral 4
resource management, of Avon-Heathcote estuary 22; of South Westland 19; of Tarawera river 21
restaurants, in Auckland 39
restructuring, of agriculture 15; of banking industry 36; and business 36, 46; of energy industry 40; of forestry sector 18; of the health sector 49; of housing stock 47; of international airports 41; of labour market 46; local government 35; and Māori 45; of trade barriers 37; transport sector 41, 42; on West Coast 19
retail sales, in Auckland 39; by month 36; by region 36; by store type 36
riverine lakes 1
rivers, longest 1
road network 14, 42; traffic volume of 42; and volcanic hazard 24; in Wellington Region 43
rohe 45
Ross Dependency 29
Rotorua, Lake, area 1
Ruapehu, Mt, 1995/6 eruptions from 24; ash cloud from 24; formation of 2; hazards from 24; highest volcano 1; large volcanic cone 1; visitor numbers 24

Ruatoria, high temperature at 10
rugby, boundaries of unions 50; first-class grounds 50; Super 12 franchises 50
rural-urban drift 30; reversed 31, 32

S

SALPEX (Southern Alps Experiment) 8
Samoa, Western see Western Samoa
sandstone, formation of 3
Sanford, fishing company 16
sawmills, large 18; on West Coast 19
schools, offering Māori medium education 45 see also education
sea floor, New Zealand region 2
sea level, during Ice Age 6
sea swell, natural hazard from 23
Seafox seamount, size 2
Sealord, fishing company 16
security and intelligence, expenditure 44
sedimentary rocks, location 3
sediments, buildup of 22
Selwyn River, upper 6
settlement hierarchy 14
sewerage system, in Christchurch 22
sheep farming, area of 15; and bush clearance 14; in nineteenth century 28
shipping 41; overseas cargo loaded and unloaded 41
skifields, risk of avalanche 23; and Ruapehu eruption 24
snowline, during Ice Age 6
socio-economic indicators 54; Index of Deprivation 47
soils, classification and distribution 11; of Pureora 13
South Auckland, ethnic diversity 34
South Canterbury, flood 23
South Island, topography 1
South Pacific, aid allocation 29; territorial boundaries 29
South West Cape, wind gust at 9
South Westland, resource management strategies 19
Southern Alps, formation of 2; mountain-building, glacial dissection 1; nor'wester and 10; rainfall 8; storms propagated in 25
Southern Hemisphere cyclonic and anticyclonic activity 7

Southern Hemisphere Pressure
Field 7
Southern Oscillation Index (SOI) 9;
and 1983 El Niño event 25
Southland, floods 23, 25; losing
migrants 32; rainfall of 8
sport 50, age trends in 50; cricket
50; golf 50; netball 50; and
provincial identity 50; rugby 50
State Highway network, traffic
volume of 42; in Wellington
region 43
State-Owned Enterprises, forestry
18; Timberlands 19
steepness, of land 14
stewardship areas, distribution of 20
storms, convective 8; hailstorm
occurrence 23; natural hazard
from 23; thunderstorms 8;
tropical cyclones 8
subduction, mechanism of 2
Sugar Loaf Islands Marine
Protected Area Act 1991 20
sunshine hours 7; distribution of 10
superstructure icing, natural hazard
from 23
surface rock, age of 3
Sutherland Falls, highest waterfall 1

T

Taieri River, length 1
Tainui, spread of 45
Tamatea-pōkai-whenua 27
Tangiwai, lahar disaster 23, 24
Taranaki, losing migrants 32; wars
28
Tarawera Mt, 1886 eruption 23;
large volcanic cone 1
Tarawera River, pollution of 21
tariffs, deregulation of 37; effect on
industry 46
Tasman Forestry forests, mill 18;
waste from mill 21
Tasman Glacier, largest glacier 1
Tasman Sea, anticyclones in 7
Tasman, Abel, voyage of 26
Taupo Caldera, ash from 5; lake-
filled 1; last eruption 13
Taupo Volcanic Zone, formation of
2; volcanic activity of 4
Taupo, Lake, area 1
Tauranga, inflow of young adults to
32; intense rainfall 8
Te Anau, Lake, area 1
Te Atatu, and dairies 39
Te Awamutu power station, most
recent station 40
Te Rapa, landslide 23

Te Reo Māori 45
Te Tiriti o Waitangi *see* Treaty of
Waitangi
Te Whanga Lagoon, area 1
tectonic lakes 1
tectonic plates, activity 1;
mechanism, plates near New
Zealand 2; and mountain-
building 3
Tekapo, Lake, area 1
telegraph network, in 1870s 28
temperature, distribution 10;
extremes 9, 10
Territorial Local Authorities (TLAs),
location of 30; Māori population
33; Māori unemployment in 33;
population 30, population
change 31
Thames Valley, flooding 23
Think Big projects 40
Three Kings, formation of 5
Timaru, low rainfall 9
timber, mills 18; production 18;
projected yields 18
Timberlands West Coast, forest
interests 19
Toi-te-huatahi 27
Tokelau Islands, NZ territory 29
Tongariro Mt, formation of 2; large
volcanic cone 1
Tongariro National Park, area 20;
date established 20; volcanoes
within 24
tornado, 1983 25
tourism 38; accommodation 38;
country of origin 38; destinations
of tourists 38; employment in
industry 38; and foreign
exchange 37, 38; and forestry on
West Coast 19; length of visit 38;
and mountain areas 14,
Ruapehu visitor numbers 24; and
the State Highway network 42
Town and Country Planning Act
1953, and flooding 25
towns and cities 14; colonial 28
TRADENZ (Trade New Zealand),
overseas representation 44
trade 37; major partners 37
traffic, State Highway network 42;
in Wellington region 43
Transit New Zealand, Act 1989, and
data gathering 43; and local
authorities 35; transport funder
42
transport issues, air and sea 41;
mode of transport 43; public
transport 43; road and rail 42;
Wellington region 43
Tranz Metro, passenger numbers 43

Tranz Rail, formation of 41, 42; inter-
island ferry numbers 43;
tonnage flows on railways 42;
Tranz Metro 43
Treaty of Waitangi (Te Tiriti o
Waitangi), impact of settlements
45; signatories to 28
tsunami, natural hazard from 23
Tuhourangi, and Tarawera pollution
21
Tuhua Orogeny 3
Tuhua, maritime park 20; obsidian
from 4, 26
Tui Mine Tailings, and contaminated
site 21
Tuke Hut, intense rainfall 8
Turangi, single-purpose town 33
Turoa Skifield, and Ruapehu
eruption 24
Tutaekuri river, flood 23
Tuvalu 29
Tuwharetoa, spread of iwi 45; and
Tarawera pollution 21

U

unemployment 33; levels since 1931
46; and Māori 33
United Nations, membership of 44
unpaid work, on the farm 15;
household labour 46
urban areas, and cultural
landscape 14; development and
vegetation 12, dominance in
sport 50; migration between 32;
compared to Pacific Rim 14,
population 30, 31; population in
1874 28
Urewera National Park, area 20;
date established 20
USA (United States of America),
tourists from 38; trade with 37

V

vegetable production, by area 15
vegetation, 1840 12; distribution 12;
in early nineteenth century 27;
exotic 12; forest burning 27;
during Ice Age 6; native 12;
Pureora mountain; and soils 11
volcanic lakes 1
volcanoes, Auckland Volcanic Field
5; eruption of 5; geology of 3;
minerals from 4; natural hazards
of 23; prominent 1; Pureora 13;
Ruapehu 24; types of 5;
undersea 2

W

Wahine, and Cyclone Giselle 25; sinking of 23
Waiau River (Southland), length 1
Waikaremoana, Lake, area 1
Waikato Carbonization Ltd, and contaminated site 21
Waikato River, different courses 6; longest 1; pipeline from 40
Waikato, retail growth in 36; spread of iwi 45; war in 28
Waimate, low rainfall 9
Wainuiomata, link to Wellington 43
Wairarapa, Lake, area 1
Wairarapa, unusual rainfall in 9
Wairau, earthquake 23
Waitaha, early Māori settlers 22
Waitakere Ranges, formation of 5
Waitaki coast, coastal erosion 23
Waitaki River, length 1
waka, landing places of 27
Wakatipu, Lake, area 1
Wanaka, Lake, area 1
Wanganui River, length 1
Washdyke, coastal erosion 23

waste disposal 21
water crisis, Auckland 40; and electricity generation 40
water quality 21, 22
Waterfall Creek, intense rainfall 8
weather, and climate 7; synoptic systems 7
Wellington, 1855 earthquake 23; airport expansion 43; head offices in 36; location of workers 46; quickest air route to 41; retail growth in 36; size 14; transport issues in 43
Wellington, Mt, formation of 5
West Coast Accord 19
West Coast, beech forests 19; fishery 16; forestry 19; land ownership 19; losing migrants 32; rainfall 8; sawmills 19; tourism 19; wind 10
westerly winds, dominance of 10; and rainfall 8; influenced by topography 1; zone of 7
Western Samoa, NZ territory 29
Westland National Park, area 20; date established 20

wetlands, and Avon-Heathcote estuary 22; distribution 12; at Pureora 13; threat to 21
Whakapapa Skifield, and Ruapehu eruption 24
whakapapa, example of 27
whaling stations, location 28
Whangaehu river, and lahar flows 24
Whanganui National Park, area 20; date established 20
wheat, in nineteenth century 28
Whenuapai, intense rainfall 8
White Island, eruption 23; formation of 2
wilderness areas, distribution of 20
Wildlife Act 1953 20
winds, circumpolar 7; damaging 10; direction of 10; formation of storms 25; natural hazard from 23; nor'wester 10; westerly 1, 7
women, in the city 48; income levels 46; in the workforce 46
World Bank, multilateral agency 44
World Heritage Areas 19, distribution of 20